LIGHT MEDICINE

A New Paradigm —

The Science of Light, Spirit, and Longevity

Ana Maria Mihalcea, M.D., Ph.D.

ARTHEMA SOPHIA PUBLISHING

LIGHT MEDICINE
A NEW PARADIGM –
THE SCIENCE OF LIGHT, SPIRIT, AND LONGEVITY
Copyright © 2021, Ana Maria Mihalcea, M.D., Ph.D.
All rights reserved.

Cover design by Melissa Peizer
Edited by Patricia Richker and Michelle Horkings-Brigham

Disclaimer: The statements and research presented in this book have not been assessed by the FDA. Therefore, these are not meant to serve diagnostic purposes nor as a treatment or prevention solution for diverse medical conditions.

ISBN: 978-0-578-85028-3

ARTHEMA SOPHIA PUBLISHING
715 E Yelm Avenue, Suite #5
Yelm, WA 98597, U.S.A.
Phone: (360)960-8538 / Fax: (360) 252-7023
https://ammedicalmd.com/

ACKNOWLEDGEMENTS

This book and AM Medical LLC would not exist in its current form without the support of Laura Mooney. I have been blessed to have her by my side. JZ Knight wisely worked to open my mind to possibilities and allowed me to explore a new world of healing in her Mercy Blu Room program. I am always grateful for her generous support, vision, and unconditional love. Ramtha the Enlightened One has been my beloved Teacher, and I treasure the enormous knowledge I have learned over the years and the innumerable "runners" that have changed and expanded my life. Ramtha's School of Enlightenment has been the greatest academy of mind I could have ever dreamed of attending. The Mercy Blu Room team—JZ Knight, Terri Stuart, Brandy Knight, and Mike Wright—have all been instrumental in the work with the Mercy Blu Room program and my own transformation as a result. My beautiful, fellow RSE students have taught me so much over the years. My patients have always been amazing teachers and it is a privilege for me to serve them. I have worked with great people on this journey and am now blessed to have the wonderful AM Medical LLC staff. I am grateful to Daniel Stanciu, Ph.D., for his inspiration and collaboration in cancer research. Thank you to Patricia Richker and Michelle Horkings-Brigham for their editorial work. Thank you to Robert Wynne.

DEDICATION

I am a servant unto the God that lives within me.
The knowledge I have garnered from
Ramtha the Enlightened One and JZ Knight
has inspired this publication.

TABLE OF CONTENTS

LIGHT MEDICINE

PROLOGUE
IN SEARCH OF THE LIGHT

This book is a culmination of my journey to understand many questions. How did I begin documenting the extraordinary healings of the great American channel JZ Knight? Why did I explore a new paradigm of medicine?

I am a physician who is convinced that Ramtha's School of Enlightenment is the greatest academy of mind in the world. Furthermore, Ramtha's model of reality is the basis of a new futuristic approach to medicine. It combines knowledge of science and spirit and explains how the Spirit's observation of thought creates either disease or health in the body.[1]

Without background knowledge, this might seem preposterous. I must surely be out of my mind. That is correct . . . I now am outside of my former mind.

I am traditionally a well-trained physician who has been everywhere and studied everything—from allopathic medicine to many healing modalities to religion and philosophy. I have journeyed the world searching, only to find answers to some of the most profound questions in a most unusual place, Yelm, Washington. It was my own deepest questions that led me to Ramtha, where the answers I experienced were beyond my wildest imagination. The answers did not come in written texts. They came in life experiences.

What drove me was not just understanding my purpose in life and attaining personal achievement but finding meaning in my emotional, physical, and spiritual challenges. I did not just want to learn to heal others. I wanted to know how to heal myself and how to become my dreams.

What really was healing? Was it possible for me to do something like Jesus Christ, to lay my hands on someone and heal them? Was I worthy to know such knowledge? Was there God? Was God some man in the sky? And if I resented men, did that mean I resented God? Did God care about me? And, if so, why did I suffer so much and feel so alone? Was I a sinner and would I burn in hell because I did not know what love is and was afraid to express it? Where did poetry come from, and music, and inspiration? What about geniuses like Mozart and Beethoven and great writers like Dostoyevsky; where did their gifts come from? And what about life and death; where do we come from at birth and where do we go after death? Most of all, I wanted to find meaning to my own journey.

My whole life has been a war between my intellectual and scientific ability and my spiritual experiences and love for God. It was imperative that I combine the two, even though they were clashing all the time. The more I wanted to advance my career as a medical doctor and researcher, the more people from that category would claim that talking about spiritual matters would ruin my career.

In this other part of my life were the healers and spiritual experiences and all the possibilities of that realm. There was a constant war within: "I can live secretly over here but these other people can't know about it," and vice versa.

I love both areas. I love science. I love to go down into every detail of science. That is a beautiful world to me. The spiritual world is everything to me because it is what gives meaning to the grand picture. Allowing the whole of myself and expressing it all—that has been my struggle.

I often tried to conform to someone else's ideal, and it never really worked. It was just not me. In this book, I did not conform to anything.

In writing about the unusual nature of my story, I hope to allow others an understanding of how I arrived at some of my conclusions. People may find a connection with someone like myself who has been searching their entire life—and I mean their whole life.

Eventually I was drawn to attend a beginning event, now called Class 101—Remarkable Mind, at Ramtha's School of Enlightenment where I heard a teaching from JZ Knight about the cell she named "Gladys®" and I thought, "Oh, my God, I found it."[2]

As a child, I had always dreamed of becoming a doctor and eventually curing cancer. I believed in miracles. Those dreams never manifested quite as I envisioned them, until I had garnered much knowledge at Ramtha's School of Enlightenment.

Years later at a private event, Ramtha told me I was still stuck and that he would make me a genius if I let him. Without Ramtha, I would never have pursued the path leading to who I dreamed long ago I could become.

JZ Knight later engaged me in her work to research the effects of the Blu Room she had created.[3] She took my then completely closed mind—that was so afraid to step out the door of what I had achieved—and said, "Go look over there. Research this." She was like an angel who opened the door. This journey of life is beautiful, and I am so grateful to have it.

Let me tell you about my search for the light . . .

PART I

A New Paradigm

The Science of Light, Spirit, and Longevity

CHAPTER 1
THE BEGINNING OF THE JOURNEY

I grew up in Hueckelhoven, a small, mining town in western Germany. My parents had fled from the oppression of communism in Romania in 1972. Raised as an orphan, my mother was able, through her brilliant mind, to excel in her schooling and earned a scholarship to medical school, where she graduated as one of the top physicians in the country. My father was a mechanical engineer.

Growing up in a small town in Germany was not my favorite experience. I had very few friends, due to the stigma that I was a "foreigner." At home, my parents would often fight. My father was a brilliant man, but he had a mean temper and an appetite for emotional cruelty. I grew up resenting and fearing him and not understanding why my mother allowed herself to remain in this situation. He only cared about intellectual achievement, and I never met his demands or impossible high standards. I spent most of my youth as an introvert in my own world—reading books, writing poetry, and playing the piano.

When I was 10 years old, I started working in my mother's office as a medical assistant during my vacations. In small steps she began teaching me how to file basic charts and perform other simple duties. She would take me on house calls where she attended to the ill and elderly. I would watch her wrap bandages around leg ulcers and care for her patients, while I ate homemade pie baked by old ladies who looked forward to my mother's visit. On weekends and evenings when she was on duty, I would take messages while she went on emergency house calls at all hours of the day and night. She was loved by many and had a huge practice. She worked nonstop.

I was very athletic in elementary and early high school and part of a running club as a young teenager. My trainer was a 17-year-old, young woman, Gabi, whom I shyly adored. Gabi developed uterine cancer and died within a couple years when I was 13 years old. This was my first encounter with cancer. Her grave was located at a cemetery near a beautiful forest, and on many weekends I would visit her grave to talk to her. I did this periodically over the years until I left Hueckelhoven for good. I told her someday I would cure cancer and understand why people die.

When I was 15, I applied to be an exchange student in the United States and spent six months with a Native American family in St. Ignatius on the Flathead Indian Reservation in Montana. This was a great time in my life. My host dad was friends with the local doctor, Bill, and they would take me on hiking trips up into the Flathead mountains. There my host father would go hunting with a bow and arrow, and we would fish and camp at the mountain lakes, an absolute dream for me to experience. It was there that he told me, "Look at this, Ana," pointing to the beautiful scenery. "This is just a local phone call to God."

I often spoke to Bill about my desire to become a doctor in the United States. When it was time to leave, he gave me a book called *The Tao of Pooh*, by Benjamin Hoff.[1] Its main message was this poem, which remained a source of encouragement for me throughout the following turbulent years:

> *To know the way,*
> *we go the way,*
> *we do the way.*
> *The way we do,*
> *the things we do,*
> *it's all there in front of you.*
> *But if you try too hard to see it,*
> *you'll only become confused.*
> *I am me and you are you.*

As you can see;
but when you do
the things that you can do,
you will find the way.
The way will follow you.

Bill wrote in the inside of the book: "You will achieve everything you want. Go for it!" I kept this book as my talisman. The Flathead mountains of Montana is where I fell in love with the United States. In our class yearbook we noted who we wanted to be in the future. I wrote: "A doctor of genetics and I want to know everything there is to know."

Upon returning to Germany, I missed the United States very much. So after my high school graduation, I went back on a cross-country trip to the U.S. for a couple of months. At the Hollywood Walk of Fame, I stood where Anthony Quinn had put his hand- and footprints in the concrete and written the words, "Dreams do come true." It was there that I made a promise to God that I would live in America no matter what it took. I always want to keep my promises.

My parents did not want me to go to medical school. My mother wanted me to have an easier life than she did. My father wanted me to pursue a career in business administration and management consulting. When I was eighteen, he sent me for entry exams to an elite M.B.A. school in Koblenz. I did not tell my parents that behind their backs I had already taken the medical school entrance exams. In preparation, I had specialized during my last two years of high school in the best science education, with majors in biology, chemistry, physics, mathematics, and philosophy. I knew my only ticket out of Germany was through a good education. The combination of excellent high school grades and my medical school entry exam landed me a spot at the Rheinian Westfalian Technical University Medical School in Aachen, Germany.

I was eighteen when I was accepted to medical school. Before starting, I had to do a three-month practicum as a nurse's aide. My mother had connections at the local hospital where she knew the chief surgeon and she landed me a position. This was a time when nurses were able to abuse the new, future medical students and teach them a lesson in humility.

The chief nurse made sure she taught me that lesson by assigning me to only emptying bedpans on the hospital ward, while accompanied by derogatory comments from some of the nurses. The extreme rift between nursing staff, physicians, and the hierarchical order among the medical staff was something I did not appreciate. Most physicians were male, and they treated women as if they were servants. I did not like the atmosphere of male superiority and could relate to the resentment of the nurses.

One day the chief surgeon, who knew my mother well, called for me to come to the operating room. I was to scrub in and help with his surgeries. He soon saw in me a natural talent, and I spent the rest of the practicum as his assistant. I learned a great deal from him, and I loved every bit of it. He told me I would make an excellent future surgeon.

During this rotation, our neighbor was admitted to my ward at the hospital. He appeared to have had a gallbladder attack and wanted me to be with him through the surgery. I was scheduled to assist. The surgeon opened the abdomen and found it filled with an inoperable cancer. When I saw this and understood what it meant, I had a panic attack and fainted. That was my first lesson on the importance of detachment. I should have never assisted in the case of someone I knew with whom I had an emotional attachment.

In the course of his illness, our neighbor's wife was getting very tired from not being able to sleep while caring for her husband, so my mother sent me to their home to keep watch during the night. I was terrified he might die while I was on duty, as I had not yet seen a dead body. I was afraid of death. I spent several nights with him before he passed away. In a quiet moment together, I asked him what advice he would give me because I wanted to be a doctor. He told me to make sure to listen to my patients.

A short time after that, another neighbor was diagnosed with liver cancer. I also visited him and talked with him about what he would want his doctor to be like. He told me the same thing, to always listen well to my patients.

It was these cumulative experiences of people in my life dying of cancer that made me wonder if that might be the purpose of my life—to cure cancer.

When I arrived at medical school, I had the strangest sense of déjà vu, as if I instinctually knew what they were teaching. In my second year I took pathology courses and had already read the entire textbook before the year started. To the great annoyance of the professor, I solved many of his cases. His was my favorite class. I told him I wanted to begin my Ph.D. thesis and that it needed to be about cancer. He argued for a while that it was too early but, in the end, he allowed me to start. My thesis studied the Ki67 proliferation kinetics of gastric cancer. I analyzed the growth patterns of stomach cancer and the areas of accelerated growth.

During this time I was trained in preparing tumor sections, freezing, and staining methods. I participated in other cancer research projects as well and learned how to analyze and prepare various tumors for analysis and staining for different markers. I absolutely loved the work and spent most nights and weekends in the lab studying cancer under a microscope. The thesis took me several years to complete. As a result of my studies, I participated in a number of research publications on different cancer types while working at the pathology department.

Throughout my training, I never forgot my goal to leave Germany and move to America. Medical school in Germany only costs $60.00 per year. There was no way I could afford expensive American medical universities. Instead, I completed my German state exams and American medical boards in parallel. This was my absolute focus. In five years I completed four German medical board exams and three U.S. medical licensing exams.

I also never stopped wondering about all those questions regarding the nature of God.

Initially, being around death and suffering was a difficult experience for me. Yet from being afraid of seeing death, pathology became one of my most fascinating subjects—dissecting and studying human deceased bodies. What a strange thing it was to see those cold bodies, looking like used puppets . . . Where did they go? That which was them, their spirit, what happened to it?

In a summer break in the first year of medical school, I visited my brother. At the time he was doing his Ph.D. at Stanford University in Palo Alto, California. He introduced me to a psychic from whom I received a psychic reading that was recorded on a cassette tape. She told me that I was very "sensitive" and should learn more about energy in the body, study acupuncture and the work of Barbara Brennan. She recommended the book, *Hands of Light.*[2] Even though this was the first time we had ever met—and I had given her no information about me—this psychic knew about many of my challenges. I was extremely impressed, so I followed her advice.

After purchasing several energy healing books, I signed up for a course in acupuncture at the University of Shanghai, China, in my second year of medical school. In China, I learned not only the basic principles of acupuncture but was also fortunate to learn Chi Gong from a master.

I saw many interesting things in China and observed how acupuncture helped in the most outrageous ways. For example, there were businessmen who came from America to get acupuncture treatments for their tinnitus—a constant ringing in the ears—that no other treatment could help. Their symptoms resolved after ten sessions. My professor spoke to me about evil spirits attached to the body that would cause disease and guided me to ancient Chinese medical scriptures that mentioned such attachments and how to free oneself from them.

After one such conversation, I was in my hotel room at night when I became aware that I was trapped in my body while a dark, black shadow hovered above, endeavoring to pull me out of my body. It seemed to me that if it succeeded, I would die. It was a terrifying experience, and that shadow definitely appeared evil to me. I prayed to God to protect me and saw a candle in my room that was lit. When the attack was over, I woke my roommate and we both noted the ice-cold temperature drop in the room. I told her that one of the healers in our class had been there in my experience in the form of a candle. Suddenly there was a knock on my door, and this same lady healer stood there in a sweat and described what she had seen happening to me. She said my Chinese professor had also been present in the room.

The following morning, I asked him if he had been thinking about me last evening. He handed me a seven-page letter that he had written during the night that was intended to help me remove these evil spirits. He told me he saw the shadow attacking me and that he wanted me to bathe in a crystal-clear waterfall and release the dark attachments and ancient curses.

All of this was highly unusual and disquieting. Whenever I was around this lady healer, I would start seeing ghosts and beings around me. I decided I needed to leave and travel alone to get away from all this. I had no idea what to do. Was there something about me that was evil? The thought crossed my mind that maybe I needed to learn about black magic and how to detach demons and rid myself of curses.

After my class, I traveled through China to Guilin and then all the way back to Beijing. Traveling in China was absolutely fascinating, and I always followed my intuition to go anywhere I wanted. I did not use a map. I just listened to the voice inside of me. It told me where to go and I always arrived safely. For a time I stayed on an island beside a Buddhist temple. While there I pondered what it would be like to just disappear and contemplated why I was living such a strange life.

During my medical school training, I continued traveling to many countries for my practical medical education, as the German university allowed international completion of clinical rotations. In search of a new home, I journeyed everywhere I could. After my stay in China, I spent four months in Germany and then left for South Africa, hoping to find a way to transfer my medical studies to the University of Cape Town.

Because of my bizarre experiences in China, I wanted to know if black magic really was something that could make people sick, and if that were true, could I learn to reverse it? While hitchhiking in Swaziland, a man gave me a lift and took me to his family property. His father was the administrator of the local hospital.

Of course, I wanted to go and experience what working in a hospital was like in that beautiful country! Walking through the ER and seeing patients lined up with gunshot wounds and horrible trauma from civil unrest was shocking and too much for me. I had never seen the effects of war.

Upon leaving Swaziland, I hitchhiked to KwaZulu-Natal. The little, native bus took hours to arrive, so I sat and talked to the local women at the bus station, asking them how to get to the coast. During the conversation I heard about a witch doctor in the area who I then wanted to meet.

As I continued hiking to the ocean shore, I noticed native women with white paint on their faces sacrificing chickens in some strange ritual. I did not understand the ceremony. At the town market, after staying a week in a small hut with some girls from New Zealand, I saw the witch doctor in his traditional garb.

Some of the locals told me about curses and the use of voodoo and that people had gone missing in the area. I was scared when I saw him, and it dawned on me that maybe trying to study black magic to understand how to heal demonic possession was not a particularly good idea. After eight weeks of hitchhiking, I left South Africa. I was incredibly lucky that I had stayed safe and, once again, still had no answers for my strange, life experiences.

A few months later, I spent another four weeks in clinical rotation at a hospital in Constanta, Romania, and stayed with my grandmother. This was right after the revolution to overthrow the dictator Ceausescu. Visiting Romania for the first time was an experience that made me appreciate how blessed I was to have parents who had escaped oppression, allowing me to roam free in the world.

I stood in line early in the morning to buy bread, only to be told that the bread was sold out. Despite having money to buy food, the grocery stores I went to had empty shelves. Garbage was piling up in the streets to one-story high because the garbage companies were on strike.

In Constanta, I worked in the emergency room at one of the main hospitals. My senior advisor was a fifth-year medical student. There was no doctor on duty. Mold was growing on the walls. A child came in with a large laceration on her face. We had no supplies, only what came after the revolution in international aid. We sewed the child's face with suture needles used for horses and used no anesthetic, because we had none. Lacking adequate facilities, I observed women going into labor on mattresses in the hallway.

I learned much about medicine but under, what seemed to me, horrific circumstances. The conditions in Romania were worse than Africa. For a while I had entertained becoming a part of Doctors Without Borders, but after seeing the situation in Romania, I knew this was not for me.

I remember being back in Germany after that experience and walking into a bakery with shelves stocked with more than forty kinds of bread and having an uncontrollable crying attack. Traveling, and the life experience that it brings, will change anyone.

During the following clinical year, I also spent a month at the University of Birmingham in England. Britain had a very good medical training program and I learned much to add to my clinical skill set, which prepared me well to excel at my home medical school.

In Germany, medical school is a six-year program. I completed the fourth- and fifth-year courses in one year, as I wanted to graduate one year early. I knew I would not be allowed to start my sixth year—which was all clinical—and would have a year off, so I tried to figure out what to learn next while I waited.

My mother became quite ill over the years, and we traveled to France in my fourth year of medical school to meet the Dalai Lama's physician, Dr. Tenzin Choedrak. Mother had gotten several consultations from him, and while staying at the compound, I asked for permission to come to Dharamshala in India to study with him. He agreed. It appeared that the Far East was to be my next destination during my year off. However, I was also still thinking about the psychic reading I had received in Berkeley. I wanted to learn more about how that psychic had been able to read my mind and tell me things about my life when I had never met her before.

I still had her name—Victoria—and found her phone number. My heart pounding with nervous excitement, I called and told her that she had done a reading for me years before and that I now had a year off from medical school. I wanted to learn how to do readings and train as a psychic. I asked if she would accept me as her student.

To my delight, she said yes. I was 23 years old when I went to my mother and told her that I was leaving for America and that I would never return home.

CHAPTER 2
A VERY DIFFERENT EDUCATION

When I arrived in Berkeley, California, a one-and-a-half-year psychic reading study course had just started. I told Victoria that I only had a year and to give me the fast-track. I ended up moving into Victoria's house. Because I wanted to learn healing and psychic reading, she had me study with her teacher, Laurie, a great psychic in the Bay area. The two ladies took me under their wings. Through them I was introduced to psychic surgery, initially the noninvasive form. I also met many different hands-on healers and worked with them. Doing readings was a natural gift to me. Finally, I could develop my abilities in seeing and knowing.

One day I learned a Curandero healer was coming to town who taught psychic surgery. Laurie told me I should go. That night I dreamed I was sitting in an audience with what appeared to be a native-Indian woman. She suddenly turned around and looked at me with steel-gray eyes. Then she said, "You, come up here! You are going to be really good at this!"

"How strange," I thought, when I woke up. Later that morning I drove to the place in Marin County where over a hundred people had gathered to meet this healer. Many there had illnesses. Starr, the teacher, was explaining methods of healing when she turned and stared at me in the back of the room. Pointing toward me, she said, "You, come up here. You are going to be really good at this."

Astonished, I went to the front of the room where a massage table was set up for treating patients. Starr had me palpate the breast of a woman with cancer. The lady had a golf-ball size, rock-hard tumor in her right breast. Starr went into a trance and focused and started coughing. Suddenly she coughed up a walnut-size piece of gray-looking tissue that landed on the floor. She told me to look at it. With my pathology background, I looked at what appeared to be definite fibrous irregular tissue. I had dissected enough cancers to know this looked familiar. Starr again had me palpate the woman's breast. The tumor was less than half the size of what I had palpated earlier.

Starr looked at me and said, "I can teach you this!"

I was impressed and onboard. I was to follow instructions, not think, and just do. There was a man in the audience requesting healing for a cancer on his cheek, which was an ulcerative lesion about 1.5 cm in diameter. Starr told me to put my hand under his bottom while he was sitting on a chair and visualize from my hand a green fire going through his prostate, up his spine, coming out of his head. That was all I was to do while breathing deeply.

As I followed her instructions, suddenly my body went into an absolute tingling sensation. It felt as though a firestorm of unbelievable electricity was racing through me. All at once the green fire completely took over my senses. The energy flowing through my body became so intense, it almost seemed like I was about to lose consciousness. I do not quite know how, but suddenly the tumor fell off his face. His cheek was completely normal, and a necrotic piece of tissue lay on the floor.

I had met my next teacher.

I flew to Texas and spent a month with Starr at her ranch to learn about the Curandero way of healing. There were many things I did and learned: walking on hot coals without burning my feet, holding a rebar on the soft spot of my neck between myself and another student and melting the steel with our minds, bending the rebar, and manifesting things like rice kernels out of thin air. Some people who came to the ranch were healed, many felt better, and others did not.

People in wheelchairs and on crutches lined up while a group of us at a time worked on healing them. We learned a noninvasive form of psychic surgery. Although I had seen many phenomena and learned about many things, I was still not any closer to understanding God or the cause of my own deep sadness and emotional outbursts. Results from my own healing were not consistent. I had no idea why I was racing so fast and where I was going. At the same time, I knew I had not yet found what I knew absolutely I was supposed to find.

During my year off, while engaged in psychic training, I applied to several medical schools. A letter of recommendation from the chief of surgery at my German university introduced me to the chief of the laparoscopic surgery division at the University of Southern California in Los Angeles. After I met with him, he talked to people he knew in the medical department and put in a recommendation. I could stay for a short while, based on their department's approval, but in no way would the admissions office allow me to stay for the whole year. They would only allow me one month.

With no other options available, I talked to God in my head to pray for help about the matter. There was no way I had gotten this far only to go back home. Walking into a lecture hall at USC, I quietly sat down to listen. Suddenly the speaker stared at me. After his lecture he moved towards me, called me over, and said, "Hey, who are you?" I told him I was a medical student from Germany doing my Ph.D. in cancer research and that I wanted to study here. He said, "Come with me," and that is how I became a member of his research lab, allowing me to extend my stay at USC.

Together with this professor I researched hematopoietic stem cells as well as beta HCG in the treatment of Kaposi's sarcoma. Under his tutelage I was introduced to great minds in the fields of oncology and hematology. With the help of several professors and through my belief in the grace of God, I was able to stay at USC for my last year. There I did research work that led to my first author publication, "Treatment Update for AIDS-related Kaposi's Sarcoma," published in the journal *AIDS* in 1999.[1]

At USC, I completed my last year of medical school in four-month rotations of internal medicine, surgery, and psychiatry. The internal medicine rotation was spent on the oncology and hematology wards. In Germany, that was considered the last of my six years of medical school.

One morning at USC I interviewed a new patient at the clinic. When the door opened, I looked at her neck and was surprised to see, in X-ray vision, a tumor on her thyroid that was later confirmed. I told my professor what I had seen. Despite noting I would have a brilliant future in cancer research, he warned me: "Forget about this psychic stuff. It's going to ruin your career!"

Concerned about adverse consequences by openly sharing my mind, I dove back into the research world and spent most of my time in the lab. This research and the subsequent publications from my medical student work earned me some excellent letters of recommendation. Those letters helped open the door to an interview at the elite University of Virginia combined residency program in Internal Medicine and Psychiatry in Charlottesville. I was accepted as the first foreign, medical graduate in the history of the program.

I was excited because Dr. Ian Stevenson, M.D, researcher of past-life experiences in children, used to be the chairman of the psychiatry department. It seemed that my life journey was finally getting closer to having my deeper questions answered! "The university must be really open-minded," I thought. Yet that was not the case.

The next three years required a superhuman effort. During residency we worked up to 120 hours a week, not sleeping every third or fourth night while continually studying. I had to catch up on a lot because I was not trained in the United States. Keeping up with many of my colleagues who had attended Ivy League medical schools was tough.

Secretly I was still searching for answers. My favorite rotations were on the cancer and hospice wards where I did all of my electives. At one point, as an intern in residency, I was on the cancer ward taking care of a young woman, my age, who had metastatic melanoma. Her name was Amy. As an intern, you are the primary person who takes care of that individual. I would see her multiple times a day. If anything was going wrong, I was the first one to be there.

I took care of Amy in the last three weeks of her life. She was a beautiful individual with a wonderful family and friends. She told me she had never been to Paris, had never fallen in love. The more I took care of her, I did something healthcare practitioners are not supposed to do, which is falling in love. I thought she was an angel, innocently beautiful. We were both 27 years old, but she had been sheltered and protected her entire life. I became depressed seeing her decline—and started bargaining with God. I said, "You know, I don't have family nearby. I don't really have friends. All I do is work. I've been to Paris and I've fallen in love. Why don't you take me instead and spare her?"

Some supervising physicians took note of my overprotectiveness and gently advised me, "You can't do that. You can't love patients like this because you'll never make it in this profession. It will destroy you." I did not care.

As Amy declined and came closer to her passing, if I did not have to attend to other patients during the night, I would just sit by her and pray to God and try to understand suffering.

Then one night while sleeping in my bed at home, I woke up startled. Amy was standing at the end of my bed. She looked radiant. There was a golden light around her. She did not say anything. She just smiled. Then she disappeared. I looked at the alarm clock, and it was 3 a.m. The next morning, at 6 a.m., I went to the hospital to do my rounds. I went straight to the nurse's station to speak to the nurse on night shift. "Where is she? Where is Amy?" She quietly responded, "She passed away at 3 a.m."

While part of me was devastated, I realized that Amy had appeared by my bed to let me know that she was fine and to not drown in grief. This experience was my first personal evidence that we do not die.

On the same oncology ward was a section for hospice and end-of-life care. One of my elderly patients was at the end of her life. She was in a terminal delirium, which is an experience of profound agitation before death. Hers was a single room, and I was called frequently during the night by the nurses because the patient was screaming. I had given orders for multiple different drugs to calm her, including morphine and lorazepam. I even tried antipsychotics. Nothing could calm her.

When I walked into her room and heard her cries, I realized that this was not agitated crying but a soul in horrific pain. I moved towards her bed and held her frail body in my arms and put my hand on her heart. I was endeavoring to simply be there with her and give some healing energy that would allow her to let go. In the corner of the room I saw a light appear that looked like a tunnel. She saw it too.

There was a subtle presence of beings felt in the room that came from the light. The moment they arrived, she put both of her hands up and started loudly groaning as if to hold them off. I knew they were coming to escort her into the next realm. The sounds she was making were of profound, spiritual pain. I asked God to tell me how to help this woman. I heard a clear voice in my head: "Call the family."

Outside the room I asked the nurse if her family had visited. The nurse said no. I read the chart files and there was a phone number listed for a daughter. It was two o'clock in the morning. I called, and a lady on the other side answered. I said, "Your mother is dying, and you need to come now."

My work required that I attend to multiple other patients, and I was not able to return until about five in the morning when I was called by the nurse to pronounce the patient's death. At the moment I arrived, a man and woman came out of the patient's room holding hands. The woman looked at me and asked me if I was the doctor who called her. I said, "Yes." She was crying and thanked me.

She told me that over 10 years ago the family had a falling out, and neither of the children had seen the mother since that time, nor had the children spoken to each other. The patient was unconscious and unable to speak when they arrived, but the spirit of their mother recognized them immediately. She calmed down, took her daughter's and son's hands and put them together, and then she exhaled with a relieved smile on her face and passed on.

The daughter told me that she thought her mother was waiting to die to heal this wound in the family. I knew it was so. When I walked into the patient's room, her eyes were still open, and she had a big smile on her face. The atmosphere in the room felt angelic in its lightness. I gently closed her eyes and understood that a great healing had taken place here. These kinds of spiritual interactions happened all the time, particularly at night and with dying patients. I was grateful for my ability to witness these things.

About a year later during my residency, one of my acquaintances told me that a healer was coming to town. "What kind of a healer?" I asked. "He's a priest from the Philippines and he is part of an order that believes in the healing ministry of Jesus Christ and uses it to perform psychic surgeries."

Of course, that was right down my alley. I went to meet him. At that time, I had stomach problems. He asked me why I was there, and I told him I occasionally had some pain in that area. I had pancreatitis several times in my younger years and an ulcer from stress. He had me lie on a massage table.

He said a prayer over the Bible that was about the healing ministry of Jesus Christ. He asked me to close my eyes. I said, "I don't want to. I want to watch you. I'm a doctor." He agreed.

He took his bare hands and opened the skin of my abdomen and created a ten-centimeter long incision that was perfect. I have assisted in many, many surgeries and one of the things that happens when you cut the tissue is arterial bleeding. There was no bleeding, and he continued to open the abdominal cavity. I was able to see the fat layer above my organs.

With his bare hand he dug into my abdomen. I was able to see my liver under my rib cage and my spleen. He took his hand and buried it in my abdominal cavity. He pulled tissue out that he deposited in a Mason jar. During the procedure I had absolutely no pain. In fact, there was a slightly blissful feeling.

If you know anatomy, with his hand he went through my aorta, the main artery of the body. He looked at some other structures and held them in his blood-covered, bare hands, then closed the skin just by pulling it together. There was no evidence that I ever had anything done to me. He handed me this little Mason jar containing some fibrous tissue as well as some blood clots and told me to bury it under a tree. I thought that he was quite impressive and a genuine healer. I took what I had seen him remove from my body and buried it under a young sapling in my yard.

There were many more unusual experiences during my residency that I of course never shared with anyone at the time. In my third year I was a senior resident and in charge of the code team. This means that if anybody dies in the hospital and you hear the radio signal go off—"code blue, room 221"—the team goes wherever that code occurs in the hospital and starts resuscitation.

In one particular case, in the middle of the night my beeper went off with the code blue alarm. I sprinted to the patient's room and arrived as the first responder on the scene. It was an elderly woman, and I started chest compressions. Her ribs and sternum cracked like broken glass under the strain of my compressions. I had a sense that this was not going to go well. The rest of the team arrived, and as the team leader I stepped back at the end of the bed and gave orders to coordinate the team efforts. The patient was being intubated. An intravenous access line was placed into the groin, while chest compressions continued and medication was given.

As this was occurring, all of a sudden my beingness was pulled backwards and a tunnel vision occurred. I could still hear everything that was happening. I was able to continue to give orders, but I suddenly became aware that from the corner of the room, I was being watched. In the corner of the ceiling I saw a shadow, and I became aware that the woman whose body we were resuscitating was looking at me from up there. Then I heard clearly in my head, as if someone were standing behind me, "What are you doing to me?" I could sense her puzzlement at the commotion in the room. I continued the resuscitative effort and called the code to stop the procedure after about twenty-five minutes. I did not tell anyone what I had seen or experienced.

A few years later I had a conversation with a patient who had flatlined during surgery and he told me about his experience. He suddenly was out of his body floating in the corner of the room and observed the surgical team as they were performing the resuscitation. He described himself as feeling detached.

Although he knew it was his body, he had no emotion and was just observing the scene. I told him about my experience, and he said, "I totally believe you." He said that it is the most curious thing to understand why there is so much commotion happening and people are working on this body and you are somehow aware that your body is dead but you are not.

I have asked every patient who has had a cardiac arrest about their experiences out of the body. There have been some fascinating conversations about my patients' experiences—which would always brighten my days—and I was the only physician that ever asked about them. Many of those people never even told their own family what they experienced for fear of rejection. Those who have had genuine near-death experiences often completely change their life thereafter because their entire worldview and purpose in life has changed.

During my residency program, I would spend my weekends at the Satchidananda Ashram in Yogaville, where I befriended one of the senior monks, a former artist and sculptor. He was in his eighties, and we were best friends for about six years. We were both socially withdrawn people, misfits, who did not belong anywhere. We would roam the forest together, swim in the river, or spend hours in the meditations hall and have long conversations about the Divine.

I had absolutely nothing in common with any of my classmates at the residency program, but Swami Tyagananda and I shared a world of imagination and love for spiritual mysteries. He listened to my strange life experiences and was fascinated by them. By that time I was a Reiki Master, and when off duty on weekends I worked on people with hands-on healing using the multiple modalities I had learned over the years. I started a spiritual support group for women with cancer and had many wonderful experiences. What I loved most about this work with people who were facing their own mortality was the fact that the fear of death removed their mask. In the face of limited time left, many things that had been so important no longer were. To others, speaking the truth and expressing love became imperative to them in their journey. I had the wonderful privilege of being with many dear friends at the end of their lives.

During this senior year in residency, I was battling profound exhaustion. Sometimes I had second thoughts about the elite medical program and my ambition to continue and succeed. I looked at alternative medical fellowships, but my desire to find an answer for cancer won, so I pushed myself forward with all my will to finish the training.

Inevitably I was at work one day and while standing up from a chair I felt a sharp, electrocuting pain in my back radiating down my leg. In that moment I had ruptured a disc that was pushing on a nerve, and I could not walk. This made it exceedingly difficult to finish my residency. I was in the final months. A "regular" surgeon I consulted told me, "We can operate." I did not really want that.

Despite my extensive medical training, I was scared of the healthcare system and would only go to healers. Yet I had been accepted to the University of Virginia Hematology and Oncology fellowship program and my vision of becoming a cancer specialist was remarkably close. However, six weeks prior to starting that program, the director told me they could not have a fellow unable to walk and that they would consider me for next year. I wasn't considered well enough to join the fellowship.

In one moment, my whole world broke apart. I was devastated. Not only had I lost my dream but also my visa to the United States. I finished my residency in excruciating pain. I studied to complete my internal medicine board exam, which I took kneeling on my knees, as I was unable to sit. Thankfully I passed the exam.

My mother came to stay with me and helped me dissolve my household. She told me about an individual in Brazil, John of God, and I decided to go there to see if he could heal my spine. My mother and Swami Tyagananda came with me, as I was only able to walk very short distances due to the excruciating pain.

John of God has verifiably done some extraordinary things. I had no idea at the time about his sinister affiliations that led to his later conviction in multiple crimes. He is a medium and had spirit entities who worked through him. Thousands of people have been healed. Some surgeries happened spontaneously; others were visibly done with instruments. With no sterilization, I watched him perform the most impossible procedures without infections occurring.

When the time came, I wanted visible surgery because I wanted to see what he was going to do. The day that I had surgery, I was standing in the room. John of God came through the door. At the other side of the hall I remember hearing him speaking words that sounded like "Deus pode todo, Deus cura todo." I don't remember the exact words, but I remember their meaning. I understood him to be chanting, "God can do anything" and "God can heal anything." I was asked to close my eyes, and while he was still standing at the other side of the room, I saw in my mind three entities of light walking towards me. One of them had what looked like a light saber in his hand. All I remember is that this middle entity took the light saber and cut through my body. When I woke up, I was in a different room and I could not move. I was paralyzed from the neck down. I said, "What happened?"

"Well, you passed out and you had major surgery."

I said, "How did I have major surgery? Nobody even touched me."

He said, "There were entities who worked on you."

After a while, the anesthesia wore off. This was a "spiritual" anesthesia. That night I had a hysterical crying attack for no reason. Two of the healers came in and started saying prayers from the Bible. As they did so, the midsection of my body raised up from the bed and a black, visible cloud lifted from my body and went through the roof. I immediately calmed down but was stunned and asked what in the world was that? The healers told me that it was a possession.

A couple of days later I was able to walk again.

From Brazil I traveled back to Europe with my mother and stayed with her in Portugal. I thought my life was over. I saw no purpose for my life if I could not cure cancer. I wanted to throw my whole career away and applied in Germany to work in a medical bookstore selling books. The response was that I was overqualified. When I became severely depressed, my back pain would come back. It took me many months to regroup.

During that time, I went to Fatima, where the vision of Mother Mary was seen by children. I wanted to learn more about Mary's life and her miraculous healing abilities. I had previously been to Ephesus in Turkey and visited Mother Mary's home where she had allegedly died. The idea of a female healing deity spoke to me. In all those places I had a strange sense of familiarity. I read that Mary had been to Egypt and that there were secrets in the great pyramids. I dreamed I was in the pyramid and discovered information about Mary. Following such messages of premonition had always been my map, so I decided to travel to Egypt. There I toured the Nile for two weeks, visiting all the historic sites. I crawled into the Great Pyramid of Giza, excited that I would have some sort of spiritual experience of knowing. But I did not, and I never met Mother Mary in the pyramid. It was just a hot, sticky, narrow space. No answer there.

When I arrived in Karnak, I stood on the road lined with figures of seated rams and was so impressed by them. I did not know then that this road was created in honor of my future Teacher, Ramtha the Enlightened One, the great Ram.

After returning to Portugal, my brother Radu talked to me and reminded me of why I had wanted to go to medical school in the first place. He urged me not to throw away my career and told me that I could still be a doctor. He wanted me to get over my profound sense of failure in not meeting my life's goal of healing cancer.

I decided to return to the United States. To meet the United States visa requirements for my J1 waiver, I had to spend three years in a medically underserved area. I flew to Virginia where I received a position at a clinic in the Appalachian Mountains and moved to Meadows of Dan, a town of 400 people. I found a small cabin to live in with its own lake, and my road was called "Light Ridge Road."

There I spent the next three years serving at a large community clinic and hiking in the wilderness during my days off. I learned to listen to beautiful bluegrass music and go to community square dances. It was a simple time in my life. Despite all the teachers I had had, I knew they were not the one. Often shortly after meeting them and studying with them for a period of enthusiasm, I knew they did not have the answers I was looking for. The voice inside of me knew I had not yet found who and what I was looking for.

One day in 2005, I walked into a health food store in Virginia and found the DVD, *What the Bleep Do We Know?*[2] When I watched the movie and saw Ramtha for the first time, I bolted up from my sofa and said out loud, "I want what I see in that woman's eyes!"

I feverishly looked up Ramtha's School of Enlightenment (RSE) and ordered *Ramtha, The White Book*.[3] The words I read were unbelievably beautiful to me. A short time after that, I was sitting in my outdoor hot tub gazing at a starry night sky. I asked the sky out loud, "So am I supposed to go to Ramtha's School?" In that moment, the biggest and brightest shooting star I had ever seen flew across the sky. I took that as a yes and flew to Washington for my Beginning Retreat a couple months later.

When I studied in this beginning class, I knew I had found what I had been searching for my whole life—real answers. Ramtha's greatest message is "Behold God." In Yelm, Washington, I discovered that the divine entity I had been talking to and looking for had been in me all along. While there, I discovered Ramtha and JZ Knight are two separate entities who share the same body through a process called channeling. To explain this process, I include the following clarification from *The Encyclopedia of American Religions*:

> "One of the more controversial aspects of Ramtha's teachings is the form in which he chose to deliver his message. Ramtha's form of communication is by no means arbitrary and superficial. He has pointed out explicitly the reasons behind such a format and explained that in order to grasp his message, it is important to become aware of the paradigms of thought, the roots of preconceived ideas, unconscious prejudices, and molds in which we normally perceive ourselves and evaluate reality.
>
> "Ramtha communicates his teachings through the phenomenon called channeling. In fact, it was Ramtha who made the term known, before the New Age movement adopted it in the 1980s. He uses the body of JZ Knight to channel himself and teach his philosophy in person.
>
> "A channel is different from a medium in that the channel is not the intermediary between the consciousness coming through them and the audience. The channel does not remain in a

transfixed, altered state while channeling; rather they leave their body completely and allow the consciousness coming through to have full faculty over all their bodily movements and functions."[4]

At this Class 101 beginning event, the teaching on Gladys®, a description of the cell by JZ Knight, was the most brilliant exposé on how we function that I had ever heard in my life.[5] In this funny, genius teaching of absolute simplicity, she answered some of the most profound questions that I had never learned about in medical school. How does a thought create physical reality? How do our attitudes cause illness? She answered it all. I was absolutely enchanted and thought I had found the Holy Grail. From the RSE campus parking lot I called my brother in Brooklyn, New York. I told him, "Radu, I finally found it. This is it, and you must come. This school is the real thing." He came to the school two months later, and my mother came a couple of months after that. All of us are still students of RSE.

After my Beginning Retreat, I flew back to Virginia and suddenly noticed that my vision had dramatically improved. For several years I was required to wear glasses and could not see while driving at night without them. In the week after that event, while driving and forgetting to put them on, I realized I could see perfectly. I immediately stopped at a large dumpster and threw my prescription glasses away. I have never needed them since.

Shortly thereafter I had some X-rays done of my abdomen. The calcifications from chronic, recurring pancreatitis, which I had suffered from a lot, had disappeared from my X-rays. Those were the first of many miraculous healings that I have experienced after applying the disciplines of RSE.

Ramtha talked about change and not living in the past. When I flew back to Virginia, I burned every piece of property that reminded me of who I was, every picture and personal diary. Of course, that was not the kind of change Ramtha was talking about. It took many years for me to understand what it was that needed to change.

I moved to Washington State after two years of regularly commuting to RSE events. I spent every vacation day I had at Ramtha's School of Enlightenment studying and learning how to apply the knowledge in my life. Ramtha's School is not a fast-track school. You cannot consume information intellectually like I was used to and know what these teachings mean. They must be experienced, which is done through engaging a series of disciplines that allows the student to focus their mind on a concept to create a desired outcome.

Ramtha teaches by sending runners, which are the manifestation of his words into a reality for a student to experience. As explained in *Ramtha, A Beginner's Guide to Creating Reality:* "A runner in Ramtha's lifetime was responsible for bringing specific messages or information. A master teacher has the ability to send runners to other people that manifest their words or intent in the form of an experience or an event."[6] These realities can be so bizarre that there can be no doubt they came from Ramtha. For example, one day Ramtha taught that he was going to send a runner and that we would know that it came from him.

The next day I went for a walk on the trail behind my office. I looked up and saw a man in a tie, shirt, and business blazer running in Birkenstock sandals towards me. I kept looking at this man's figure, and after recognizing him as my primary care section chief, I started laughing and asked him what he was doing. He said he was sitting in his office on the east side of town and suddenly had the overwhelming urge to go for a run. So he did. But now he felt he should return to his office. I watched him run off and thought only Ramtha can send such remarkable displays of words manifested into reality, and I got a real "runner" to prove it.

CHAPTER 3
REALITY CHECK

When I moved to Yelm, Washington, to be close to the school, I was oblivious to the extraordinary disinformation campaign that was going on against RSE and JZ Knight. Newspapers were producing exaggerated lies to the detriment of many students that came from all over the world, just like myself.

Not knowing about the community's prejudice, I interviewed for a position at a local medical clinic. It seemed like a great match and I was told I would get the position. I was invited to an evening dinner where I was asked why I came to the area. When I excitedly shared that I was going to Ramtha's School of Enlightenment, the job offer was retracted the next day. That was my first rude awakening to the extraordinary prejudice against the school.

In a later position I had a supervisor who hated Ramtha's School and gay people, and he started religious and sexual harassment. I had to get an attorney to protect myself and underwent two years of bullying at the workplace.

What we see today happening to President Trump—the lies, the threats, the newspapers going against the president and painting a negative image—is exactly what has happened to JZ Knight, Ramtha's School of Enlightenment, and its student body for decades. The lies told could not have been farther from the truth.

CHAPTER 4
MY JOURNEY OF HEALING CANCER

In May 2012, I was with my partner Laura in our little cabin. I was on my way out the door when Laura playfully pulled me backwards and tickled me. Suddenly she paused and pressed on my abdomen and asked, "What is that?" I palpated my abdomen and felt something hard under my belly button. This caught my attention. I kept pushing on it and noticed that it was quite large. It did not hurt. I was alarmed and decided to go to my own house to have my mother, who was in Yelm at the time, examine me.

When I arrived at my house and lay back on the sofa in my living room, my mother palpated my abdomen and determined the mass to be the size of about a three-month pregnancy, reaching from my pubic bone all the way to my belly button and filling the majority of my lower abdomen.

I called my office manager, as I did not have a primary care physician, and asked if possibly one of my colleagues would see me as a patient and look at this mass. My colleague declined, but my office manager contacted a partner office, where one of the physicians was willing to see me the next morning at 7:30 a.m.

I had worked with my new doctor a few years earlier in that very office. I was grateful that she was willing to see me on such short notice. She examined me and confirmed there was a large mass in my abdomen. She then sent me to the hospital for an immediate ultrasound. At the hospital, the ultrasound showed a large uterine mass and what appeared to also be a large ovarian mass.

My doctor called me with the results of the ultrasound and scheduled an immediate CT scan to have this further evaluated. I went to the office of the local radiologists, who knew me well, as I had referred hundreds of my patients to them over the years. Waiting for my CT scan, I was quite nervous and asked the technician if a radiologist would be willing to review the scan with me. Very kindly, since they knew me, one of the radiologists pulled me into his office and we looked together at the scans.

The results and the pictures were shocking to me. There was a large uterine mass that was displacing the bladder and a large 11 cm mass pushing adjacent to tissues, which appeared to be of ovarian origin. The scan also revealed lymph node enlargements in the pelvic area. Why hadn't I known this? The radiologist tried to calm me down by saying it was still possible that this was benign and not necessarily a malignancy. However, because of its features, the mass needed immediate surgical intervention.

Now I was really getting worried. One of the blood tests performed by my doctor was a CA 125. This is a tumor marker for ovarian cancer. I had access to my medical records online. That evening while checking my emails, the result was posted. My CA 125 was 36, with the upper limit of normal being 35. This is when I really understood the shocking possibility that I might be dealing with ovarian cancer.

The following day I had an appointment with the gynecologist to discuss the results of the CT scan. My partner Laura came with me. The gynecologist explained to me that I did need surgery and that because of the elevated tumor marker and the size of the tumor, she was referring me to a specialty clinic for gynecologic oncology in Seattle. The main reason for that was the need to get intraoperative pathology on the tumor. If it turned out to be malignant, the surgery would need to be more extensive.

Almost two weeks passed before the surgery date was set. I went on medical leave. I was afraid of dying and afraid, after having been obsessed with cancer for all my life, that I had actually manifested the disease from my focus. But I was also aware, from Ramtha's teachings, that the true reason for my having gotten ill were all the recurring emotions that had been with me throughout my life.

Anger, rage, blame, and resentment—I was aware that my emotional, stormy intensity had pushed the genetic buttons. I was terrified of my light review. I had learned at Ramtha's School of Enlightenment that at the end of life we see our every thought and action and their true intent. The divine being that we are, the God within, would review everything that I had done to other people and I would realize that I had done it to myself.

When this unfinished soul business—emotions never brought to wisdom over lifetimes—was reviewed at time of death, I would realize that I had missed an opportunity in the cycle of my spiritual reincarnations and just run another body into the ground for emotional addiction.

I remember one morning sitting down with Laura and telling her every bad thought I had ever had and every bad thing I had ever done in a rescue confession. After I was solemnly finished, she simply said, "That's it?"

I replied, "That's it."

She said, "Hmm, that's not so bad. Do you want breakfast?"

I called my mother and my brother to tell them how wrong I was and how sorry for all the difficulties I had created for them. I tried to clean up just in case I was not going to survive. I prepared a will and set my affairs in order. During this period I spent most of my time doing RSE disciplines focusing on a benign outcome, as in no way would I accept chemotherapy or radiation.

I survived the surgery with the large uterine and ovarian masses removed. My focus manifested that there had been no metastatic spread. Postsurgically I had internal bleeding that caused a large hematoma in my abdomen. A lymph vessel had been cut during the surgery and was leaking and not healing.

I was discharged with an undiagnosed urinary tract infection and a temperature, as well as internal undiagnosed bleeding. The infection caused urinary retention, which is the inability to urinate while having extreme urgency to go, and excruciating pain. In the first days after being released from the surgery, I continued having a temperature. I went to the bathroom and there was a pool of blood gushing down my legs.

My partner rushed me to the hospital, and I was readmitted. A CT scan showed the internal bleeding with a large hematoma pressing on the bladder and a new mass from a lymphocele that developed as a result of the cut lymph vessel. I had two drains put in, one in my back and one into my abdomen, and was started on intravenous antibiotics due to concern for an abscess in the abdomen. The lymphocele drain stayed in and did not stop draining for weeks.

Eventually it became infected again. My temperature started to rise and the abdominal pain was getting worse. I knew I had to get to the hospital. There was an event with Ramtha, and I wanted to go regardless of how sick I was. I just wanted to hear from my Teacher that I was going to get out of this mess. I passed out at the event, as the temperature was spiking. Later I was told by a participant that Ramtha had spoken to my Holy Spirit and that I was going to be all right.

The next day Laura drove me to the University of Washington, where I was admitted with an intra-abdominal abscess. I was started on a morphine drip and IV antibiotics. The medical team assembled to figure out how to solve the problem with the lymphocele that was still draining, and they were discussing surgery.

Throughout my recovery time, I was using the disciplines learned at Ramtha's School to heal myself and relieve my pain. While in the hospital, I pushed my IV pole with morphine and antibiotics along the corridors, while doing my Neighborhood Walk®. This discipline is defined in *Ramtha, A Beginner's Guide to Creating Reality*, as: "The Neighborhood Walk® is a technique created by JZ Knight for raising consciousness and energy and intentionally modifying our neuronets and set patterns of thinking no longer wanted and replacing them with new ones of our choice."[1]

I would repeat over and over that I have always been radiantly healthy and that I do not need any more surgery. There were multiple delays for a decision by the doctors. I finally had a small procedure done to change the drain. After another week in the hospital, the radiologist said, "The drain is in the right place and your lymphocele has stopped draining." After more than six weeks, this was an absolute miracle.

The drain was removed, and I went home. I continued to focus and apply Ramtha's disciplines, and at a follow-up CT scan a month later, the 10 cm lymphocele was gone. It had completely disappeared.

The doctors were watching my left ovary because I had internal bleeding and changes there as well. A few weeks later I went for a follow-up ultrasound. This was after I had indulged in more anger outbursts. The radiologist came to me and said, "I don't know what happened to you, but your left ovary has grown significantly. It is now almost 10 cm and a fistula to the vagina has developed." He showed it to me on the ultrasound. He told me this would require another surgical intervention and he was concerned that it was malignant because it had grown so fast compared to the scans just a month earlier.

I understood from Ramtha and JZ Knight's teachings that a complete healing required a complete neighborhood move in my brain. After the experience of knowing that I had healed the lymphocele, I was listening to another teaching by JZ Knight. This reinforced that I could do this, that I could apply the discipline successfully and that I needed to continue to self-correct.

At the Class 101 event, self-correction is a discipline taught at RSE that interrupts old patterns of thinking that are harmful.[2] By self-correcting I become, and am, a new mind! I applied the disciplines very diligently to conquer my anger and continued to focus on radiant health. A follow-up MRI scan one week later showed that the mass was completely dissolved, the left ovary was normal, and no fistula was present.

The application of the disciplines has saved my life. It was my own patterns of thinking that were causing all of my suffering. Changing my mind allowed me to have another chance.

CHAPTER 5
HEALING MIND ACROSS TIME

Experiencing a concept allows personal truth. Imagine how much of my life I had spent thinking about cancer, what was causing it, and why people died. My own experience answered that question.

In 2012, during this healing journey from ovarian cancer, I was continually plagued by my fear of death, and even after my healing from surgery this concern persisted.

I decided to dedicate a full retreat at Ramtha's School of Enlightenment—the All Group Follow-Up, November 28-December 2, 2012—to focusing on resolution. I drew a card with the intent of being fully aware as my conscious God self in an out-of-body experience. I wanted to resolve my fear of dying. I spent the five days focusing on nothing else.

Two days after the Follow-Up event, while asleep I became aware that I was lying on a gurney in a hospital. Suddenly I knew that I was about to die and found myself screaming, "Nurse! Help." I heard the code blue sirens go off, as a medical team rapidly assessed me. I felt my consciousness falling backwards out of my body into darkness. I could hear in the distance the resuscitation efforts and orders of doctors being yelled out while administering electroshocks and CPR.

I was aware outside of my body. This was not the first time I had experienced myself out of body, so I thought the command, "I want to go out into space." In that moment, a pair of golden eyes flashed in the Void and I knew I could not control where I was going but had to surrender to the journey.

I was aware that I had just died but was completely detached, and not the least bit upset. Traveling through the Void in darkness I knew I was going somewhere. I "arrived" from darkness into a room with some furniture, a sofa, and on it was sitting my current dog Rajani. I looked at her and went to embrace her, asking her what she was doing here, since my former identity had just died. As I touched the dog, she transformed into a black-haired, approximately 40-year-old woman, who grabbed me by my neck trying to choke me, asking, "How do you like me now?" I knew this woman was my lover in a previous lifetime.

I detached from her and moved through the room towards a door and opened it. There was a dusty road and some buildings that looked like a storefront from a town in a Western movie. It was a strange place because I was aware that I was being observed. It appeared to me that I was being observed as a man in a former life. Something made me aware that I had died as a man before I became Ana in this lifetime.

I was conscious that the beings who were looking at me were all "dead," yet alive. All were female, and I was the man they hated. I had used and abused, as a reckless, controlling, violent, selfish man.

Two police officers were taking away a handcuffed woman with a black eye, who glared at me with hate and jealousy. I knew that black eye was my handiwork and she was a lover in this former life. At the same time I knew this was my mother in the life as Ana.

As the magnitude of what suffering I had provoked in these women's lives as a selfish man came fully into my awareness, I heard a loud voice thundering over the road. It said, "This is how you become a crossover." A crossover is a gay person, a lover of their own kind.

I looked into the hateful eyes of the woman with the black eye as she was taken away.

Then my awareness shifted to a new room, representing another parallel reality. I was observing from the corner of the ceiling a scene in which I, as Ana, was sitting at a dinner table with my partner Laura, to whom I am married in this current life.

Laura had glowing, golden light around her head. I was aware that I was dead and Laura was alive. Even though I saw myself from above and that my body below me was alive, it did not seem real—only my awareness that I was dead was real.

A waitress with a short, gray apron approached us from the right to get our order. On the other side of our table was a window, framed by dark wood, and outside was a body of water with waves. My conversation with Laura was beautiful and peaceful. Suddenly I could faintly hear the voices of the doctors and nurses from far away bleeding through from a different reality still occurring. I was traveling through darkness and heard, "She has been gone twenty-five minutes. We have a pulse." I became aware of my body on the hospital gurney drawing in my first breath, returning from death. At that same moment, I woke up from the dream, shaken. I became aware that I was in my room at home staring into darkness. I thought, "WOW—I just died. That was not so bad! And I had been in so many different realities all at once!"

It was early morning, 3:30 a.m., and I decided to get up and create my day, doing my Neighborhood Walk® in my bedroom in the dark. While engaged in this discipline, I began to notice a powerful presence in my room. I said, "Hello? Who's here?" while the hair on the back of my neck stood up. As I stared into darkness, a bright flash of white light filled my room from nowhere, and for a moment the room was as bright as day.

I realized the powerful presence I was aware of was my spiritual self. Standing in my bedroom I understood that I was currently alive, engaging my Neighborhood Walk®, and simultaneously I had died and was haunting my room, bodiless. I was also aware that at the same time I was in between lives on a road gazing at the woman with the black eye while in the room with Rajani, my dog. I was also sitting with Laura at a dining table.

As I kept walking, I continued to be totally aware in all of these realities and thought the words, "I have always been future Now," knowing that all timelines were being simultaneously affected and healed by my declaration.

I walked in this powerful state for moments of no time, absolutely detached, observing, now. At some point my awareness came back to just Ana here. I was stunned by what had happened. As best I could, I shared the experience later that day with Laura. It was the complete manifestation of the reality I had focused upon during the RSE event. My fear of death was gone, and I understood more about being a matrix mechanic.

Through Ramtha's teachings and my experience, I understood our multidimensional reality in the quantum field occurs simultaneously, and we are right now experiencing all of our past and future lives. Being influenced by the past means reliving an emotional experience that has been repeated over many lifetimes and has never been resolved.

It was now clear to me that my anger against men was caused by my own spiritual rejection of my actions as a man towards women. I was resenting a part of myself that was reflected in my environment. A matrix mechanic is a mind engineer that can look at specific patterns of thought and the reality that they create and change them so a new reality can manifest.

A few weeks later, my mother and I got into an argument. Though the time was stressful, I already knew the outcome. I understood that in my out-of-body experience I had seen a past, but also a future, and knew this was purposeful.

Intermittently, the angry, tyrannical man I used to be and saw in my experience would come out of the closet of my mind. Some situations would trigger rage in me to fight this reflection, even try to destroy it, so I did not have to look at it anymore. This resulted in much conflict that periodically threatened my beautiful life with painful chaos. I understood that this was for me to own, especially knowing that I could not get angry because it would pose the risk that I would get sick again. I knew that I had started to rapidly manifest my thoughts, and that to lose control of my own self-correction could mean manifesting further illness.

Dutifully, I applied the disciplines of C&E® and

Neighborhood Walk® daily, focusing always first on what I had NEVER been, and in C&E® blowing out every day control, anger, hate, insecurity, victimization—every negative word I could think of that I might have held as an emotional propensity. The discipline of C&E®, an acronym for Consciousness & Energy®, is defined in *Ramtha, A Beginner's Guide to Creating Reality* as ". . . the fundamental discipline of manifestation and raising of consciousness taught in Ramtha's School of Enlightenment. Through this discipline the students learn to create an analogical state of mind, open up their higher seals, and create reality from the Void."[1]

At some point I eliminated enough denial about what was buried within me that I simply looked into my environment, knowing that my mind is all things, and blowing out any negative attitudes I saw in others. It was not important to identify if this was relevant now to me but simply if it was in my reality that I took responsibility for its creation and changed it.

I understood from my experience that this was the way that in increments I would be able to change my life and affect my own matrix towards the future I desired.

Much change has happened through this journey of awakening, and many things I have wanted all my life began to manifest.

For my fortieth birthday, Laura took me to the Salish Lodge at Snoqualmie Falls for the weekend. On April 12, 2014, we went to the hotel restaurant for my birthday dinner. We were talking about amazing concepts we were reading in the book, *Alien Interview*, edited by Lawrence Spencer.[2]

The waitress came in. She had a short, gray apron around her waist. I looked up at Laura, and her hair was bathed in a golden glow. I looked at the window and its wooden frame that I recognized.

I absolutely froze when I realized that I was sitting in the restaurant I had seen two years before, but it was its mirror image. The window and table were on the opposite side I had seen, but the scene was the same. The body of water was the view of Snoqualmie Falls. I looked into the reflection in the window, and there was the scene I had lived before.

My expression changed to utter shock and I could not speak. I could only stare at Laura, who was asking me, "What happened?"

Tears were flowing down my face, as I realized that I had made it to this destiny point that I had already lived. I WAS ALIVE. I WAS IN THE FUTURE THAT HAD ALREADY HAPPENED AND I WAS ALIVE IN IT BOTH THEN AND NOW.

In the weeks that followed, I realized that some of the last residues of my personal war and anger were diminished, like a shadow that had lifted. I looked at Laura one day and said, "It is gone, you know." She said, "Yes, I know."

In the following years I started attending Intimate Day with Ramtha events. These were small group gatherings to learn from the Master Teacher.

The Intimate Days became a catalyst for change in my life by virtue of the runners that I received from them. During one of these special events, Ramtha told me I was still stuck and that he would make me a genius if I let him.

One of the things that Ramtha talked about was the corruption of the healthcare industry, which I was a part of. He talked about the detrimental effects of vaccines on human health. By this time I was the Medical Director for the Geriatric Center of Excellence and the Medical Director at a large nursing facility in Lacey, Washington. I had advanced in my leadership role. I was paid very well and lived an extremely comfortable life.

A major opportunity presented itself when, in 2018, I became JZ Knight's supervising physician for the Mercy Blu Room program. This started a fantastic journey of research and discovery. It was as if she and Ramtha woke me up from a deep sleep in my predictable comfort zone.

In JZ's program I used alternative therapies in conjunction with the Blu Room to treat patients, including those with cancer. I also became JZ's personal physician. I was constantly researching and reading. JZ would give me assignments to research different compounds for the patients at her program. She also wanted me to help her reverse her own atherosclerosis.

Despite many colorful experiences with a variety of psychic and other healing methods, I relied on my traditional knowledge base in my profession. Working with JZ, I found myself consuming knowledge and new information with astonishing speed, as I discovered alternative healing strategies. I was eager to find solutions and delighted when JZ was happy with something that I found.

JZ Knight can see into the future and is an extraordinary, visionary genius. Everything I learned, because of her, reshaped my own database of information. The more I learned, the more I realized what I did not know. During this period I read many thousands of pages of books and articles.

I wanted to know what JZ knew and how she was able to construct the Blu Room and why was it helping people. I bought all the science books that were sold in JZ's Closet from her own library on subjects like sacred geometry, quantum physics, chemistry, and antimatter physics. I devoured them all and then went after many of the references that were quoted by the scientists and found even greater depths of information.

Suddenly I found myself living a lifelong dream. Runners from Ramtha changed everything in my life. I became more and more restless though with my own hypocrisy of still being in the healthcare system and having influenza vaccines given in my name. As part of a pay-for-performance incentive program at work, we had to prescribe statin drugs that I knew were toxic. I had learned more and more about healthcare corruption and that much of what I was practicing as standard of care was a lie. I was always hiding when I told my patients about alternative ways to treat cancer or other diseases.

I just could not live with myself anymore and finally had to exchange financial security and professional success for truth. I contemplated a question from JZ about what is life without truth.

I had to overcome my fear and just do it. During that year

of discovery and contemplation, I participated in every labyrinth scheduled at RSE. The labyrinth is affectionately called The Tank® at Ramtha's School. The book *Ramtha, A Beginner's Guide to Reality*, explains this challenging discipline: "The Tank® is the name given to the labyrinth used as part of the disciplines of Ramtha's School of Enlightenment. The students are taught to find the entry to this labyrinth blindfolded and move through it focusing on the Void without touching the walls or using the eyes or the senses. The objective of this discipline is to find, blindfolded, the center of the labyrinth or a room designated and representative of the Void."[3]

In several of these sessions I successfully completed the journey to the heart of the labyrinth. This exceptional training in focus was imperative to give me the confidence that I could maneuver the unknown in my life and unfold my destiny.

After having spent so many years in a comfort zone conforming to social expectations in the medical healthcare system, I had buried my sense of adventure and courage. The Tank® and other disciplines in Ramtha's school helped me find that spirit again.

Finally, in 2019, I quit my job, gave up all my leadership roles, and changed my career to go into private practice in integrative medicine. Laura became my business partner and we worked together to make this happen.

One morning while setting up the office, I was engaged in a Neighborhood Walk® in the parking lot. I looked at my new office building. Oddly, it was a strange building that looked like a Western storefront.

Suddenly I had an overwhelming sensation of déjà vu, as I realized that this was exactly the Western storefront I had seen in my dying experience in 2012, seven years earlier.

This future that I was now living was the dream of having my own practice fulfilled. This reality already existed seven years earlier as a potential future, and the continuous change in addressing past emotions allowed me to quantum shift to this parallel reality in which I have always had my greatest dreams.

Many of those voices of emotional, soul bruises had been made wise, and now a new future could be experienced.

I did not understand over the years how captured in my own mind I had been. Applying the disciplines taught at Ramtha's School, I had continued for many years every day to blow out negative emotions during C&E® and create what I wanted to be instead. Over time, my life changed completely. Certain attitudes like fear had manifested earlier in my body as lifelong asthma. As the fear left, the asthma disappeared, and from having to use an inhaler multiple times a day, I went to not needing one at all.

I began to heal myself enough that the old, captured self was no longer there. Instead, my new life in the Western storefront, an office building in Yelm, lay ahead of me. I had seen far into the future in a Now and realized the multidimensional nature of myself as a spiritual being.

Physical healing occurs through healing the spiritual being that has lived for eons and is stuck in old, emotional patterns of attitudes. When we heal those patterns—these voices of the past that still haunt us in this lifetime—we can heal this body and our soul.

Chapter 6
Living the Future Now

Time travel is not only possible right now by means of technology that is already available in black projects, but a trained mind can travel in time. If we envision a future and dream it into being, everything that we dream about will come true. Such is the quantum physics law of observation.

As I described earlier from my dying experience, I understood how past emotions would affect the Now in my life if I were to still live them. I learned it was possible to change the matrix of one's life towards the future by owning these emotional expressions.

Ramtha teaches his students how our future self can redeem us here now. I was absolutely enchanted with that idea and often envisioned who I would be millions of years into the future.

In 2014, I was taught by JZ Knight at an event at RSE how to make a plan to create my future life. The idea was to envision my future incarnation as if it were simply another day. I did so, and in the document I described and dreamed a being that was unlimited, immortal, able to fold space/time, know all sciences, and had realized becoming the love of God. I outlined where I would go and what I would experience at the time of my physical death.

When I was told at Ramtha's School that there are no rules in the quantum field, I developed a theory that I did not want to wait for my death to live this amazing person who knows so much. Consequently, I wrote instructions to my unlimited self, living millions of years in the future, to download that future knowledge to me now in my current incarnation as Ana.

Specifically, I wrote that I come back from the future and download future technologies, which include the panacea of healing all diseases and the molecular solution of immortality medicine.

I wrote that my future self would appear to me here now and manifest through time warps and wormholes transferring information between universes and dimensions. I would be taken through wormholes traveling to see future civilizations and meet extraordinary beings on spaceships.

My future self would insert future time tiles into my existence, which include books of the future downloaded. I wrote to be taken out of my body at night and to be taught the extraordinary science of the future, of medicine, physics, healing, and clean energy. I asked to be taught the unconditional love of God and downloaded with the absolute love and pure joy of being. I wrote to intentionally open my brain to fully see and know and be given full memory of the future and erase the memory of any past karma.

Two years after I wrote this plan, I had an experience in which my Orb self was pulled out of my body through wormholes through the roof of my house. I watched two torsion fields that began in my body from my shoulder blades and went straight through the ceiling.

I was pulled up through one of the torsion fields out of my body. In the first experience, I saw a craft made from blue-living tissue, transparent, and I could see space through it. There was some type of medical equipment for procedures.

Twice that same night I was pulled out of my bed through a torsion field. Laura told me I was screaming in bed and could not be awakened for some time. Waking up briefly, I told her that I had been taken through a torsion field into a craft, when seemingly I fell back asleep and it happened again.

When I went through the torsion field the second time, I was standing in front of a blue being, who I recognized as my future self. The spaceship was a giant, blue-living cell and it was intelligently controlled by this blue being's consciousness.

It was exactly what I had written in my plan. I was absolutely amazed that what I had written had happened exactly as detailed. That meant that everything else I had written would also occur. From then on, I focused on this blue alien.

On one occasion while I was seeing patients at the Mercy Blu Room complex in Yelm, JZ Knight walked in to visit. She told me that when she goes into the Blu Room she works on remembering here in this time what she knows when she leaves her body. Another time when I visited JZ at her house, I showed her a picture I had drawn of the alien I saw. She told me that my future self is dreaming me here. I focused for years to understand and experience what she said.

Every day I focus on my future self, to be this blue being. I have no question in my mind that advanced civilizations are real, and I have seen them even when I was a small child. I would tell my mother that the people without faces were there again standing by my bed. They had large eyes but no nose or mouth. My mother did not know what to do with her strange daughter. I had profuse nosebleeds after they appeared.

I have seen unidentified craft across the hills from my house, as wide as the entire hillside, illuminating the night sky and other strange objects flying at night over my house.

The idea of personal redemption, not by some external savior but my own future who already knows the path, was a concept taught by Ramtha. I wanted to know what that meant. In fact, the teaching on Light Medicine in this book was something I had always wanted to understand. Ramtha often presents concepts and ideas that lie completely outside of the understanding of his students. But we can know and experience the wisdom of what he teaches by contemplating, exploring, and focusing on the manifestation of living our own answers.

Artificial intelligence is not the greatest future of humanity. There is an alternate future for humanity in which we understand as divine beings that we can focus on any concept and download the information from the quantum field, the mind of God, just like Ramtha has taught for the last four decades. We can know what future civilizations know. We can rethink and re-create our future.

This book explains in many words, and hundreds of pages, what Ramtha is able to express in just a few simple sentences. The above is just one of thousands of teachings from a library of knowledge spanning forty-three years of work that can illuminate humanity to achieve this alternate future.

I know parallel realities are real. I know that information transfer between parallel universes is real. I know the great work we do now in our life heals us in many parallel lifetimes. I know we get downloaded and wake up in the morning with an idea of how to proceed. We have a knowingness on what book to read, what article to seek out, where to search, all the while knowing that there is a greater picture and a path to the destiny in which we will be able to understand it all.

As we evolve in our understanding, we will be able to interface with greater and greater futures and more advanced civilizations. Scientists like Nikola Tesla, who was centuries ahead of his time, brought humanity extraordinary progress. Unfortunately, much of this knowledge is still withheld from the public.

We can have free energy, immortality medicine, cures for all diseases, the eradication of all pathogens, the restoration of our world, antigravity propulsion systems, and folding space/time. We can quantum leap, levitate, bilocate, and travel through wormholes to other galaxies in space.

We must learn to listen to our own voice inside. That is the path in front of us, just as described in the poem, *The Tao of Pooh.* The expectations, roles, and identities we play for others are traps that only we can free ourselves from. We must tune out the noise so we can hear our own small voice. The unique spiritual journey is an alone journey that takes us home to our God within.

CHAPTER 7

LIVING IN THE PRESENCE OF A GREAT LIGHT

I now understand the quantum nature of our mind and the power of our spirit to create reality from an experiential level. This spiritual knowledge is the great unifier between scientific and spiritual aspects that give meaning to my life. The great unifier is the love of God.

I am grateful to my Teacher, Ramtha the Enlightened One, who taught me all these things, and JZ Knight for her visionary inspiration. All the topics that I write about in this book and the scientific evidence I present I studied because I was inspired by JZ to do so.

My love for her grew so profound and intense that I wanted to do everything to help heal the diseases that she experienced, because her body was used by a great being and became worn down by the process of channeling. I studied chelation as a mode of atherosclerosis reversal, exosomes and peptides and many other modalities described in this book in the hope I would find something that could help her with this challenge. As I document in the chapter regarding her medical history, she has always healed herself.

JZ is an extraordinary healer, a visionary who can see the future, and a being of profound love for all people.

In my life, she has been like the rising sun who shined so much light and love into my world that it healed everything. In her presence and warmth, I was like a closed flower that could open and exude color and perfume—unique and individual. I was completely allowed in my own journey and never had to conform to anything. In freedom I had the opportunity to answer my own questions and make my own discoveries.

JZ is this sunlight, this love of God, for thousands of people—countless individuals around the world who connect to her on social media and who email her daily for help and guidance. She tirelessly responds and helps everywhere. When she puts her mind on someone, their life is illuminated, healed, and changed. I have witnessed that.

Her far vision has saved many people's lives. People with life-threatening illnesses have felt her presence at night when she was working on them, and their condition improved in a couple of days. She sent me a message on one such person, stating that his breathing should be much better and his mind much clearer after encountering a life-threatening illness. Not only did this patient feel better two days after this message, but he himself mentioned that his mind was clearer than it had been in years. He felt tremendous energy and healing and knew that JZ had worked on him.

Her awareness and consideration of other people were never just displayed in empty words but continuous action of unending generosity. Despite all the adversity that she has experienced, JZ has never been afraid to live her truth and never stopped being love.

She never hesitated in being tested in every scientific way, because she had absolute knowledge of who she is and who Ramtha is. Her consistency and authenticity have been documented over a staggering span of many decades. JZ never needed anything from the world. She was not out there to glorify herself—only to glorify and love God.

She was an icon in the eighties and viciously attacked by the deep state. Despite that, she never wavered in being an incorruptible light to the world. From her far travels to the other side, she brought not only exquisite and rich wisdom, but she gifted the world with the futuristic technology of the Blu Room. Its science is far advanced of this time.

JZ only sees divine possibilities in everyone, never their flaws. She always profoundly respects an individual's choices and free will. She does not reprimand mistakes but understands that developing wisdom requires time and patience. She is a shining example of allowing and unconditional love.

For a time, I became a witness to this elusive, mystical creature in the form of a beautiful woman. Her marvelous mind and mysterious great light are how JZ Knight should always be remembered.

You can see from my experience that Ramtha and JZ Knight gave me knowledge that changed my life and led me to find peace within myself. All of my searching finally led to that quiet voice inside of me that already knows the way and is the voice of God.

This journey of spiritual awakening is what inspired me to write this book

PART II

A New Medical Model for Beings of Light

CHAPTER 8
THE FOUNDATION FOR A NEW MEDICAL PARADIGM

Many models of understanding and disciplines of science address healing the physical body. The standard Western medical model is one in which healthcare describes the mechanistic management of chronic diseases. Unfortunately, chronic illness is accepted as an inevitable outcome of the human condition.

As the aging process and manifestation of chronic illness progresses more and more, pharmaceutical drugs and invasive procedures are used to maintain a level of function and quality of life that is less than optimal. This requires the ongoing management by a practitioner who understands the foreign artificial language of disease and pharmacotherapy.

Within this model the human being is trapped in a lifelong dependency to chemical medicine. The basis for this model is the belief in disease, as well as corporate interest, that only allows solutions to be scientifically viable that can lead to profitable margins for drug companies.

Disease is considered an irreversible process leading over a life span to the ultimate end—the death of the biological system.

The model does not have room for healing as an understanding of restoration to original, optimal function and health—a restoration of balance in the body through mental, emotional, spiritual, and physical healing. This model has its place when chronic disease has so progressed that without pharmacological or surgical intervention the body would die.

True prevention based on nutritional optimization and the knowledge of cell physiology and biochemical metabolism is marginalized in our current healthcare system. Corporate interests have waged war against any discipline of healing that could restore the patient back to health. However, we will discuss how knowledge of the biochemistry of the cell allows us to access mechanisms that could slow down and even reverse many diseases of aging.

Optimization of cellular function is not just the nutritional supplementation of proper vitamins in adequate doses but also entails the understanding of environmental health and detoxification of the body from toxins present in our food supply and environment.

We have the possibility through vitamin therapy, nutraceuticals, peptides, hyperbaric oxygen therapy, intravenous nutritional therapy, and other regenerative approaches to treat the cause of diseases and prevent them from further manifesting in the body. We can reverse diseases and aging.

Moreover, there are biological sciences of genetics, physiology, biophysics, and quantum physics that expand our view of the human condition so far beyond that which is now considered. Even though this knowledge exists, it is rarely incorporated in a comprehensive approach to the patient. And yet all scientific approaches and explanations are but a shadow of a true causality that explains all: Why do we get sick in the first place? How do our thoughts influence the body? Who are we, and what is the purpose of our life?

In an even broader view, the current understanding of allopathic and integrative medicine does not integrate consciousness, self-awareness, and self-responsibility for our thoughts as a key factor in the causality of disease and restoration of health.

Light Medicine requires a complete reevaluation of the very nature of the human being as an incarnated spiritual being of light—an immortal essence of light that chose to utilize a physical body like a garment for the purpose of physical experience and evolution.

The basis for this evolutionary model of Light Medicine is the body of teachings of Ramtha the Enlightened One. Over the last four decades Ramtha has provided teachings regarding the nature of reality, the origin of the human Spirit, and the material manifestation as a divine being through seven levels of consciousness and energy.

The medicine of the future is based on a spiritual understanding of God as a being of light and the journey of making known the unknown in a physical body that is animated to experience material reality.

The evolution of science, medicine, and healing will occur when we realize that we are incarnated spiritual beings and divine creators of reality. Our mind and DNA are inextricably combined, and it is our mind that evolves our genes for generations to come. Understanding how diseases originate in the mind is a cornerstone of broadening our understanding of true healing.

The most compelling case for the proven reality of this model is shown in the discussion of the medical history of JZ Knight, channel of Ramtha the Enlightened One. In Chapter 13, I will be discussing in detail the DNA tests that show Ramtha and JZ, remarkably, have different DNA when utilizing the same body, indicating that the spiritual being changes the physical body at will. These test results compile the most stunning evidence of latent potential for all human beings.

Incorporating the spiritual, divine being and its power to bend light into matter through observation brings about the path to a new science and a new future of promising potentials.

When we understand how the mind of a spiritual being can affect DNA and modify its transcription, then we are no longer bound by a limited idea of simply maintaining health in an aging body and preventing disease through healthy nutrition, hormonal optimization, peptides, and other means.

Now we are in a new realm of possibilities. If we can train divine human beings to change their mind and access unlimited potentials, we open the door for them to alter their own physical, genetic, predetermined program.

We can create superhumans, to whom superhuman abilities, longevity, and immortality are real possibilities of mindful creation. It is not that we are created in some external creator's image but rather every human being can now create themselves in their own ideal image and enjoy the adventure of their own creation as a physical experience.

Health is then redefined by the endless capacity of DNA to rediscover, reinvent, and make oneself anew in endless variations of adventure. As our minds reach for the stars, our genes comply, for they too are made of the stuff of stars.

CHAPTER 9

HEALTHCARE POLITICS AND SUPPRESSION
OF NATURAL TREATMENTS

Science, involving healthcare, has come to be owned by corporate interests. The quest to heal people is marginalized by the need to keep the Medical-Industrial Complex going. In order to profit, it requires sick patients, and when people are healed from their chronic diseases, they are a lost-profit potential.

The pharmaceutical industry, the most powerful lobbyist in Washington, D.C., has significant influence over the Food and Drug Administration, and science is no longer objective but a handmaiden of Big Pharma. The industry has systematically suppressed and destroyed unconventional physicians who have healed or cured cancer, autism, atherosclerosis, or other chronic diseases. They persecuted them, like the witch hunts of the Middle Ages, by destroying their reputations, labeling the solutions as quackery, and charging physicians with fraudulent accusations, leading to endless trials, and loss of their licenses. This has happened over the past one hundred years to numerous, brilliant physicians who were relentlessly punished by a corrupt system for healing those in their care.

This profit-driven industry has caused the death of hundreds of thousands who were subjected to drugs with severe side effects—toxic chemotherapy, radiation, and other expensive medical procedures—without consideration for the evaluation of less expensive, less toxic, treatments.

The big business of coronary heart disease and coronary artery bypass surgery is far more profitable than giving patients the proper vitamins to reverse the process of atherosclerosis or consider chelation of heavy metals as a first line of therapy. In order to free science from its lucrative lies and artificial barriers to investigating true natural and cheap cures for diseases, our whole mechanism of scientific exploration needs to change.

Any system can be controlled when its information is controlled. The monopoly and information control of corporate healthcare started when John Rockefeller—whose company, Standard Oil, was controlling 90% of oil in the United States—expanded his empire by developing the ingredients for petroleum-based medications in the early 1900s.

Rockefeller's Company, Standard Oil, purchased the controlling interests in the German drug and chemical company IG Farben. IG Farben operated as the backbone of the Nazi war machine. During the Nuremberg trials it was learned that the business leaders of IG Farben were involved in operating concentration camps like Auschwitz and Buchenwald.

At the turn of the twentieth century in the United States, there were many medical practices that encompassed natural and holistic medicine. However, Rockefeller and his colleague, Andrew Carnegie, decided to take control of medical education in the U.S. during this period for the purpose of "reeducating" the medical profession to prescribe more pharmaceutical drugs.

In 1910, the Carnegie Foundation commissioned Abraham Flexner to reform medical and higher education in the United States and Canada.[1] Flexner then wrote a report that concluded all-natural healing practices were unscientific quackery. This opened the pathway for the control of information that persists today. Founded in 1897, the American Medical Association was given the authority to issue new licenses and evaluate colleges. A special department to eliminate what was considered medical quackery was formed in 1913.[2]

The American Medical Association continues to be funded by drug manufacturers, while natural remedies and alternative treatments have been continuously discredited. After the Flexner report, medical schools that offered training in homeopathy, phototherapy, and electromagnetic field therapy dropped these courses from their curriculum to avoid losing accreditation. Every medicine, other than allopathic medicine, was subsequently labeled as unscientific.

The Rockefeller and Carnegie Foundations controlled the curriculums at universities within the U.S. and Canada through their philanthropic organizations. They instituted their own people as university board members. As these universities were interested in continuing the flow of money, nutritional and other natural healing courses were eliminated. Instead, courses taught were exclusively about chemical drugs.

This has led to extreme bias in favor of pharmaceutical drugs and caused the lack of training and education to all doctors regarding natural treatments, herbal remedies, nutrition, homeopathy, and electromedicine.

These influences continue to this day, with an ongoing bias against natural and inexpensive therapeutic treatments. Physicians who dare step outside of this rigid system can face being ridiculed, threatened, and disciplined by medical boards and the FDA. With this brief historical context explaining the dominance of pharmaceutical medicine, we can now understand the potential problems of such a unilateral medical system.

The Dangers of Our Healthcare System

Every day 290 people are killed in the United States by prescription drugs. According to the FDA, these adverse reactions cause about 100,000 deaths per year. This makes prescription drugs the fourth leading cause of death in the country.[3] As a comparison, the number of deaths for heroin overdose was 14,996 deaths, as reported in 2018.[4]

According to Johns Hopkins patient safety experts, 10% of all U.S. deaths are due to medical error. Medical errors are the third highest cause of death in the United States and still considered underrecognized. As a cause of death, medical errors are behind cancer but remain ahead of respiratory disease.[5]

A December 1, 2018, update by the U.S. Health Resources and Services Administration (HRSA) on the federal Vaccine Injury Compensation Program (VICP) reported that the total amount of awards to children and adults who have been injured or died after receiving federally recommended childhood vaccines have surpassed $4 billion. The HRSA report reveals that over the past thirty years (since 1989), the VICP has received 20,123 petitions claiming vaccine injury and death.[6,7,8]

Researchers at the Department of Radiation Oncology at the Northern Sydney Cancer Centre studied the five-year survival rates of chemotherapy on 22 types of cancers in the U.S. and Australia. They studied 154,971 Americans and Australians with cancer, age 20 and older, who were treated with conventional treatments, including chemotherapy. Only 3,306 had survival that could be credited to chemotherapy. The overall contribution of curative and adjuvant cytotoxic chemotherapy to five-year survival in adults was estimated to be only a shocking 2.3% in Australia and 2.1% in the U.S.A.[9]

One would think if we discover that something doesn't work, we would stop using it. To the contrary, chemotherapy and radiation have long been advocated.

It is well known that many chemotherapeutic agents may increase the risk of developing other cancers like leukemia. If the chemotherapy successfully treats the original cancer, later on there is a higher chance for developing other cancers due to the initial treatment. A quarter of the total Medicare budget is spent on chemotherapy services to beneficiaries in the last year of life, with 40% of that cost occurring within the last thirty days of their lives.[10]

A study published in 1980 in the journal *The Lancet* evaluated the survival of breast cancer patients who received chemotherapy. The survival rate of 78 patients who received chemotherapy from first detection of metastases (including single-agent chemotherapy) was no better than that of the 80 who did not receive chemotherapy. The abstract states: "Overall survival of patients with primary breast cancer has not improved in the past ten years, despite increasing use of multiple-drug chemotherapy for treatment of metastases. Furthermore, there has been no improvement in survival from first metastasis, and survival may even have been shortened in some patients given chemotherapy."[11] Several cytotoxic chemo drugs have not changed significantly since then. They were developed after World War II and continue to be in use.

In 1979, *JAMA* *(Journal of the American Medical Association)* published an article finding: "The incidence of diagnosed breast cancer showed an 18% increase between 1935 and 1965 and a 50% increase between 1965 and 1975. However, breast cancer mortality has remained unchanged for at least the past forty years. Analysis of survival curves of women with breast cancer suggests that two or more populations exist, with about 40% suffering fatal outcome unaffected by treatment. The remaining 60% exhibit a relative mortality only modestly different from that of women of similar ages without evidence of disease."

Of note, according to the *JAMA* article, patients who refused medical procedures had a lower mortality rate than those who had them. Ironically, early diagnosis was associated with accelerated chemotherapy treatment and subsequently an earlier death.[12]

A more recent 2016 study published in *The Lancet* evaluated 23,228 patients with breast cancer and 9,634 patients with non-small cell lung cancer. Results showed that of those patients who received chemotherapy, almost 1,400 died within a month, which equated to 8.4% of lung cancer patients and 2.4% of breast cancer patients. However, at some hospitals this figure was much higher, with death rates of 50.9% at one particular hospital.

According to the authors, patients dying within thirty days after beginning treatment with chemotherapy are unlikely to have gained survival through the palliative benefits of the treatment and, in view of the side effects sometimes caused, "are more likely to have suffered harm."[13]

Zelek S. Herman, Ph.D., wrote an article in the *Journal of Orthomolecular Medicine* discussing alternatives to the current model of statistical survival analysis for cancer patients. He points out that the current Kaplan-Meier survival analysis, which has been used by biostatisticians and physicians to assess the effectiveness of cancer treatment, has significant deficiencies. These include questions pertaining to the death rate for patients in a group receiving a specific treatment. The article explains multiple mathematical and statistical factors that would influence the outcome and conclusion. It also analyzes cancer treatment studies that have indicated improvement in survival; however, when the mathematical data is analyzed further, that statistical improvement in survival cannot be sustained.[14] This illustrates the importance of meticulously analyzing statistics of any given research article before drawing clinically relevant conclusions.

In the book *The Illusion of Certainty: Health Benefits and Risks,* Dr. Erik Rifkin, Ph.D., and Edward Bouwer, Ph.D., discussed how easy it was to manipulate data to favor a certain outcome.

One such application is evident in statements made by medical organizations that praise the benefits of screening for cancer. PSA tests, colonoscopies, and mammograms are all advertised as reducing the incidence of cancer and therefore reducing the number of deaths from this deadly disease. This is not necessarily the case.

A recent report showed how death rates for most forms of cancer continued to decline, including a 1.6% annual decline in cancer deaths for men from 1992 to 2003 and a 0.4% annual drop among women. However, another article reported that an examination of the annual statistical data compiled by the American Cancer Society revealed that the rate of mortality from cancer has changed very little over the past fifty years.[15] These are opposite messages based upon the evaluation of statistical data. In understanding this fact, we can now fathom that today's medical science is not unbiased but can be easily manipulated according to any intentional agenda.

The current COVID-19 pandemic has exposed the fake news media, which spins and twists any narrative to misinform the public. What is also being revealed is that science can be similarly twisted.

An example is hydroxychloroquine that has been shown in numerous studies early in the disease to treat COVID-19. It helps reduce the progression of the patient into cytokine storm, which then leads to initiation of respiratory failure and the need for ventilator support. However, due to the media spin to prevent this solution, studies are being fabricated that paint a false narrative. A large-scale study on the use of hydroxychloroquine for treatment of COVID-19 was published on May 22, 2020, in the renowned medical journal *The Lancet*. This controversial article titled "Hydroxychloroquine or chloroquine with or without a macrolide for treatment of COVID-19: a multinational registry analysis," was later retracted after the database was found to be made up.[16,17] This was a fraudulent study that was featured in the fake news as proof that hydroxychloroquine has no effect. Just one of many examples, this shows how science is being manipulated by political and corporate agendas.

This same approach has been used for decades in corrupt science that is just as fake as the media. For example, studies about laetrile (or vitamin B17), which in the original Sloan Kettering research showed anticancer properties, were debunked by corrupt studies. The reputation of laetrile was subsequently destroyed in the United States and the drug banned. The same has occurred with a chelation therapy drug called EDTA (ethylenediaminetetraacetic acid), which in numerous studies has been shown to reverse atherosclerosis. However, since the industry of coronary artery bypass grafting is so lucrative, numerous attempts to discredit this treatment have been undertaken. In supporting the benefits of EDTA, scientists who are reputable and in good standing with medical societies may become subject to ostracism. The principal investigator, Dr.

Gervasio Lamas of TACT (Trial to Assess Chelation Therapy), is such an example.

Lamas' trial was designed with the purpose to once and for all show chelation does not work, and the researcher himself was a great sceptic. However, when the results of the double-blind study were revealed, he became convinced by the scientific data. Despite the fact that chelation had been shown to have greater efficacy in preventing further cardiovascular events in diabetic patients than any other commonly used medications— like aspirin, statins, beta blockers, ACE (Angiotensin-converting enzyme) inhibitors, and others—chelation was not made a new standard of care.[18] The researchers were instructed to perform another trial that would last for several years and, as of this writing, the TACT2 trial is still ongoing.[19] The consequence is that patients continue to not have access to this potentially lifesaving treatment because it is not being recommended by mainstream primary care physicians.

Many natural cancer cures have been discovered in the last 100 years by brilliant physicians. Those cancer cures have been systematically discredited and framed as quackery. The physicians were persecuted through the Food and Drug Administration (FDA) and American Medical Association (AMA) while pharmaceutical companies continued to profit by promoting outdated chemotherapeutic agents that not only do not work in prolonging survival but that they themselves cause cancer and are harmful to the body.

The cancer industry is a 500,000 billion-dollar-a-year business. Some novel cancer agents can cost as much as tens of thousands of dollars per month. There are 1,500 cancer centers in the United States. Consider the hospitals that depend on taking care of sick cancer patients with their radiation oncologists, extremely expensive radiation equipment, chemotherapy oncologists, home-care agencies, and nursing facilities that are all supporting the cancer patient. It is projected that one in two women and one in three men will develop cancer in their lifetime. Profit is the driving force in this industry—not the desire to find a cure, which would put this very profitable apparatus out of business.

Surely something must be done to improve the current failings of our healthcare system.

In 2016, when President Donald J. Trump was elected, he made the promise to drain the swamp, the corrupt political establishment in Washington, D.C. Since then we have witnessed the reveal of unprecedented corruption and lies within our government by the deep state. While this treason and corruption are becoming more and more evident, appropriate steps are being taken to preserve the Constitution of the United States and defend the prosperity and freedom of all Americans.

Similarly, the long-term effects of healthcare corruption are unparalleled in its consequences. Instead of creating wars that kill innocent lives to keep a corporate war machine going, the corporate healthcare system perpetuates war on the health of people who become chronically ill customers to an unscrupulous industry. Physicians are misled and trained unilaterally to favor pharmaceutical drugs, all the while being indoctrinated that all other alternative modalities are marginalized and considered quackery.

Evidence abounds that the science of today was bought and paid for by pharmaceutical companies who have manipulated results in their favor. Any natural solutions that did not provide the possibility for multibillion-dollar profits, secured by patents, were never investigated. As the standard of science was set, all solutions had to undergo clinical trials—and so it was ensured that cheap, natural solutions would never receive funding and be investigated; therefore they would have no chance of receiving scientific credibility.

Furthermore, the AMA and FDA always undertook every possible means of bankrupting, discrediting, and threatening the physicians who dared to care about their patients and provide solutions that worked and did not cause any side effects. Many physicians who worked on natural cures for cancer and other diseases had their offices raided, and some even met untimely and mysterious deaths.

Erin Elizabeth, from *Health Nut News,* has been tracking and exposing the many murders of holistic doctors.[20] Additionally, Robert F. Kennedy exposed the financial ties of Big Pharma to government agencies like the CDC (Centers for Disease Control and Prevention) and identified the organization as a privately-owned vaccine company. Millions of dollars have been funneled to such agencies to become not the protectors of the people but the right hand of corporate interests, leading to abominable health recommendations and the ignoring of vaccine-related injuries.[21]

Needlessly patients have died without access to natural healing cures in order to maintain antiquated treatments with cytotoxic chemotherapy that has a very high toxicity on normal tissue. In addition, radiation therapy—which has not been proven to have any survival benefits to cancer patients—is used with a risk of developing secondary cancers from the treatment later.

There has been a fight by a few brave individuals for decades to have the right, in the land of the free, to heal people who by their own choice did not want to undergo toxic treatments like chemotherapy and radiation.

The solutions described in the natural cancer healing chapter are not new and by no means complete. So many more exist. There are brave doctors who found cures for cancer and documented thousands of case histories. They were found dead under mysterious circumstances, threatened, persecuted, and/or had their licenses revoked.[22]

Freedom cannot be achieved without a nation having the right to safe healthcare and medical freedom of choice. What the AMA has accused doctors who found natural cancer cures of— namely, quackery and worse—is exactly what they have committed in the name of greed.

Harmful vaccinations cause chronic illness and injury in children and adults alike. With billions of dollars paid out through the vaccine injury fund, mainstream never questions the recommendation that advises people to take vaccines that make them ill.

Health misinformation needs to be addressed for America to have a scientific future in the medical field that can lead to true health and well-being of the population. Does this have huge consequences for the multibillion-dollar healthcare industry? Absolutely. Could healthcare be politically too big to fail?

The current system ensures that people remain sick so that Big Pharma has another client they can make money off of until the day they die. Transparency is needed to dismantle that flawed system.

Today we have artificially elevated costs of care for unnecessary treatments of diseases that could have been prevented with proper education. But who will have the courage to touch this monster? Healthcare is a thriving economy and it needs sick people to continue its spin of scientific lies. Nowhere has this political agenda been more clearly expressed than in the extreme war on any natural cancer cure and suppression of any such solution to reversing the disease in the United States.

The FDA utilizes their own policing force to intimidate physicians, terrorize their offices, threaten them, and litigate with endless lawsuits. The journeys of such physicians who endeavored to stand up against this tyrannical regime are described in the book, *World Without Cancer*, by Edward Griffin.[23]

In Griffin's book, the story of "vitamin B17," or laetrile, is such an example. The original researchers at Sloan Kettering Cancer Center clearly found anticancer properties in this medication made from bitter apricot seeds. However, the positive research results were altered, and false publications were intentionally circulated in medical journals.[24]

An investigation by the Senate into the conduct of the FDA and AMA in suppressing any natural cure for cancer is detailed in the 1953 Fitzgerald report called "A Report to the

Senate Interstate Commerce Committee on the Need for Investigation of Cancer Research Organizations." In the document, the extreme bias and harassment against the cancer cures of Hoxsey, Krebiozen, Burzynski, Gly-Oxide, and Mucorhicin—that with independent evaluation have helped ease the suffering of hundreds and thousands of cancer patients and even in many advanced cases cured the disease in natural ways—have been maliciously attacked and discredited. The famous quackery watch board still exists to this day, and one can easily find the disinformation surrounding these natural treatments.[25]

This same controversy goes on today in many areas of medicine. The FDA's relentless war against Stanislaw Burzynski, M.D., Ph.D., in his use of the anticancer treatments called antineoplastons is another ongoing example. Burzynski's antineoplastons have been shown to have substantial remission rates in some of the most difficult to treat cancers, like childhood glioblastoma. There have been ongoing trials and lawsuits for decades. An excellent report of this war against an individual's cure for cancer is the documentary *Burzynski*.[26]

The Fitzgerald report is a historical document that still applies in healthcare politics today. This report discusses how surgery and biopsy of malignancy may spread the disease and that radiation therapy has not benefited cancer patients after breast malignancy. Of course this treatment regimen continues to this day even though we have large studies that indicate no survival benefit has been achieved by chemotherapy or radiation over the last 40 years.[27]

To quote from the Fitzgerald report: "A neoplasm should never be incised for diagnostic purposes, for one cannot tell at what split moment the cancer cells may be disseminated and the patient doomed. Aspirating the neoplasm to draw out the cells by suction. This, too, is a very questionable procedure, for what of the cancer cells that may be present below the puncture point and around the needle which have been set free? It must be realized that while cancer cannot be transplanted from man to man, it can be transplanted in the same host.

"There is a report from another source in which Dr. Feinblatt, for 6 years pathologist of the Memorial Hospital, New York, reported that the Memorial Hospital had originally given X-ray and radium treatment before and after radical operations for breast malignancy. These patients did not long survive, so X-ray and radium were given after surgery only. These patients lived a brief time only, and after omitting all radiation, patients lived the longest of all."[28]

Similar parallels and methods through the exposure of scientific corruption are evident in the COVID-19 era.

To many scientists it would be almost incomprehensible to acknowledge that much of the current scientific education is disinformation created by the self-serving agenda of an elitist group that has made healthcare part of their population control mechanism in which people who are sick become ongoing customers. So-called reputable scientists and institutions tell us how we should think about health, while anyone or any type of solution outside of that preprogrammed paradigm is labeled as quackery and conspiracy.

Over the past decades some physicians have questioned the conflicts of interest the FDA has shown due to its close ties to big pharmaceutical companies. Dr. Marcia Angell was the editor of the prestigious *New England Journal of Medicine* and she sounded the alarm about the FDA, the profit-making machine of pharmaceutical companies.

Angell wrote in her Op Ed, "What Ails the FDA? Payola," published in the *Boston Globe* in March 2005:

"FDA's hasty evaluation and approval process for drugs with lethal side effects and unproven clinically significant benefits has substantially increased industry's profits at a cost in sacrificed lives. Even when the FDA knew about a drug's lethal adverse effects, it allowed it (e.g., Vioxx) to stay on the market for four years 'after a clinical trial showed it was probably more likely to cause heart attacks or strokes than to prevent stomach ulcers.' Furthermore, FDA routinely allows drug manufacturers to misrepresent the risk/benefit ratio of their products in beguiling advertisements that conceal the hazardous effects— 'it's a beautiful morning . . .'

'Why is the nation's most important regulatory agency appeasing the pharmaceutical industry instead of protecting the public? One answer is that it is on the industry's payroll. Literally.' When Congress passed the 1992 Prescription Drug User Fee Act, it put the FDA under industry's control—'he who holds the purse strings holds the powers.'"[29]

A study in the *Journal of the American Medical Association (JAMA),* published in January 2010, attempted to quantify U.S. funding of biomedical research by the pharmaceutical industry, government, and private sources.

At that time, researchers estimated that U.S. biomedical research was standing at over $100 billion annually. The pharmaceutical industry proved to be the largest contributor to research, funding over 60 percent. The government contributes to about a third of the costs, with foundations, advocacy organizations, and individual donors responsible for the remaining investments.[30] This investment is ever-increasing. If scientists are paid to achieve certain outcomes, thereby keeping their research funding going, what kind of bias does that introduce? In addition, medical journals are biased through the influence of pharmaceutical companies and special interests. Only those studies get published that present a favorable view of their donors.

In 2017, the *British Medical Journal (BMJ)* conducted a study of the number of medical journal editors who had received payments from pharmaceutical companies. Of the journals that could be assessed, 50.6% of editors were receiving money from the pharmaceutical industry—in some cases hundreds of thousands of dollars. The average payment in 2014 alone was U.S. $27,564, plus research funds. Worst on that list is the *Journal of the American College of Cardiology (JACC)*, where

19 of its editors received, on average, U.S. $475,072 personally and an additional U.S. $119,407 for "research."[31]

Much of what we currently call "standard of care" and acceptable medical science is disinformation. This, in addition to the suppression of natural cures, is part of the cause of a broken healthcare system that is corrupt at its core. Why is not every possible option allowed and evaluated, including natural supplements and high-dose vitamins, Light Medicine, frequency medicine, homeopathy, and repurpose drugs to treat any chronic illness? The reason is simple: because it would destroy the profits and control of the giant pharmaceutical industry.

The FDA has rules in which studies done in other countries are not accepted as the basis for allowing Americans to use new drugs developed elsewhere. United States policy requires that all the clinical trials that show benefits in other countries be re-created. This costs millions of dollars and causes lengthy time delays in treatment approval, which those who suffer from terminal illness do not have.

UV light therapy as used in the Blu Room, referred to earlier, has been found to be effective in the treatment of many diseases and was used in hospitals more than a century ago. However, due to the rise of the pharmaceutical companies and their propaganda machine, UV light therapy was marginalized.

Vaccine Misinformation

The medical industry's push for vaccination of the population is based on scant, verifiable, beneficial data. Yet the globalist vaccination program is being relentlessly pushed by the healthcare system. People are constantly bombarded with this misinformation, while the link to autism and other side effects is being ignored.

In the latest Cochrane review, there were fifty-two clinical trials of over 80,000 people which assessed the safety and effectiveness of influenza vaccines in North America, South America, and Europe between 1969 and 2009. Inactivated influenza vaccines probably reduce influenza in healthy adults from 2.3% without vaccination to 0.9%, and they probably reduce influenza-like illness (ILI) from 21.5% to 18.1%. Seventy-one healthy adults require vaccination to prevent one case of influenza, and twenty-nine healthy adults need to be vaccinated to prevent one of them experiencing an ILI. Vaccination may lead to a minimal reduction in the risk of hospitalization in healthy adults from 14.7% to 14.1%.

Vaccines provide little or no reduction in days off work. Inactivated vaccines are known to cause an increase in fever from between 1.5% to 2.3%. The authors who assembled the data concluded: "However, whilst the vaccines do prevent influenza symptoms, this is only one part of the spectrum of 'clinical effectiveness' as they reduce the risk of total 'clinical' seasonal influenza (i.e. influenza-like illness) symptoms by around 1%. When the results of our analysis are expressed as RD the effect appears minimal. This is remarkable as healthy adults are the population in which inactivated vaccines perform best. We found no evidence that vaccines prevent viral transmission or complications."

In other words, according to the researchers, the results of the review appear to discourage the utilization of vaccination against influenza in healthy adults as a routine, public health measure.[32] One study with a group of college students showed that influenza vaccination actually increased the risk of spreading the virus.[33] In the elderly, another study showed that while vaccination rates increased as much as 67% from 1989 to 1997, there's no evidence of vaccination reducing hospitalization or death.[34]

If the science itself does not support mass vaccination, why are the medical associations, doctors, and media pushing it and declaring anyone who doesn't take it is a risk to society?

The answer is hidden in plain sight and was recently revealed by Bill Gates: "The world today has 6.8 billion people. That's heading up to about nine billion. Now if we do a really great job on new vaccines, healthcare & reproductive health services, we could LOWER that by perhaps 10 or 15 percent."[35]

The current trend with rapid implementation of mRNA vaccines against COVID-19 without any long-term safety data is very concerning. Already we are seeing unprecedented severe adverse effects, including deaths, after COVID-19 vaccine administration.[36]

The vaccine safety and effectiveness issue needs to be addressed as part of the greatest disinformation campaign in medicine. If we want to increase health and longevity, we must stop injecting toxic substances into the body.

The free flow of information allowing all possibilities of healing is part of a free nation and an awakened, bright future for its citizenry. Without understanding how our highly respected scientific medical system has been corrupted, people will not understand why change is needed. Physicians will not be able to reeducate themselves contrary to how they were indoctrinated, unless they understand the lie. Patients will not be able to make different choices unless they understand that other possibilities exist and can find those physicians able to facilitate a more holistic approach to medicine.

I have been part of the corporate healthcare system for almost twenty years. The process of reeducating myself and waking up to a different reality was a very arduous journey. I can understand the resistance of conventional healthcare providers to question their current paradigm, as these questions come at a great cost. Understanding that our current system is based on manipulated and incorrect science explains why we need to implement a new model for the health of human beings.

CHAPTER 10
THE SCIENCE OF LIGHT MEDICINE

Imagine how our understanding of healing and treatment could change if there were to be a new unified theory for medicine, one that takes into consideration not just the body and the treatment of ailments with specific interventions but also the mind and spirit of a person and how that affects their health. I wish to present a science that can bring together all these views and allow different and novel perspectives on treatments.

In the current medical model, spirit and body are seen as separate, and our approach is mechanical in nature. Allopathic healthcare is disjointed. If there is a heart problem, the patient needs to see the cardiologist. If there is a problem with another organ, they see another specialist. In the middle is a primary care provider who is coordinating the specialized care.

Pharmaceutical drugs are there to maintain a chronic disease state. The expectation is not the restoration of optimum health. The patient will be maintained on medications that are ever-increasing in number for each new complaint developed. Nutritional optimization is marginalized, while consideration for the spiritual self is ignored.

In the integrative medical community, the idea of reversing the effects of aging is an important cornerstone of treatment. Nine hallmarks of aging, and thereby mechanisms of disease development, have been described: genomic instability, which includes mutations of genes, telomere shortening, epigenetic changes, dysregulation of protein biology, deregulated nutrient sensing, such as insulin resistance, mitochondrial dysfunction, cellular aging, stem cell exhaustion, and altered intercellular communication.[1]

Alongside correcting nutritional deficiencies, balancing hormone levels, and detoxifying the body, there are numerous treatment modalities that can help reverse these nine biological processes.

Both the allopathic approach and the functional medicine approach are valid viewpoints that provide models of understanding in which to treat patients. When combining both models, there certainly is a broader knowledge base in addressing disease and the appropriate treatment.

Yet these perspectives are still limited, as they do not explain the greater causation for disease. As my personal experience with cancer taught me, we have the ability to return to optimum health by considering how our thoughts, beliefs, and emotions are directly affecting our well-being. Perspective is everything. How to look at a problem and see a different solution, a new explanation, could bring a new means of treatment.

We have been looking at health in a fragmented way. In our separateness we cannot comprehend the whole that we are part of, which includes but is not limited to the functioning of our physical body.

Quantum physics and biophysics add additional dimensions to viewing health in a more expanded way, which would then encompass a greater level of wholeness. Quantum physics includes the effects of the Observer on our material reality.

Physicist David Bohm in his book, *Wholeness and the Implicate Order*, explains: "The proposal for a new general form of insight is that all matter is of this nature: That is, there is a universal flux that cannot be defined explicitly but which can be known only implicitly, as indicated by the explicitly definable forms and shapes, some stable and some unstable, that can be abstracted from the universal flux. In this flow, mind and matter are not separate substances. Rather, they are different aspects of one whole and unbroken movement."[2]

Other prominent physicists have written about the implications of the Observer and mind over matter. Henry Stapp stated, "We have known for almost a century that this theoretical creation of the human mind called 'classical physics' is a fiction of our imagination." John Wheeler said, "Observation is the mechanism of Genesis. The Observer is the creator." Max Planck stated, "I regard consciousness as fundamental. I regard matter as derivative from consciousness. We cannot get behind consciousness."

In this book I discuss topics from a vastly different perspective than conventional healthcare would consider. The Observer is paramount to this new view.

In the coming pages I introduce the light value of molecules, the electrical ability of natural compounds to restore health, the ideas of clean nutrition and detoxification to help the body restore its function, the natural treatments for cancer, and the reversal of chronic diseases. In my view, restoring the body electric is a key to longevity and ultimately a path to immortality.

Proof that a human body can be completely transformed and healed by an unlimited consciousness has existed for forty-three years within our midst. The medical documentation of the transformation of JZ Knight's body when she is channeling Ramtha the Enlightened One demonstrates this.

The question is: How open-minded and how untainted can we be in our perception to broaden our own mind and leave our ignorance behind us?

The world has long been controlled through fear and disinformation. Our perceptions have been molded to the agenda of elitists who believe in atrocious things. Science has been misused as a cover to control society by fabricating diseases and using its research for mind-control purposes. Viruses, like COVID-19 and other vectors of illness, are created in laboratories and then released upon the world to create profitable chaos, bending society to the twisted vision of an enslaved, human future. There is so much to undo in our own programmed disbelief and ignorance.

Models of science that can explain to date unexplainable and legendary phenomena do exist but have been suppressed, such as the torsion physics of Russia and the antigravity propulsion technology of Nikola Tesla.

Ramtha has explained that a limited mind cannot comprehend an unlimited mind. We can only understand that mystery when we become the mystery within ourselves. This mystical aspect of self is teaching us and thereby continually changing our perspective. In experiencing our change, we garner more knowledge, understanding, and wisdom. Let's never presume we have figured the miracle out, lest we risk having closed our mind to new possibilities.

As an internal medicine physician, my views about health, healing, and true causality of disease changed greatly through the many events that I attended at Ramtha's School of Enlightenment. My training started in 2006. In January 2018, I became the supervising physician for JZ Knight's Mercy Blu Room program. Seeing the beneficial effects of this Blu Room technology inspired me to broaden my mind to understand how it worked.

Ramtha's teachings, as transcribed in the next section, became the foundation and beginning of the new Light Medicine model of science as described in this book. As you read the documentation of the transformation occurring through JZ Knight's Blu Room creation, her own medical healing and, separately, the documented physical changes that occur in the channeling process described further into this book, ask yourself with what perception are you reading?

A Model for Light Medicine

On May 11, 2018, Ramtha gave the teaching, included below, to a small group of students about the topic of Light Medicine. I was invited to attend this rare opportunity for

86

transformation. The journey of studying and researching the science of what Ramtha taught that day paved the path to my pulling together information from all scientific fields—biology, biophysics, quantum physics, torsion physics, mathematics, physiology, biochemistry, genetics, and spiritual teachings—a new, yet ancient perspective, called Light Medicine.

"Ramtha: The channel has given to the world a super technology. Its value will not even be celebrated until decades to come. But because it is given by her and designed by her, those who are prejudiced and biased—and would rather hold onto their hatred and biases rather than be cured—will always stand against it. Why? Because it takes control out of their hands.

"That always threatens people. The least relief from elsewhere threatens those who are in control of suffering.

"The channel—this applies to you in all of your dreams—always wanted to be a healer, running around healing plants in her mother's home. She made them worse by what she thought she was injecting them with, a pink liquid, something 'Pepto.'

"But it did not go unnoticed, just like with you. Your deeper dreams do not ever go unnoticed. So what is destiny? A plan. Well, obviously she didn't become a healer the legitimate way, but it was always there. And loving God with all her might and all her being, as you do as well, allowed her to prepare a path for me—to allow—a rigorous process.

"And the dream of healing people and making them better would take a higher caliber of technology, knowledge, and work, taking into account extraordinary mathematics and deliverance of light that is likened to Blue Body®. She is where she is because destiny delivered to her this way of healing. Not always what we dream in our limited sense of perception will ever be recognized but when taken to a greater reality—and then if you are still open—will be utilized.

"So many entities say, 'Well, my dreams never came true.' Truly? Perhaps the dreams are faded petals of another time rather than a future time that, without knowledge, one cannot perceive. A limited entity cannot perceive higher flows of consciousness. It is only when they are trained properly, which the forty-some years of the work was about. In preparing entities to understand more broadly their place as divine beings—and in that to be able to tap into the superconsciousness, even if it is in Fieldwork®, even if it is in C&E®, even if it is in any discipline that has been created to augment the knowledge into a performed experience—the experience gives rational truth. To that person it is only important—to that person, to that being—as they accept that ability that opens them up. And now these dreams, long ago, have a place in the future. How many of you understand that? Not all dreams have a place in this time but in future times that can be augmented, as it were—a new word that I learned—into now. Instead of strong-armed, it is augmented. Now we have what common people call genius.

"Now if I may, this entity did not need to study chemistry or biology. She is grand in mathematics. Her brain thinks that way. She didn't have to train in any of these arts of persuasion that would lead to an inventive mind. You all agree? So this woman creates this machine. And Father [a student] can tell you it works, and here is why. Even if you are astute that all biology, their atomic structures, particles, chemistry, mathematics, and understand spin-ratio value, at the end how does one determine a particle's veracity? By its light. Yes or No?

"All things have a lightbody, and because it is from light, they descend to mass. You are a conglomerate of a neighborhood of diversified light whose harmony is you. You understand?

"Now if you understand that and you work in light, then you garner information from those elementals that have the highest light value. When those values are then taken into the human biological form, that light enhances the body's mechanism. So you see, healing mass to mass is absolutely necessary. Healing the mind is absolutely necessary. Healing with light is the Great Work.

"Now do you know the light value of Carbon 60? Why? Shouldn't you investigate what you kind of take, kind of don't take? Do you think it is a novel idea? Look at its light value. Study it. How can a particle that looks like the Blu Room, with so much light, override so much lack in cellular performance?

"And whereas if you are an entity of light, then wouldn't your bread be light? If you take the substance, it is so powerful that it feeds light-starved cells and, taken enough, it renews vitality in the DNA. That is why it lengthens life.

"It is not about how you feel. Remember, feeling is an emotional experience. Having no feeling says to the uneducated mind, 'Well, it didn't do anything.'

"If you swallow a light-form, does it do anything for you? How does it feel? You don't feel anything. If Orbs enter into your body and help your body, do you feel anything? Because the Source is light.

"Inflamed tissue, organs, cellular masses, are common in the aging of any lifeform. Why? Because many of the cellular constructs of matter are losing light, and when they lose light they become debris, or they become starved, and as such they are swelling with fluid. No cell can take in fluid without dispelling wastes, hence inflammation.

"Do you understand inflamed? It is dying; water in, waste out. That is the loss of light, which is the governing body of all things material.

"Let us return to light medicine. When an entity has indomitable will and they have a causal effect of their health occur—which could be an accident, could be any one thing—and yet their will keeps the body going against all odds, is that will light? And has the body got enough light or is the body receiving light from the will?

"How does mind heal the body?

"Student: It infuses light through will.

"Ramtha: Exactly. It is the God machine. So now this brings us to understand the totality of the Great Work. The Great Work in essence is to train the aspirant through a long series of specified teachings that in the end always calls upon that aspirant to utilize the focus of their will—and their will only—correct?

But it is applied in various areas and soon we have that common thought that allows the access to streams of superconsciousness in the brain because there is a place for it to be heard. There is a place for it to be lived.

"All of these transmissions are through light, and every word has a light representation. That is the reason a master speaks in certain ways."

– Ramtha
May 11, 2018

In Light Medicine, we are looking at a different model of reality. Ramtha's greatest message is "Behold God," that we are incarnated divine beings of light inhabiting a body who have reincarnated innumerable times for the purpose of spiritual learning. The journey throughout incarnations is the return to a state of "enlightenment," which is the awareness and applied knowledge that each human being is divine. The full realization of the God within each human being is the ultimate becoming. The purpose of reincarnation is gaining wisdom through the human experience by resolving all of our unfinished, emotional experiences.

Our observation bends light into form. For those who do not like the spiritual wording that explains how human beings are creators, quantum physics provides a scientific language that says the same thing in mathematical terms. Quantum physics describes how particles are collapsed into material reality by the Observer, hence this individual observation is the act that creates our material reality. The effects of observation engaged in disharmonious attitudes create incoherence and disease in the body. Biophysics clearly explains this, as we will discuss.

In Light Medicine we understand healing, not simply on a mass-to-mass level. Ramtha has explained: "So, you see, healing mass to mass is absolutely necessary. Healing the mind is absolutely necessary. Healing with light is the Great Work."

A scientific model does exist that encompasses attitudes, emotions, the spiritual self, and the physical body. The basis of

Light Medicine is understanding how the spiritual being interfaces with the material reality of the human being. This interface can be measured and correlates with the amplitude of bioelectric signals in the body electric. The body electric is the interface for the conscious being of light to engage the brain and, through the autonomous nervous system, every cell of the body.

Ramtha further explains that the human brain is like a computer and the Spirit is the operator of the machine—that every human being is divine. The divine human being creates reality through the observation of our thoughts. The process of disease, physical deterioration, and aging is not caused *in* the body but through inharmonious attitudes of the mind that are continually observed and perpetuated *on* the body.

Scientists have understood that our universe is entirely a mental construct and mathematical in nature. All gross physical matter can now be reverse engineered to ever smaller particles until we arrive at energy fields and probabilities. Electrons in atoms no longer have a physical mass but a probability smear of existence based on observation. Quantum physics understands that our universe is mental and that physical mass is illusionary.

This idea also applies to the physical body. We are not disconnected from the quantum physics effects of the Observer. Our observed thoughts and emotions create the reality of our physical experience, including diseases. The mass of our body can be kept in the mental construct of health or illness according to the will of the Observer.

Ramtha lays out a foundation of understanding that we are divine beings incarnated in a physical body and that if we understand light values in other elements or atomic structures, we can use them for medicinal purposes to enhance the light in our body.

In the following segment I will explain how higher light values correspond to the atomic structure of molecules and their ability to donate electrons. Electrons change states by giving off photons, which is light. The enhancement of the organism through electron donors, also known as molecules with antioxidant properties, increases the organism's light or electrical amplitude that in turn can heal and regenerate tissues. The loss of light leads to decay and disease.

I would summarize these foundational ideas as:

> ➢ You are a divine being.
> ➢ Your thoughts are matter.
> ➢ Inharmonious thoughts create aging and disease.
> ➢ Love is harmony and creates disease reversal and youthfulness.

Reverse Engineering of Matter

The idea of reverse engineering matter back to zero-point energy has also been taught by Ramtha. Over the decades, he has meticulously provided simple models of understanding for his students to be able to comprehend the creation of matter. His teaching of consciousness and energy creating reality from the observation of a thought has a very specific implication for viewing a new scientific approach. Ramtha has specifically taught that all energy is inextricably combined with conscious information and that this information cannot be separated from energy. This is important to note for when we discuss energy transfer through the coherent whole of the body.

For further background knowledge regarding Ramtha's model of reality, I recommend the Class 101 at Ramtha's School of Enlightenment, where it is explained as the following: "The seven levels of consciousness and energy is Ramtha's model of reality and it explains our origins and destiny. It is expressed graphically as a triad, with the seventh level at the top and Point Zero at the apex. Consciousness and energy are inextricably combined and the seven levels of consciousness correspond to the seven levels of the electromagnetic spectrum. They also represent levels of energy, frequency, density of mass, space, and time."[3]

Imagine your mind as a looking glass from the macroscopic evaluation of matter in a body and then step by step changing the perspective of the looking glass to smaller and smaller scales.

This process of reverse engineering also applies in the other direction. We can fluidly change through different levels of perspective but need to be aware of what scientific understanding applies to each level.

A different science has been attributed to each level that describes its actions—quantum physics, electrobiology, biophysics, genetics, biology, chemistry, physiology, neurology, cardiology, endocrinology, and medicine. Seemingly all of these areas are separate, but they are not. They are different areas of study, but if we want to understand creation and a new model of medicine, we have to include in the discussion theories from every level. Each section of study above is in itself correct but remains limited without the context of the whole.

Biophysical Model of Organisms

Biophysics is an area of science that acknowledges we are organisms of light. Dr. Mae-Wan Ho was a biophysicist who wrote extensively on the subject in her book, *The Rainbow and the Worm*, where she describes the physics of organisms. She also wrote *Living Rainbow H2O*, an extraordinary book about the biophysics of water. In this section I will be discussing Dr. Ho's research and how it relates to Light Medicine.

We are conscious beings of light, and the body electric has a large flow of electric fields in the organs and the entire organism. This electrical field is required to maintain health. It is known that one single photon can initiate a cascade of chemical reactions. For example, when a photon hits one cell in the eye on the retina, 100,000 chemical reactions can be set off by this one photon. This is how the signal from one photon can be amplified millions of times over the whole when in a coherent state.

Living systems are very sensitive to specific weak signals. There is a large amount of energy stored in the body; therefore it automatically amplifies weak signals into macroscopic effects. This is how small energy and information transfer can affect the entire organism. The concept will become even clearer in the chapter on torsion physics.

This transfer can explain how the electron donor capacity of a molecule—which is its ability to give off light—can beneficially affect the entire organism towards healing in a multilevel cascade of effects, from subatomic to macroscopic. Nobel Prize winner Dr. Szent-Györgyi, who discovered vitamin C, wrote in his book, *Introduction to a Submolecular Biology*: "What drives life is thus a little electric current, kept up by the sunshine. All the complexities of intermediary metabolism are but the lacework around this basic fact."[4]

Here we will discuss the scientific background of how electricity manipulates genes. By increasing electricity or light in the body, we can reverse the aging and disease process.

Dr. Ho described how life is all the colors of the rainbow and all organisms emit a steady rate of light. This ranges from a few photons per cell per day to several hundred photons per organism per second. This is called bioluminescence.[5]

Human beings absorb light in several ways. Unpolluted healthy food stores the energy of sunlight. We are extracting this energy source. When we are in the sun with our skin exposed, we absorb photons through melanin in our skin. Our body converts that to energy to utilize in chemical reactions. In the same way, molecules, that are electron donors, can increase the light energy field of the body, thereby enhancing health.

Dr. Mae-Wan Ho explains that communication in the human body occurs not just on molecular and chemical levels. It also happens on an electric, magnetic, and vibratory basis. That is because light consists of electric and magnetic fields.

Molecules vibrate at various characteristic frequencies. This produces electromechanical oscillations, which are phonons or sound waves. It also produces electromagnetic radiation, which are photons or light waves. These phonons and photons extend over macroscopic distances.

The communication within the body occurs through the entire electromagnetic spectrum of wavelength of light and over seventy-three octaves of sound, hence we are beings of light and music.[6]

Ramtha said, "All things have a lightbody, and because it is from light, they descend to mass." It is important to understand that light is the origin and causation of matter—not a consequence of matter.

It is known that organisms are liquid crystals. These are dynamic and have vibration and coherent motion on every scale. Water is aligned in this structure. Liquid crystal contains proteins, enzymes, molecules, and acts like a matrix. This matrix is due to the properties of collagen, which make up more than 70% of all the proteins of the connective tissues. The fluid and liquid crystallinity of the organism is what allows for rapid information transfer and the function of a coherent whole.[7]

That is in line with quantum physics entanglement, where any particle in the universe always knows what is happening to any other particle in the universe. Excited molecules vibrate into collective modes of oscillation. They produce sound and light waves. This is applicable to any biological organism and all matter because all matter is made up of light.

Music is being created in endless variations, and the symphony that we are is varied and always influenced by our moods and physiology. This is the scientific knowledge currently known and related to what Ramtha said: "You are a conglomerate of a neighborhood of diversified light whose harmony is you."

The matrix that makes up our body contains the properties of a superconducting, quantum computer.

Most biological liquid crystals are arranged as a helix. Cholesterol molecules, DNA, and collagen have this specific organization. This is called the "cholesteric organization" of molecules, which endows living matter with a variety of crucial, physical properties. It enables the optimization of DNA compaction in the nucleus of cells. When unwound, chromosomal DNA can reach a length of two meters.

This organization in animals allows for the ability to reflect light with a color, depending on the helical twist, with a predominance of left-handed torsion. If the pitch is very tight, reflection occurs towards the blue or even ultraviolet range. If the helix is loosely twisted, reflection is in the red or infrared range. The color changes with the angle of observation.[8]

Resonant recognition is the primary mechanism of all molecular processes in the body.[9] Due to the nonlocal properties of the wave function of electrons, the electron has a probability of being found anywhere within the system. This means the information encoded in the electron is also nonlocal and can affect cellular mass within the entire body.

The excitation of a single photon to a single electron can provide an information cascade in a coherent, living organism in which the signal spreads over the entire whole. Information travels at the speed of light. We will discuss in Chapter 12 how information travels via torsion fields faster than the speed of light.

A coherent system has no space/time separation. This is because particles like photons and electrons are entangled on the quantum level. All information in a coherent system is transmitted instantaneously across all time and space.

The liquid-crystalline organism is extremely sensitive to electromagnetic fields. Therefore human beings can have significant health effects from electromagnetic interference like cell phones.

The electrical properties are based on water molecules that are bound in and around the collagen triple helix. Liquid water exists in two states: a coherent phase, which is about 40% of the total volume at room temperature, and an incoherent phase. "The remaining 60% incoherent phase is extracted by thermal fluctuations from the coherent phase."[10]

In the coherent phase, the water molecules oscillate between two electronic configurations in phase with the resonating electromagnetic frequency. Organized water close to surfaces, such as a cell membrane, is able to induce a very long-lasting, electronic excitation of the different molecular groups present.

Coherent water is excited water with a plasma of almost free electrons that can easily transfer electrons to molecules on its surface, literally facilitating an electrical current. The interface between fully coherent, interfacial water acts as a battery in the body.[11]

There is independent evidence that molecules taking part in a biochemical reaction share a common frequency. They attract each other by resonating to the same frequency.[12]

The collagen, liquid crystal structure of connective tissue with its associated structured water, constitutes a semiconductive electrical matrix that extends throughout the organism.

This matrix is linked to the intracellular structures of individual cells. They form an excitable electrical continuum for rapid intercommunication throughout the body. Remember when I discussed the proposed theory that electricity manipulates genes? High amplitude electricity in the body creates health and longevity.

Liquid crystals play an important role in biology because the combination of order and mobility is a basic requirement for self-organization and structure formation in living systems. Liquid crystals are present everywhere in living matter. They address the major types of molecules essential to life. In the animal and plant kingdoms, the cholesteric structure is a recurring design, suggesting an evolution to an optimized left-handed helix.[13]

Asymmetry is a feature found in biological organisms. This left-right asymmetry is seen throughout the body on every level from micro- to macromolecules with the rotational direction of DNA being a preferred twist to the right. In the opposite twist it has no activity in the cell. Proteins have a preferred twist which affects their function—amino acids are mainly biologically active in their left-handed form. Only one twist direction is found in the living organism.[14] This helical twist encodes an important optical property of living molecules. It determines how these molecules reflect light, which is part of a communication mechanism that holographically encodes the entire biological program in space and time.

The physical crystalline structure operates optimally in quantum coherence, coherence being another word for harmony. Memory is thought not only to be localized in the brain but over the entire liquid-crystalline continuum, which serves as a holographic medium.

Dr. Claude Swanson writes that biophotons generate torsion waves, which propagate beyond the body and form a holographic standing wave pattern around the body.[15] Torsion waves are created by the Observer. This field interacts primarily with particle spin—which we will discuss in the next chapter—wherein the physical body is projected as a hologram into physical reality.

Quantum coherence is the prerequisite for conscious experience. Water, which constitutes 60% of the human body, is quantum coherent; therefore cells and organisms are also quantum coherent. Dr. Ho writes: "Most of all, the quantum coherent organism is a macroscopic quantum being, with a unique, evolving wave function spread ultimately throughout the entire universe, entangling the wave functions, or consciousness of all other quantum beings."[16]

Quantum coherence has been suggested to occur in the brain microtubules with the collapse of the quantum wave function being essential for consciousness.[17]

It has been shown that all information is being transmitted via ultrafast, resonant energy transfer within the organism.[18]

Coherent energy is stored and comes together anywhere in the system so it can be used to do biological work. Incoherent energy goes in all directions and cancels itself out. Coherent energy is stored over all space/time and can be utilized to optimize healing in the body. In our Light Medicine model, we subscribe to this key point, which is that the higher the energy state in the body, the greater the level of health, youth, and vitality.

There is a quantum nature to all biological processes. All molecular reactions in the body start with one photon exciting one electron, initiating a molecular reaction cascade. When we are looking at molecules that act as electron donors, this quantum nature of biological processes applies. The electrons given to the body elevate the entire quantum state to a level of higher energy or light.

I propose that higher energy state is translated into macroscopic upregulation of genes that encode health and downregulation of genes that encode disease. This is one answer to Ramtha's question on how a molecule like Carbon 60, containing so much light, can override so much lack in cellular performance. As Ramtha said: "If you take the substance, it is so powerful that it feeds light-starved cells and, taken enough, it renews vitality in the DNA. This is why it lengthens life."

This can be applied to any molecule that has the capacity to give off electrical energy in the form of electrons or protons.

Water and the Void – As Above, So Below

The concept of "as above, so below" can be applied to all scales of creation. Just as original creation arises from the Void, all living organisms arise within the structure of water. In Ramtha's teachings, "The Void is defined as one vast nothing materially, yet all things potentially."[19]

Water creates the liquid-crystalline matrix that holds in solution molecules of life that create living organisms. The state of quantum coherence is the "I," the divine being, living in all things and expressing in endless variations of color and sound, vibration and music.

The "I Am" is the Observer that, in the observation of thoughts, changes the organism, the body, through creative free will. Expanding on Dr. Mae-Wan Ho's vision, the additional viewpoint is the divine Observer.

The geometry of life in water is equivalent to the first building blocks of matter in the Void. We misunderstand the spiritual as separate from science. However, the multi-dimensional existence described in string theory and quantum theory is explaining the spiritual realms all the way to the beginning of creation itself, which is zero-point energy.

In her book, *Living Rainbow H2O*, Dr. Mae-Wan Ho describes how water has been shown to be an infinite energy donor and is responsible for the ability of proteins, enzymes, and DNA to function in nanospaces.

Water has quantum properties in several phases and is essential for the building of the liquid-crystalline structure of the organism. It has been shown that the arrangement of water molecules around proteins and enzymes is what allows their functioning to occur at such an efficient rate.[20]

Water's structural configuration is the tetrahedron, the original geometrical building block of life. Whether interacting with hydrogen atoms or hydroxyl groups, water has a versatile binding capacity which allows life to occur. Imagine water as the Void, the substance of God, which provides the energy and animation to all life.

This is how God operates, by allowing any creation to be animated with the energy of life. Water is such a substance—acting like the original substance but in harmonic proportions at a larger scale. It is equivalent to the matrix of life and therefore has such extraordinary, versatile properties, as affected by the Observer. No two snowflakes in the universe are the same. Dr. Masaru Emoto definitively showed in his experiments that water molecules reconfigured according to intention and thought.[21]

Further Study of Light

One of Nikola Tesla's contemporaries was Walter Russell. Russell was not an educated scientist but an individual who had a spiritually enlightening experience and was downloaded with extraordinary scientific and spiritual knowledge.

Russell described a new mathematics of the universe, which was prominent in the last century. He shared his theory with other scientists, including Einstein. He described God's mind as expressed in light. This mind is spiritual substance. In fact, it is the ether that Tesla was able to access with his zero-gravity propulsion systems. Russian scientists call it manifested force torsion, as we will discuss in Chapter 12.

Russell describes in poetic ways how all of life is light and that God and matter are one and the same thing. He stated, "There is only one language and that is light, and the alphabet of this language is color and that the color in its vibration has sound."[22]

Walter Russell accurately predicted, based on the vibration of elements, the discovery of plutonium. He said about healing: "Nor can information concerning the material body alone, its chemistry and its functionings, heal the body. Bodies manifest life, but life is cosmic. Life is not in the body. Life is spirit, and spirit is still. Life is not chemistry or germ of matter. To heal the body so that it can manifest life of the spirit Self of the body, one must give the unbalanced body the balance of the spirit. Knowledge of the Light can alone do this. All the information in the world will not heal a body unassisted by the Light in him who heals and in him who is being healed."[23]

As previously mentioned, Ramtha also spoke about this light and its relationship to will when he said, "Let us return to light medicine. When an entity has indomitable will and they have a causal effect of their health occur—which could be an accident, could be any one thing—and yet their will keeps the body going against all odds, is that will light? And has the body got enough light or is the body receiving light from will?"

"How does mind heal the body?"

"Student: It infuses light."

Russell explained that electrical and magnetic forces are always in perfect balance. He developed a way to predict, based on vibrational frequency, the atomic structure of atoms.

In his book, *The Secret of Light*, he describes how carbon alone expresses the idea of matter and that the nine octaves of the elements are stages of unfoldment and enfoldment of carbon. Only carbon creates a cube sphere. All spheres behave like suns. They become radiating, zero-point energy fields. Hydrogen is a one-octave-younger prototype of carbon. Nitrogen is the next element beyond carbon. Elements are not fixed, created things. They are pressure conditions of light waves. Russell explains how the spectroscope has been able to divide light rays through its prisms into the component parts which make up the life history of each stage. Each element tells the story of its entire previous incarnations, literally, as if each element is a living being of light. The elements of matter are not different substances or different things. They are different pressure conditions of light waves, all alive, as the light of God is life.[24]

In our universe, hydrogen, carbon, nitrogen, and oxygen are the most abundant elements. The saying that "we are made of star stuff" is based on the literal elemental configuration of the human body, which is 65% oxygen, 18% carbon, 10% hydrogen, and 3% nitrogen. We indeed *are* the composition of stars.

These molecules have a resonant frequency spectrum in the composition of the body, a vibrational, quantum signature that is frequency specific to each individual human being. This vibrational signature composition can be enhanced in its light.

How can a substance increase the light within an organism? Because the electron energy transfer occurs across the entire system. It changes its quantum state and vibrational properties across the continuum.

Molecules that act as electron stealers cause vibrational disruption in the organism. It is the energy vibration of the intervention that causes the effect. We can affect the crystalline structure of water molecules through a loving thought or hateful thought. The effects on the entire organism are that of harmony or disharmony. In the same way, giving the body a healing substance or a toxic substance brings about a beneficial or harmful effect.

We can explain how 65 trillion cells are changed profoundly. The function of genes rearranged in their activities, as a secondary event occurring after an intervention, increases coherence and energy in the biological system.

The vibrational frequency shift is primary. Gene activity changes represent an effect, not the ultimate cause. High light value molecules can alter infinite amounts of genes when the information is related to health. In a state of quantum coherence and enhancement of the light value of the entire organism, the genes of health will be turned on. The higher the coherence, the greater the repair. Quantum incoherence occurs through disruptive, negative thoughts and emotional attitudes and toxic environmental chemicals that turn on harmful genes, which leads to sickness in the body.

Biophoton Research

All organisms are one coherent photon field, or lightbody, from which living matter is derived. Professor Alexander Popp, a world leader in biophoton research in Germany, showed that the death of an organism starts with a very sharp increase in the loss of light, measured as biophoton emission, up to 48 hours prior to death.

The disease and aging process is initiated by the loss of light in the body. There are studies which have evaluated biophoton emission as a form of an optical biopsy that can predict the presence of cancer via the increase in biophoton emission.[25]

In different cell lines, the addition of cytokines, like tumor necrosis factor alpha, increase the biophoton emission. Cells in stress have variations in biophoton emissions.[26] It is also possible to differentiate malignant from nonmalignant cells using biophoton emission.[27]

Light has been used to control biological systems to facilitate rapid and reversible manipulation of highly dynamic cellular processes. Instead of using chemicals or drugs, researchers have used light-sensitive proteins and their ability to transform or interact with other proteins to manipulate all aspects of cell cycle.[28]

Light-sensitive regulatory proteins occur in nature. These regulate processes, such as plant development, gene expression, circadian rhythm, and facilitate the communication of visual information. Genes that are light sensitive, called optogenetic systems, are based on natural photoreceptors that have been used to control intracellular processes. These photoreceptors contain an area called chromophore that undergoes a rearrangement of its atoms upon absorption of a photon. This leads to a change in the photoreceptor. Most photoreceptors mediate interactions within the cell or between cells in response to light. The cellular processes are manipulated by light, ranging from gene transcription, genome engineering, transmission of cell signals, and changes within the skeleton cell.[29]

The future of medicine will include the ability to modify cellular body functions with light. This is done with light therapy and, for example, in JZ Knight's Blu Room. Our current scientific understanding is not yet fully integrating the fact that our biological system can be manipulated, treated, and healed through use of light, frequency, and sound.

Mathematical Structure of the Universe and Its Relationship to Healing

In my desire to understand Ramtha's teaching regarding the Blu Room technology and how it might function in healing, I researched geometry and elementary physics. I wanted to know if there was a pattern, a language that would provide new avenues of discovery in relationship to healing molecules and Light Medicine.

I found some fascinating correlations in theories presented by mathematicians and physicists. Whether or not this is truly the foundation of the science of the Blu Room is challenging to know. However, the correlations to its geometry are interesting enough to describe in this book for the reader to contemplate.

Nikola Tesla stated, "The day science begins to study non-physical phenomena, it will make more progress in one decade than in all the previous centuries of its existence."

The understanding of how spirit interacts with matter is the advancement of science. Nikola Tesla knew about sacred geometry. He said, "If you only knew the magnificence of the three, six and nine, you would have a key to the universe."[30] Much speculation has arisen regarding this quote attributed to Tesla.

Interior angles of polygons mathematically and numerically end up being the number nine. The number 9 is significant in the 22.5-degree arc of a circle. A circle consists of 360 degrees. In many divisions of 360, the digits equate the number 9 ($360=3+6+0=9$, $180=1+8+0=9$, $120=1+2+0=3$, $90=9+0=9$, $72=7+2=9$, $45=4+5=9$, $360 / 40 = 9$, etc.). The number 9 also appears in many other mathematical representations. For example, the speed of light, 186,624 miles per second, can be calculated to add up to 9 ($1+8+6+6+2+4=27=2+7=9$). The same applies to proportional relationships between the Earth and the moon. The phi golden ratio is seen in vortexes in nature from the spin of atoms to the spin of galaxies. The angles in golden ratio triangles can be added up to 9.

Related to these numbers, the mathematician, Marko Rodin, discusses that the mathematical fingerprint of God is the number 9. He described vortex mathematics and showed that the numbers 1, 2, 4, 5, 7, and 8 represent the physical world, and that the numbers 3, 6, and 9 represent the spiritual world that govern our material reality from the quantum level.

In his theory, 3, 6, and 9 represent the pathways that force, energy, and information take. Rodin also discusses that inside the major groove of DNA exists a higher dimensional template defined by the mathematical number pattern 3, 9, 6, 6, 9, 3.[31] Rodin's mathematics certainly look interesting as periodicity in DNA configuration has been described by others and correlates with ancient mathematics and sacred geometry.

The number 3 also occurs in quantum physics and quantum law. In 1970, a theoretical physicist, Vitaly Efimov, described equations of quantum mechanics in relation to the Borromean rings. Efimov was looking at the behavior of sets of three particles, regardless of their size. He found that whether one compares subatomic particles or atomic particles like the proton, the neutron, and the electron, they come in sets of three. The symbology of the Borromean rings, which was used in the fifteenth century to describe the relationship of the Father, Son, and the Holy Spirit, and that God is surrounded by the word, light, and life, represents the Trinity of Creation.

When light is expressed into form, torus mathematics is recurring. It has been found in calculations that our universe is the shape of a torus and can be described either in this torus form or in the sacred geometry based on triads. This geometry is everywhere in nature.

Whether you look at a galaxy or subatomic particles, the dimensions are not important. The ratios stay the same. They evolve according to the Fibonacci series and the golden mean. In all of nature we see this code expressed.

The mathematician, Dr. Stephen Phillips, described in his book, *The Mathematical Connection Between Religion and Science*, an interesting theory. He mathematically analyzed the tree of life and the Pythagorean solids and found an embedded code. I was fascinated by his hypothesis in relationship to the octagonal shape of the Blu Room.

He described two connected circles, representing matter and antimatter. Within those two circles arises the triad, the square, the pentagon, the hexagon, the octagon—all sacred geometry. He developed a systematic representation in which he divided these mathematical shapes into triads, the basic, geometric shape of creation. The corners of each triad were represented by a dot called yods. When he added up the number of yods in the geometric shapes, he found a code.[32]

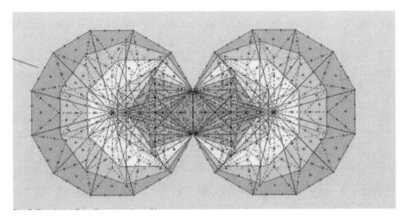

Figure 1: Polygons enfolded in 10 trees of life. Stephen Phillips © 2009.[33]

One of the numbers encoded was one of the most mysterious numbers seen in physics, called the fine-structure constant. This number governs the properties of all atoms.

String theory, which is an alternative theory to quantum mechanics, describes in multiple dimensions how light strings are bent into form and create reality.

The laws of string theory are encoded in sacred geometry. Dr. Phillips also discovered that encoded are the number of bones in the human skeleton, all the classical acupuncture points on the body, as well as the codons of messenger RNA and anticodons of transfer RNA. His theory also describes accurately the instances in the genetic DNA code of stop codons, anticodons, as well as regular codons and represents a code for the seven musical scales.[34]

Based on Dr. Phillips' discoveries, could the octagon be a code for reverse engineering the physical matter of the human being to its original property of light? Since the Blu Room has an octagonal shape, is its geometry a code that affects its beneficial healing properties?

Even in human DNA, geometrical patterns are found. Our DNA winding displays the Fibonacci series and the golden ratio. The four different nucleotides that make up our DNA contain molecular bindings in hexagonal and pentagonal shapes.

According to Ramtha's teachings, the pentagon, which creates the five-pointed star, is the symbol of Christ consciousness. The hexagon, which creates the six-pointed star, is the symbol for God/man, God/woman realized. This geometry encodes the divine human, the being of light that has descended into mass as a conglomerate of diversified light.

What genius has spoken this mathematical language throughout history? Plato originally proposed that the laws of the cosmos could be deciphered in geometry.

Johannes Kepler, in the fifteenth century, described the planetary distances in our universe accurately through sacred geometry. He depicted the view of the universe based on the application of regular polyhedra. He inserted an octahedron between the orbits of Mercury and Venus, an icosahedron between Venus and Earth, a dodecahedron between Earth and Mars, a tetrahedron between Mars and Jupiter, and a cube between Jupiter and Saturn. This model accurately predicted the proportional distances between the planets and the sun. Kepler wrote in his book, *Harmony of the World*, in 1619, "Geometry, which before the origin of things was coeternal with the divine mind and is God himself . . . supplied God with patterns for the creation of the world."[35]

Crop circles all over the world have been shown to encode advanced mathematics and harmonics. These mathematical relationships are found everywhere in nature.

How could this apply to identifying healing molecules based on their structural and electrical properties?

Imagine if a molecule has only been studied for a certain effect. If all other effects have not been studied, then we do not know all that this molecule can affect. Our fundamental, scientific approach is limited by definition.

For example, a new drug will not be studied for several years in looking at long-term side effects. Many adverse effects come to light once the drugs have already been released to the market. On the other hand, many vitamins have only been studied in extremely small doses; therefore the therapeutic effect of larger doses has never been evaluated and so they are falsely discarded.

Our viewpoint determines the boundaries of our knowledge. What if we look at a molecule from a different perspective, that of the language of light? We understand that the original lightning spheres of creation were carbon, oxygen, hydrogen, and nitrogen. These molecules are the same molecules that the body is made of and essentially needs. If we desire to heal the body in the most natural ways, not by artificial means, we are going to give it the molecules that it already naturally has within it.

We can utilize the premise that the greater the energy transfer electrically that a molecule is capable of, the greater its potential healing ability to the quantum coherent whole. Understanding how matter originates and what theoretical properties determine the veracity of a molecule's light would lead us to examine the origins of matter—the birthplace of original particles that make up the large.

String Theory and the Ether

The most elemental building block of matter has been called the Anu and has been described in mathematician Stephen Phillips book, *Extra Sensory Perception of Quarks*. In the book, Phillips describes the theosophist occult chemistry of Charles W. Leadbeater and Annie Besant. These two visionaries viewed the most fundamental beginning particle via extrasensory perception and recorded the most fundamental geometry of the subatomic makeup of atoms.

The smallest unit of light bent into matter is the Anu. It is roughly spherical, slightly flattened, and has a depression at the point where the force or energy flow is causing a heart-shaped form. The Anu is spinning and pulsating as if breathing. Each atom is surrounded by a field formed by the finer atoms of the higher planes which surround and penetrate it. Each Anu is composed of ten coils lying side by side but without touching one another. Each coil is itself a spiral containing 1,680 turns. If we continue unwinding each spiral, we end up with an enormous circle of the tiniest, imaginable dots flying like pearls on an invisible string. These strings are the most basic structure in which light is bent into form, the original building block of matter. Stephen Phillips showed mathematically that subatomic particles are made of these Anu's.[36]

Pythagoras noted about the ether: "An infinitely subtle substance, out of which all other substances are constituted, in varying forms, passes back again into simplicity. The same principle underlies the harmonies of music and the motion of heavenly bodies." [37]

John Keeley, American inventor, working on an etheric force engine in the nineteenth century "affirms, with other philosophers, that there is only one unique substance, and that this substance is the Divine spirit, the spirit of life, and that this spirit of life is God, who fills everything with His thoughts; disjoining and grouping together these multitudes of thoughts in different bodies called atmospheres, fluids, matters, animal, vegetable, and mineral forms."[38]

These scientists have shown how the original substance of light, the ether, is the very matter of our reality using a mathematical code as the language of creation. Via intentional observation of thought, we can influence that light substance.

Everything is a representation of everything else, all in divine, harmonic proportion. The human body is also a representation of the whole of creation. Imagine a quarrel between two people in your orbit, and they represent two cells. There is now an inharmonious ripple in your environment. Because everything is connected to everything else, the whole is affected by that quarrel.

This is the idea behind what has been called the morphogenetic field of the mind of God, that one thought can affect creation millions of miles away. Our intent can affect nature and the survival of the natural world. Our attitudes, how we perceive things, is everything. The same quarrel as described above can be allowed until it simply dissolves. Harmony is then restored and the whole is again uplifted.

The greatest understanding of our time is that quantum theory and string theory are depictions of the spiritual realm that are profoundly scientific as well as profoundly spiritual. The scientists who can see the interconnectedness of all things, who can see the harmony of interplay, are the greatest mystics.

The ocean of light in the Void consists of the original building blocks of matter. These are the strings in string theory that form the Anu described by the clairvoyant psychics. Scientists have called it the God particle, the smallest building block of matter. From this light, of which all matter is made, arises all reality. There is only one substance, which is the mind of God. There is only one overarching science, which is the science of divine light manifested.

Thought is the coagulating principle that allows light to be bent into form. The light strings form God particles, these form subatomic particles, the subatomic particles form atoms, the atoms form molecules, the molecules form DNA, proteins, and other conglomerates of function. DNA, proteins and other molecules form organs, organs form the physical structure of the human being. Ramtha explains this descent into matter in his model of reality: a triad divided into seven levels of the light spectrum.[39]

Each scale of size and description in this coagulating descent of matter maintains the same harmonic, mathematical ratio, the song of God. Therefore, self-awareness of "I am," as the Observer, is the awareness of all of life—past, present, future—all present in a Now. This awareness of wholeness, of harmony, provides unlimited access to all energy, all knowledge, and all life.

We are not disconnected from anything in creation. Our thoughts and conscious awareness affect life everywhere through harmonious or inharmonious vibration, creating an immediate quantum entanglement of particles. All of life is like an ocean of subatomic particles defined as strings of light.

If we want to understand creation, we must look at the harmony affecting all things. We will find the small represented in the large, the near represented in the far. We never lose sight that regardless of the scale, all life vibrates in harmony in infinite variations. Any disharmony causes its effect, which ultimately becomes the destruction and neutralization of the source of disharmony itself. The law of harmony in the universe is absolute. Cause and effect are absolute in equilibrium.

There is nothing else but God. In the cycle of reincarnation, the same laws of cause and effect always play out. Regardless of perhaps millions of incarnations needed to harmonize disharmonious attitudes by turning them into wisdom, all beings are returning to one state—the perfect balance and the perfect harmony of being one with God.

I contemplate the music of the spheres as not just a faraway, celestial, spiritual imagination. The harmony, inter-connectedness, and vibratory song of creation are all around us. The music of the spheres could be the microcosm of what we hear in the larger world through the sounds of nature. The wind, the birds, the flora and fauna on macroscopic levels are an orchestra of vibrational creation that plays a symphony together, to each other, and in interconnected harmony.

If we could change our perspective to understand and appreciate what creates and makes up the large, it is the infinite interplay of subatomic particles that makes up the ever-greater scales of life's symphony.

According to Ramtha's model, all are God and the only thing we need to shift is our attention. By observing reality with an open-minded curiosity to know, all can know. The body of one individual person, the body of humanity, the body of celestial planets, the body of galaxies, are all one body of God. Each smallest component is connected to the large. There is no lack in God's kingdom, only fulfillment of the law, and that law, according to Ramtha's teachings, is the unfolding of a destiny of discovery through the observation of the conscious being, the living God.

Nikola Tesla and Electromedicine

Nikola Tesla had a great impact on modern medicine. He invented the Tesla coil, which produced high-frequency and high voltage currents which he used to heal the body. Tesla himself would go long hours without food, drink, or sleep. He used the electrical currents of his machine to heal and rejuvenate his body and uplift his mood. The high-frequency currents would replenish his energy, help his fatigued muscles, and increase his weight and strength. He did experiments with vibrations and resonance and how that applied to healing. He called electricity the greatest doctor. The high voltage currents also had bactericidal properties.[40]

Tesla also utilized high-frequency currents for ozone generation, which has powerful antiseptic and antibacterial effects. However, for the purposes of Light Medicine, the idea that high-frequency voltage can heal cells becomes the basis of understanding how we can reverse and heal any malady. Tesla explained that these high-frequency "vitality boosters" would generate a "universal healing agent." When applied, they would enable the body to heal disease.

Tesla began to experiment with the healing properties of his oscillators, which had remarkable healing properties.[41] Dr. Frederick Finch Strong, M.D., was a lecturer of electro-therapeutics who applied Tesla's ideas for healing. Strong discussed how the life force within the human body can be enhanced by high-frequency electricity. The applied electricity runs through the sympathetic nervous system. When voltage in the body is decreased, disease ensues. The use of high-voltage electricity can increase that voltage and thereby reverse diseased bodies back to health.[42]

At AM Medical, my office, I utilize the technology of the autonomic nervous system function test RM-3A, which provides voltage measurements correlating with internal organ function to gather information about the health status of the patient. It provides excellent information as a health screening tool based on the above scientific understanding.

It has been proven that electrical energy alone can fuel ATP (adenosine triphosphate) synthesis. A cell can respond to an electrical field and capture energy from it. AC (alternating current) fields as low as 60 V/cm have been shown to induce ATP synthesis. The rate of ATP synthesis was slow, but after ten to thirty minutes of continuous stimulation, more than 10 ATP per enzyme was obtained. With AC fields, there appeared to be a window at around 10 Hz for effective energy coupling.

Experiments have revealed that the membrane ATPase can capture energy from an electrical field to synthesize ATP or to pump an ion up its concentration gradients. Molecules have also been shown to convert energy from one form to another. A simple membrane transporter or a membrane integrated enzyme can perform this energy utilization. The membrane transporter can respond to a periodic potential, which can be an oscillating electrical field, an acoustic or sonic wave, or other types of oscillating driving forces. This means our cells are able to convert electricity, sound, and light into energy.

It has been proposed that these characteristics satisfy the concept known as the language of cells. The electromagnetic language of cells can influence cellular transport and biochemical reactions. We can neutralize the harmful effects of environmental and electromagnetic fields by an interference signal which can then cancel and abolish the harmful fields. This evidence shows that electromagnetic medicine has its basis in science.[43]

The idea of improving electrical conductivity within the cells as a mode of healing can be approached from several directions. High-frequency oscillators like the Tesla coil can be utilized. Dr. Robert Becker, orthopedic surgeon and researcher in electrophysiology and electromedicine, described a complete, operational system in living organisms which controls such basic functions as growth, healing, and biological cycles.

This functions via data transmission in an analog fashion using varying levels of direct current (DC) as its signal.

There are two electrochemical links in the operation of this transmission system: One is between the direct current and the nervous system; the other is between the DC and all body cells. Dr. Becker's concept explains the diverse effects reported with the biological effects of applied electrical currents, which includes electrical anesthesia, electrical growth control, and electroacupuncture.[44]

The Blu Room, by applying a certain ultraviolet-blue frequency and its corresponding biophotonic energy to the body, could work in the same way by increasing the life force. Our skin absorbs photons and can store them as energy. This energy can be transferred to the whole organism and allow the regeneration of biomolecules to occur.

Nutritional supplements that enhance mitochondrial function and thereby increase the electrical conductivity in the body are also helpful in this approach. Upregulating cellular mitochondrial density with appropriate bioidentical thyroid hormone replacement when indicated is necessary to address cellular energy production.

The physical detoxification of compounds that are interfering with electrical productivity of the mitochondria and removal of them from the body is just as important.

It has been shown that when a cell voltage drops, bacteria fungi and viruses are able to grow and cause disease within the body. When voltage is restored, the immune system can fight off these pathogens; therefore the restorative ability of the body is profound.

The answers on how to affect the healing of the body lie in the body electric because we can provide cells with substances that are electron donors that will help heal the body.

The future of medicine understands that the electrical conductivity and amplitude of the body electric, seen in the sympathetic nervous system—and can be measured by machines like the autonomic nervous system function test—are the connection in which the spiritual being utilizes the physical body through electric light.

If we maintain high light value in the body or high electrical value, we can maintain harmony, stasis, and health. The importance of a preventative health approach, through the early diagnosing of a loss of light in the body and taking appropriate steps to rejuvenate that loss of light, is the true meaning of preventative health. As we are referring to electricity and light synonymously, we now understand that the above measures are enhancing light throughout the body.

Proteins, DNA, and Communication

Biomolecular interactions, in particular protein-protein and protein-DNA interactions, have been shown to be electromagnetic in their nature. Certain periodicities within the distribution of energies of delocalized electrons along a protein molecule are critical for protein biological function and interaction with its target. If protein conductivity is introduced, then a charge moving through a protein backbone can produce electromagnetic irradiation or absorption with spectral characteristics corresponding to energy distribution along the protein.[45] This again indicates that regulation of cellular constructs is electrical and electromagnetic in nature.

The Brain as Quantum Computer

The interface of consciousness with the brain has been compared to a quantum computer in the scientific literature as well as in Ramtha's teachings. The idea has been discussed that the electrical activity of the body that generates spatiotemporal electromagnetic fields acts like an antenna that tunes the brain/body system into the quantum memory network that contains consciousness.

Neurons appear to communicate via fractal resonances. Their information processing exhibits quantum properties and quantum entanglement. The quantum space/time matrix contains elementary particles. With the extremely high energy of the quantum vacuum, space/time is curved to a singularity, producing wormholes.[46] These micro-wormholes may give us access to our own parallel realities. This connection between particles could be responsible for producing the phenomenon of quantum entanglement, quantum coherence, and other nonlocal phenomena, all of which occur in the brain.

The microtubule network of the cellular cytoskeleton in the brain's neurons has been identified as a key structure involved in processing information. Photons, when absorbed, will modulate the electronic properties of biomolecules, resulting in a direct functional effect. Phonons and electrical fields will also do this.

Coherent interference of cytoplasmic sources will result in holographic information processing. Holographic interference patterns can be stored in the phosphate bilayers of membranes over short time periods or hardwired into microtubules and actin filaments.[47]

The Placebo Effect of the Mind

In spiritual and medical healing, the placebo effect plays a powerful role. The patient can receive a sugar pill, believing that it is medicine, and the patient is healed. The pill is the ritual, which could also be performed by the energy healer or shaman. Whatever the patient believes is in the placebo will produce the outcome. The process exemplifies important acts of individual creation of the divine being. The patient is focused on healing, accepts the healing in the form of the sugar pill or the healer's ritual, and is filled with feelings of hope. Coherence is then created in the crystal liquid-crystalline structure of the body, and the spin of subatomic particles is rearranged to facilitate this new state of health. Thus the patients heal themselves. The stronger the belief in the setting—the doctor, the pill, the "ritual" around the healing—the greater the outcome.

Is it possible to cut out the ritual and have the individual directly heal oneself? Yes. If observation on healing is present—absolute acceptance is present—then the individual will be healed simply by the collapse of the wave function of the Observer that deems it to be so. If there is doubt, fear, concern, or anything else but the absolute knowing that the healing has occurred, the healing cannot take place. The harmony in the body has not been achieved and the denial of the healing manifests.

This is not to tell anyone to throw away their supplements or supporting medications. The mind has to be trained and powerful enough to be able to change one's quantum state. Patients need to have enough acceptance to allow healing to occur. The attitudes that have made them sick, for many people, are not easy to change. It requires much mental self-awareness and correction of destructive thoughts to be willful and powerful enough not to engage further in addictive habits and negative emotions.

In similar ways, if the patient believes in nothing, is negative towards every solution, and busy engaging thoughts of blame, feelings of anger, resentment, self-pity, helplessness, and hopelessness, the greatest support, the newest medication, the most exciting solution, cannot override that negative attitude. There are patients who communicate that they are allergic to everything and so their body will react negatively to everything in the environment. It becomes the law in their reality. These are the patients who disproportionately will manifest the adverse reactions. Self-responsibility is a bitter pill to swallow for many; however, observation is an absolute law when it comes to maintaining health in the body.

Our organism is made of more than 60% water. Water becomes imprinted with intention and thought. We also affect the spin of every subatomic particle in the body and imprint its spin with the information provided by our thoughts.

Matter responds to the observation of thought and that communication is transmitted over space and time instantaneously. Everything we think and feel is immediately transmitted throughout the entire organism and directly affects the electrical properties of cellular structures.

Attitudes Affecting Telomeres

Telomeres are the protective structures on the ends of chromosomes. In the aging process, telomeres progressively shorten. Short telomeres are associated with all diseases related to aging—cardiovascular disease, dementia, diabetes, arthritis, and cancer.

It has been found that aging is a dynamic process. Earlier it was thought that once you age, the pattern is irreversibly set. Elizabeth Blackburn, Ph.D., together with Elissa Epel, Ph.D., won the Nobel Prize following their research on telomeres. Telomeres shorten with each cell division, but the wearing-down process is what really determines how fast cells age, and some people have much more rapid telomere shortening than others.

Thanks to researchers like Blackburn and Epel, it is now understood that this rate of decline can be slowed down, telomere length can be increased, and the enzyme that repairs telomeres, called telomerase, can also be increased in its activity. Science knows that we can slow down and even reverse the aging process. Imagine if we all started working on longevity and antiaging while still young, in our thirties and forties. If you progressively halt and reverse that aging process, at age 70 you're still going to be at age 45. The age reversal process can be easier when started at a young age, as cells are still very functional. It is more challenging to age-reverse a severely ill patient or someone with advanced age. Even that is not impossible but more challenging. If we also correct the mind that leads to the acceleration of the disease process, then we can effectively create high-functioning longevity.

In telomere studies it has been shown that negative emotions accelerate the aging process. Feeling threatened, hostility, and hate shorten survival, as do unsocial neighborhoods and adverse reactions to life events for children. Once these children are taken out of the hostile environment, the telomere changes will reverse. A wandering mind and stress can accelerate the aging process, as do anxiety, depression, and chronic lack of sleep.

The longer telomeres are and the more telomerase is present, the slower the aging process. If we engage in mindfulness techniques, eat good food, move children out of neglect, focus our mind, improve our sleep, and exercise, then our telomeres can lengthen again.[48] A study on anxiety and phobia in women showed that those with chronic anxiety had an equivalent of six years in premature aging.[49]

There is the saying, "Love your neighbor as yourself." This is not just about brotherly love. When you have the emotional reaction of hate and anger, you are adversely affecting your own body through your emotional reaction. This shortens your life span through reduction of your telomere length and, as we discussed earlier, by creating incoherence in the biological system. In turn, meditation and stress reduction has been shown to slow cellular aging.[50]

CHAPTER 11
MOLECULAR SPECTROSCOPY AND ELECTRON TRANSFER

According to Ramtha: "All things have a lightbody, and because it is from light, they descend to mass. You are a conglomerate of a neighborhood of diversified light whose harmony is you.

"Now if you understand that and you work in light, then you garner information from those elementals that have the highest light value. When those values are then taken into the human biological form, that light enhances the body's mechanism."

In science, there are different ways that we can consider quantifying the light value of a compound or "elemental." One such technique is called spectroscopy.

Spectroscopy is a science that studies and measures spectra produced when matter—atoms or molecules—interacts with, or emits, electromagnetic radiation. The interaction of radiation with matter can cause redirection of the radiation and transitions between the energy levels of the atoms or molecules. A transition from a lower level to a higher level with transfer of energy from the radiation field to the atom or molecule is called absorption. When atoms or molecules absorb light, the incoming energy excites a quantized structure to a higher energy level. The type of excitation depends on the wavelength of the light. Electrons are promoted to higher orbitals by ultraviolet or visible light. Vibrations are excited by infrared light, and rotations are excited by microwaves.[1]

An absorption spectrum is the absorption of light as a function of the wavelength. The spectrum of an atom or molecule depends on its energy level structure, and absorption spectra are useful for identifying compounds.

Light is a wave or particle with a wavelength or a photon carrying energy. The energy of a photon = hc\λ h. Planck's constant is h. The speed of light is c. Energy and wavelength are "inversely proportional." Shorter wavelength means higher energy. Ultraviolet light has wavelengths shorter than 400 nanometers (nm). This is the wavelength that Ramtha discusses as the consciousness and energy of the Blue Body®. Ramtha teaches: "It is the body that belongs to the fourth plane of existence, the bridge consciousness, and the ultraviolet frequency band." "Blue Body® Healing is a discipline taught by Ramtha in which the students lift their conscious awareness to the consciousness of the fourth plane and the Blue Body® for the purpose of healing or changing the physical body." The Blue Body® is the perfect template of the physical body without polarity.[2] It is this frequency that has the power to heal the body. The Blu Room uses a wavelength of 310 nm, narrow-band ultraviolet.

Energy is measured in electron volts, meaning each electron can do 9 eV (electron-volt) of electrical work. Photons are produced or absorbed when electrons change their energy level in an atom. According to the electron cloud model of Erwin Schrödinger and Werner Heisenberg, electrons occupy probable positions surrounding the atomic nucleus. This is called the probability function, describing a cloudlike region where the electron is likely to be found. Once the electron is excited to a higher energy level, it is in a more unstable position than when in its relaxed, ground state. Therefore, the electron will quickly fall back down to the lower energy level and, when doing so, emits a photon with an energy equal to the difference in energy levels. The energy transitions for electrons of each element are unique and distinct from one another. Thus by examining the colors of light emitted by a particular atom, we can identify that element based upon its emission spectrum.

When looking at biological compounds, we can use the vibrational Raman spectrum. It is a tool to define important information on the molecular structures of a chemical substance. UV-Vis (ultraviolet-visible) spectroscopy is what occurs within atoms and molecules when photons in the UV and visible ranges of the spectrum are absorbed or emitted. In the following table, the color, wavelength, frequency, and energy of light are shown.[3]

Colour, wavelength, frequency and energy of light

Colour	λ/nm	ν/10^{14} Hz	ν_b/10^4 cm^{-1}	E/eV	E/kJ mol^{-1}
Infrared	>1000	<3.00	<1.00	<1.24	<120
Red	700	4.28	1.43	1.77	171
Orange	620	4.84	1.61	2.00	193
Yellow	580	5.17	1.72	2.14	206
Green	530	5.66	1.89	2.34	226
Blue	470	6.38	2.13	2.64	254
Violet	420	7.14	2.38	2.95	285
Near ultraviolet	300	10.0	3.33	4.15	400
Far ultraviolet	<200	>15.0	>5.00	>6.20	>598

Table 1: CRC Handbook of Fundamental Spectroscopic Correlation Charts (2005). CRC Press.[4]

By shining the light from excited atoms through a prism, it is possible to isolate these different wavelengths, which separate them through the process of refraction. Without a prism, we do not see these different wavelengths of light one at a time, but all blended together. The color emitted by each element is a distinct fingerprint of identification.

Infrared (IR) spectroscopy is a process in which lower energy radiation in the infrared region of the spectrum can produce changes within atoms and molecules. This type of radiation is usually not energetic enough to excite electrons, but it will cause the chemical bonds within molecules to vibrate in different ways. Just as the energy required to excite an electron in a particular atom is fixed, the energy required to change the vibration of a particular chemical bond is also fixed. By using special equipment in the lab, chemists can look at the IR absorption spectrum for a particular molecule and then use that spectrum to determine what types of chemical bonds are present in the molecule. For example, a chemist might learn from an IR spectrum that a molecule contains carbon-carbon single bonds, carbon-carbon double bonds, carbon-nitrogen single bonds, carbon-oxygen double bonds, and others. Because each of these bonds is different, each will vibrate in a different way and absorb IR radiation of different wavelengths. By evaluating its IR absorption spectrum, important determinations about a molecule's chemical structure can be made.

Electromagnetic waves consist of two waves perpendicular to each other. One of the waves is an oscillating magnetic field, the other is an oscillating electrical field. This oscillation determines the vibration.[5]

Electrical Properties of Antioxidants and Their Role in Healing

The oxidative damage created by free radicals is referred to as oxidative stress. This process has been associated with the development of degenerative diseases, which include cardiovascular and inflammatory diseases, cancer, atherosclerosis, stroke, and the symptom complex called "aging."

Free radicals are reactive molecular species with unpaired electrons that oxidize other molecules to gain electrons and stabilize themselves. This reaction produces another free radical, initiating a cascade of free radical stabilization and formation.

Free radicals can oxidize and thereby damage macromolecules, like DNA, proteins, carbohydrates, and lipids.

Free radicals, such as superoxide, hydrogen peroxide, and hydroxyl groups are produced in the cells and the environment. Within cells, oxidative metabolism generates and propagates free radicals, especially when transition metal ions like iron and copper aid in electron transfer. Free radicals also occur from environmental sources, including tobacco smoke, air pollutants, anesthetics, pesticides, heavy metals, and radiation.

Many organisms use oxygen during metabolism and can be subjected to oxidative stress. There are physiological mechanisms in the human body that hinder free radical formation. For example, transition metal ions are bound to proteins to limit their catalytic involvement in free radical formation. Molecular oxygen is bound to specific enzymes, which regulate its reduction to superoxide. These mechanisms can also be impaired, leading to an accelerated aging process.

In the plant kingdom we have natural compounds that have the ability to alleviate free radical damage. Antioxidants, like flavonoids, have a polyphenol structure, which contains numerous double bonds and hydroxyl groups that can donate electrons through resonance to stabilize the free radicals. The radical scavenging properties associated with the structure of flavonoids defend against oxidative stress. In doing so they reduce heart disease, prevent cancer, and slow the aging processes in cells responsible for degenerative diseases.[6]

In Light Medicine we understand that the ability of a molecule to donate electrons and even protons are equivalent to the ability of the molecule to give light to the human body. The greater the energy of the electron donation, the greater the light value of the compound. We understand that the electrical ability of antioxidants as electron donors is the ability to give light to the coherent organism. As a secondary effect this will decrease oxidative stress, therefore decreasing inflammation and henceforth slowing the aging mechanism and even reversing it.

The biosynthesis of flavonoids in fruits is regulated by ultraviolet light, and their accumulation acts as a defense mechanism against oxidative stress. When humans ingest such a compound, the body can use it to augment its own defensive mechanisms. Quercetin is a flavonol that, when reacting with a free radical, donates a proton and becomes a radical itself, but the resulting, unpaired electron is delocalized by resonance, making the quercetin radical too low in energy to be reactive.

Three structural groups aid in quercetin's ability to maintain its stability and act as an antioxidant when reacting with free radicals. These functional groups can donate electrons.

Quercetin has displayed the ability to prevent the oxidation of low-density lipoproteins (LDL) by scavenging free radicals and chelating transition metal ions, illustrating the correlation between electron donation and clinical effects. As a result, quercetin may aid in the prevention of certain diseases, such as cancer, atherosclerosis, and chronic inflammation.[7]

This understanding is applicable to many different, natural molecules. By ingesting these compounds, we can utilize the protective mechanisms that plants have developed and apply them to our human body. The identification of these compounds, based on the criteria of the electron's donor status and antioxidant abilities, will help us identify new and previously known natural cures for diseases. The key is the determination of the veracity of its light, which in our model correlates with the ability to give off electrons. It is important that the dosages are adequate to have beneficial effects in the body based on the level of disease and lack of light that exists in the individual patient's disease state.

The idea of determining the relationship between antioxidant properties of medicinal plants and their electrical current conductivity has been described in 2015 by a research group from Malaysia. Ten herbs were selected randomly: Strobilanthes crispa, Pereskia sacharosa, Ehretia laevis, Plectranthus amboinicus, Orthosiphon stamineus, Andrographis paniculata, Persicaria odorata, Clinacanthus nutans, curry leaves, and frankincense. The results show that all the extracts have a significant amount of electrical conductivity ranging from 0.06 – 0.12 Ω·cm. All the extracts also have high antioxidant properties.[8]

In a study evaluating antioxidants with infrared spectroscopy, different polyphenols were assessed. Infrared spectroscopy assesses effects on molecular bonding—in this case for lipid peroxidation. The spectroscopy showed that phenolic acids like capsaicin and catechin have antioxidant protective effects.[9]

A review article from China discussed antiaging ingredients in plant-based, traditional Chinese medicine. Antiaging effects, such as antioxidant properties, increased telomerase activity, and decreased DNA damage were identified. The compounds also had an effect on longevity genes like mTOR (mammalian target of rapamycin), SIRT1 (sirtuin 1), AMPK (adenosine 5′ monophosphate-activated protein kinase), insulin, and insulin-like, growth-factor-signaling pathways.

Identified plant-based, molecular compounds that have been used in traditional Chinese medicine can be categorized in different groups: "flavonoids, saponins, polysaccharides, alkaloids, and others: astragaloside, *Cistanche tubulosa* acteoside, icariin, tetrahydrocurcumin, quercetin, butein, berberine, catechin, curcumin, epigallocatechin gallate, gastrodin, 6-gingerol, glaucarubinone, ginsenoside Rg1, luteolin, icarisid II, naringenin, resveratrol, theaflavin, carnosic acid, catalpol, chrysophanol, cycloastragenol, emodin, galangin, echinacoside, ferulic acid, huperzine, honokiol, isoliensinine, phycocyanin, proanthocyanidins, rosmarinic acid, oxymatrine, piceid, puerarin, and salvianolic acid B."[10]

Based upon this research, I propose that all molecules with antioxidant properties also have high electrical conductivity. As seen in the research above, multiple longevity genes are activated by compounds with high antioxidant properties.

The molecular structure of these natural antioxidant compounds consists mainly of carbon, hydrogen, oxygen, and nitrogen. In Light Medicine we are assessing these molecules based on their ability to become electron donors and scavenge free radicals. This method can be used as a systematic model on how to identify natural products that enhance the body's healing mechanism. In traditional Chinese medicine, the idea is that they enhance chi, or life force energy. That is precisely correct, and we are transposing this idea to the bioelectrical Light Medicine model.

Specific Molecules and Their Healing Properties

We can apply the above model and look at the electron donor status of vitamin C (Ascorbic Acid $C_6H_8O_6$).

The many biological effects of vitamin C (ascorbate) have been shown to be related to the electron donor status. In aqueous solutions, vitamin C emits solvated electrons when excited in single state.

The UV spectrum of ascorbic acid at pH 7.4 exhibits a high absorption peak with a maximum at 265 nm.[11]

Vitamin C can react with electrons as well as transfer them to other biological systems and thereby acts as an efficient electron mediator. The strong tendency of ascorbate to eject electrons under formation of ascorbate free radicals classifies it as a very potent electron donor. In the reaction of electrons with oxygen in solutions, peroxyl radicals are formed. These have a powerful ability to kill bacteria and inactivate viruses.

Vitamin C plays an important role in the protection of cell membranes. Cell membranes consist of 20-25% proteins and lipids as well as 2-5% of vitamins C, E, β-carotene, and water.

The structure of the membrane depends on the specific function of the cell. The cell membranes in organisms are constantly being attacked by oxidizing free radicals, which are also generated in the human organism by enzymes. It was established that membrane degradation is efficiently avoided by an electron cascade transfer within these antioxidant vitamins.[12]

Dr. Nikola Getoff, from Vienna, wrote many scientific papers about hormone regeneration. He has experimentally shown that hormones can emit solvated electrons when excited into single state in aqueous or in water-alcohol solution.[13]

The emitted electron retains the specific frequency of the corresponding hormone. It thereby transmits the information of the original hormone molecule. By electron transfer from a given hormone, via the brain, to other hormones or to a biological system, communication is established. When hormones continue to lose electrons or light, they create metabolites that are able to induce the formation of cancerous cells. However, when these hormone metabolites are exposed to potent electron donors, such as vitamin C, they can be regenerated.[14]

Solvated electrons are electrons that have been released by substances into an aqueous solution—such as hormones, enzymes, amino acids, vitamins, and other organic compounds. Most biological systems in humans are capable of emission and generate—as well as consume and transfer—electrons, enabling intersystem communication via the brain.[15]

Hormones in specific emit, and react with, electrons and can transfer electrons to other systems; therefore they are classified as electron mediators in the organism. The regeneration process of hormones, for instance, by vitamin C, and hormone degradation (e.g., caused by free radicals in the organism) are in permanent competition. Therefore, Getoff, et al. recommended an adequate consumption of vitamin C. Of note, higher vitamin C concentration led to 100% regeneration of the hormone progesterone. The regeneration of hormones depends on several factors. These include the hormones' molecular structure, their concentration, the rate of chemical reaction with solvent electrons and ascorbic acid, as well as the pH of the solution.[16]

It is well known that an acidic environment increases the likelihood of disease development. An alkaline pH constitutes an electron donor state and therefore a healthier state in the body.

It is interesting that UV light irradiation induces electron emission by hormones and facilitates the regenerative process in the presence of high levels of vitamin C. When discussing Blu Room effects in combination with nutritional optimization and other high light value supplements, hormonal regeneration could be another way in which the Blu Room is able to assist in the healing process. In addition, increasing vitamin C consumption to higher levels, as Linus Pauling recommended, can have antiaging effects also based on regeneration of hormones.

Oxidizing free radicals—like hydroxyl, hydroperoxyl, peroxides, and oxygen species—are mostly generated in the liver. Whereas reducing solvated electrons—representing the basic form of the hydrogen atom—are emitted by enzymes, hormones, and redox systems as a sequence of energy transfer processes in the organism.[17]

Oxidizing transients are also involved in the degradation of consumed nutrients. Their surplus attacks the cell membrane and its components, causing an accelerated aging process. By systematic investigations into the fate of excited states of organic molecules, such as vitamins in aqueous solution, it was found that molecules having substituents like -OH, -O, -OCH3, -OPO3H2, -OPO3H-, -COO⁻, -NH2, -NHCH3 can eject electrons.[18]

Knowledge of these electron-donating, side chain molecular groups that give electrons can further assist in the prediction of possible clinical light-giving effects and thereby the recognition of novel, healing compounds. Each electron has its own spin and torsion waves, which emit the information of the original molecule to the whole of the coherent organism. DNA molecules are able to transport electrons over long distances. The electron transport through DNA occurs in a multistep-hopping mechanism. The rate of each individual hopping step decreases strongly with an increase in distance.[19]

Not only in DNA has it been proven that electron transfer in biological systems is important in communication. The energy released in the hydrolysis of an ATP molecule is the universal energy unit which is used in a great number of energy transformations in living organisms. All these transformations involve protein molecules which are generally of a very large size. It has been shown in 1976 at the Bogolyubov Institute for Theoretical Physics in Kiev that energy from ATP hydrolysis can be transferred without loss along alpha-helical protein molecules as special collective excitations, which are called molecular solitons.

All protein molecules represent very long polypeptide chains with periodic repetition of peptide groups which contain the hydrogen, nitrogen, carbon, and oxygen atoms. These polypeptide chains can exist in different configurations, which in alpha-helical proteins, the polypeptide chains are coiled into long helices—stabilized by hydrogen bonds between the peptide groups—in addition to the peptide bonds between neighboring carbon atoms within the primary polypeptide chain.

In each helical protein molecule, the peptide groups are situated along three chains of hydrogen bonds which are located at equal distances from one another and form periodic structures. The periodic structure of an alpha-helical protein molecule provides the basis for the transmission of vibrational excitations and therefore ultrafast information transfer within individual peptide groups. The basic vibrational excitation of the peptide group corresponds to vibration of this C=O (carbon-oxygen bond). Owing to the dipole resonance interactions, the vibrations in C=O of individual peptide groups are organized.

There are two types of collective excitations—excitons and solitons—and they may appear in each chain of peptide groups. Excitons spread along the chain exceeding the velocity of longitudinal sound waves. While traveling, they generate phonons; therefore they are rapidly decelerated. Solitons are collective excitations formed as a result of the combination of intra-peptide C=O vibration with a local deformation of the chain.

Although excitons are less stable, they are easily excited by light of a corresponding frequency. This means that light can alter the information transfer within peptide chains by changing the vibration of the excitons. The study of the infrared spectrum, when excitons in protein molecules are generated, is an effective means for analyzing protein structure. This explanation of how light and sound information is transported within peptide chains is important in understanding the biophysical control mechanism in the body.

Electron transfer from donor to acceptor molecules along protein molecules plays an important role in the bioenergetics of living organisms. It has been established experimentally that electrons can move without energy loss along protein molecules over distances of tens of intra-atomic distances. Protein molecules are dielectrics. The transfer process involves excess electrons that come to a protein molecule from a donor molecule. Electron transfer appears to be realized by the alpha-helical part of the molecule—an area of the protein that is used as a highway for electrons to travel.[20]

In 2017, Caltech published a paper discussing how DNA acts like a wire that is nothing but a conductor for electrons and that that is the real method of how information is being processed for cell replication.[21]

So far we have discussed the multitudes of donor molecules that can give off electrons and thereby affect proteins and peptides as well as DNA configuration. How DNA, protein configurations, and their function are altered by electrons is a further important mechanism to understand when considering a new Light Medicine model.

The Linguistic–Wave Genome Model

Dr. Peter Gariaev, a professor with the Institute of Quantum Genetics in Moscow, wrote in his groundbreaking book, *Quantum Consciousness of the Linguistic–Wave Genome, Theory and Practice,* about the fundamental flaws of the current Genetic Code Model. He describes how the genetic translational system is intelligent and able to read, based on the quantum and electromagnetic nature of the genome and the holographic whole program of the organism.

Dr. Gariaev and his coresearchers found in mathematical-linguistic analysis of the texts of DNA an independent language. They developed a new kind of spectroscopy called the "polarization-laser-radio wave" spectroscopy based on principles of holography, quantum nonlocality, and an understanding of soliton regulation (the modality in which electrons travel along DNA and peptide chains for ultrafast transmission of information).[22] The scientists were able to transfer, via DNA wave replicas and laser-radio wave processes, biological information from a donor to a recipient organism.

In this experiment the donor biosystem, represented by a tadpole of Xenopus Iaevis (a frog), was at a specific stage of development with the recipient biosystem at a different stage of development. The experiment successfully demonstrated the possibility of morphogenetic information transfer via the broadband electromagnetic field of the living tissues of tadpoles of Xenopus laevis (donor) on the cell differentiation of an embryo tissue of the same species.[23] This means that we are able to transfer genetic information via electromagnetic fields and directly influence our gene expression without physical gene editing.

Einstein, Podolsky, and Rosen (EPR) in 1935 described a paradox in physics. Quantum objects—for example, a pair of entangled photons—during their separation show an information connection. The quantum state of one photon—polarization or spin—can be instantaneously transferred to another photon. It becomes a mirror image of the first. This phenomenon occurs regardless of any distance between the photons. Gariaev describes that this EPR mechanism is a base for transmission of genetic (and mental) information between organisms.[24] According to Dr. Gariaev:

    1. Soliton and laser fields of DNA and chromosomes are optical-acoustoelectric, non-

linear wave processes, responsible for storage, reading, and transmission of genetic and other regulatory field information in the organism's space/time.

2. In biological systems, DNA, chromosomes, and proteins work in "antenna" mode, receiving external acoustic and electromagnetic fields, wherein the properties of such antennas change to perform regulatory body functions. The liquid-crystal chromosome continuum is a nonlinear optical medium and under certain conditions can function as a laser with alternating wavelengths as well as a soliton laser (on the so-called Fröhlich modes).

3. Chromosomal DNA, as a transceiver of laser radiation, linguistically polarizes its image and simultaneously performs its conversion into radio waves. The radio waves, formed according to a quantum nonlocality mechanism (teleportation), are isomorphically (linguistically) polarized in accordance with photons' polarizations. These radio waves can carry genetic-metabolic infor-mation from (both) within and outside of the biosystem.[25]

These described mechanisms for regulation of vital processes allow the ability to instantaneously transfer vast information between all cells and tissues via photons and polarized radio wave channels. This would explain why strategic, linguistic biomolecules—nucleic acids and proteins—have left-handed helical twists. These biomolecules determine the pronounced abilities of optical rotatory dispersion (optical rotation of a substance with a change in wavelength of light), circular dichroism (possible spin angular momentum states for a photon left- and right-hand), and birefringence (the ability to split a beam of light into two beams). This ability to alter the emission of light is the language mechanism used by these molecules to scan and communicate the context of their function over space and time to the whole organism. They act as an antenna for receiving and emitting information.[26]

I am convinced that this mechanism of gene control via light and sound will be used for genetic engineering in the future.

All things have this laser-radio wave signature and, theoretically, the information of any healing molecule can be captured and transferred. This could potentially be utilized for healing purposes without the necessity of taking a physical substance. We would instead become consumers of information.

Optical Properties of Carcinogens

Dr. Fritz-Albert Popp found correlations between the optical properties of biomolecules and their effects in causing cancer. He exposed 37 materials to ultraviolet light to create excited states. Some were carcinogenic and some were not. The molecules which cause cancer had the effect of reemitting the light at different frequencies, similar to a scrambling effect of the light. All of these carcinogens reacted to a very narrow band of wavelength around 380 nm. A key frequency that cells use for repairing damage is 380 nm. A weak light (low luminescence of watts/meter^2) at this wavelength is found to speed up the healing of cells. Dr. Popp discovered that carcinogens function by absorbing this healing energy and converting it to other frequencies which can trigger illness. He found that mistletoe was the one substance that was able to reverse the light scrambling effect of carcinogens.[27]

In understanding the linguistic-wave genome model by Dr. Gariaev, the question would be if carcinogens, like heavy metals, interfere with the healthy, laser-radio wave hologram of the organism and its information transfer. Is the light-scrambling effect of carcinogens literally a distortion of the holographic information that regulates healthy cellular function? It has been shown that increased concentrations of heavy metal ions in solution changes optical reflectance, which could mean signal interference in the body.[28]

Of interest is that some of the healing molecules that we will be discussing show light spectra in the 200 nm to 300 nm range and definitely less than 380 nm. Several molecules, such as vitamin C, carbon 60, rapamycin, and resveratrol are mentioned as examples. These molecules share the common basis of hydrogen, oxygen, carbon, and nitrogen. I postulate that molecules of high light value that have maximum emission spectra in the 200 to 300 nm range could be an indication of their potential healing properties. This hypothesis needs further verification but could be an additional basis for evaluating healing compounds based on their electron donor status, their chemical structure, and light spectroscopy. The next step is understanding the interaction between the holographic laser-radio wave information of compounds and the organism in the context of the linguistic genome.

As discussed above, every molecule has a laser-radio wave spectroscopy that can capture its entire information. This certainly could theoretically explain its healing properties. However, it is also plausible to me that molecular side chains that are electron donors could be responsible for a molecule's specific biological activity. These side chains may have emission spectra in different wavelength ranges that are correlated with areas of biological activity. We have a lot of unanswered questions in this area; however, the potential for scientific progress in the regulation of the human genome towards health and age reversal is substantial.

Some molecules like curcumin, which has an UV spectroscopy emission peak higher than 380 at 425 nm, still have profound healing properties. Curcumin has significant electron donor capabilities with properties like ultrafast, excited-state processes, such as solvation and excited-state intramolecular hydrogen atom transfer. These properties make curcumin an attractive agent for photodynamic therapy. Other agents useful for photodynamic therapy also have emission peaks much slower than the 200 to 300 nm range.

Curcumin is the biologically active molecule from the herb turmeric. There are studies that evaluate whether curcumin helps with diabetes, and the answer is yes. Another study investigated if it helps with inflammation, and the answer is yes. In further studies it has been shown to prevent heart disease, Alzheimer's, metabolic syndrome, and cancer. Each question posed requires a study that will provide an answer. Other researchers will then assess if certain genes are upregulated or downregulated. They will also get their answers.

Curcumin has definitely been shown to increase the antioxidant capacity in the body.[29] This means its molecular structure is an electron donor or light-giving molecule and that the electron transfer affects gene function. Curcumin, by donating electricity to the organism, can upregulate or downregulate many genes; therefore many diseases can be beneficially affected. By understanding the quantum coherence patterns of organisms, we see that the entire organism can be affected by the vibration of the molecule as in this example.

Buckminsterfullerene Carbon 60

When Ramtha asked that we look at the light value of elements and how they can assist the body in healing, he was speaking about a molecule called Carbon 60. He said on May 18, 2018:

"Now do you know the light value of Carbon 60?"

"Look at its light value. Study it. How can a particle that looks like the Blu Room, with so much light, override so much lack in cellular performance?"

"If you take the substance, it is so powerful that it feeds light-starved cells and, taken enough, it renews vitality in the DNA. That is why it lengthens life."

C60 shows two intense bands at 209 and 255 nm respectively. This is near ultraviolet radiation. We can say that the emission spectrum of this molecule is in a very high-frequency band.[30] Carbon 60 is made of carbon which, according to Walter Russell, is the perfect idea expressed in matter. Carbon is a perfect sphere and in its crystalline structure a perfect cube. Carbon 60 molecular structure has seventeen pentagons and twenty hexagons. Many of these structures are endowed with unusual rigidity for their mass because of their geometry. We have learned, according to Ramtha, that pentagons and hexagons are also a code for the perfect ideal of the human being—God/man, God/woman realized into flesh.

Carbon 60 in studies has been shown to be a superconductor. It displaces the magnetic field, levitates, and has been proposed to be a substance that will, in the future, replace plastic because it is so versatile. It is the most common molecule in the universe. While looking at the background radiation of diffuse interstellar bands, scientists found Carbon 60 was the most abundant molecule. C60 absorbs light—starlight in space—and emits light. It's an electron donor. It has been shown to exist in more than 174 vibrational states and is used in medical nanotechnology. Therefore the substance has extraordinary applications.

The medicinal properties of Carbon 60 in our understanding of Light Medicine are related to its specific molecular structure and property to give off electron currents. Carbon 60 accumulates in mitochondria, the powerhouse of the cells, and has antioxidant properties, anti-inflammatory and anticancer properties. It has been studied in humans as well as in mice.

Carbon 60 molecules were excited with a light-emitting diode lamp. The photo-excited C60 had cytotoxic effects causing a decrease in cell viability in 24 hours in leukemic cells that were resistant to the chemotherapeutic agent cisplatin. Because C60 has unique photochemical properties, it can be applied for photodynamic therapy of cancer.[31] Carbon 60 in mice models has been shown to be neuroprotective,[32] reverse Alzheimer's dementia, and heal the brain by enhancing neurite outgrowth.[33] C60 fullerenes cross the blood-brain barrier and elongate the life span in rats.[34]

Fullerenes have been shown to inhibit allergic response as a negative regulator of allergic mediator release that suppresses Antigen-driven type I hypersensitivity. Human mast cells and peripheral blood basophils exhibited a significant inhibition of IgE (immunoglobulin E) dependent mediator release when preincubated with C60 fullerenes.[35]

It has been demonstrated that water-soluble C60 nanoparticles have an efficient antitumor activity in studies and show specific immunomodulatory effects to the immune cells, such as T-cells and macrophages, both in vivo and in vitro. For example, C60 nanoparticles can increase the production of T-helper type 1 cell (Th1), cytokines (interleukin-2, interferon-gamma, and tumor necrosis factor-alpha), and decrease the production of T-helper type 2 cell cytokines in serum samples. On the other hand, C60 $(OH)_{20}$ nanoparticles show almost no adverse effect to the viability of immune cells in experiments but stimulate the immune cells to release more cytokines, in particular TNF-alpha. TNF-alpha production increased almost three-fold in treated T lymphocytes and macrophages. TNF-alpha plays a key role in the cellular immune process to help eliminate abnormal cells.[36]

A time-dependent decrease of viability was detected when leukemic cells were exposed to a combined treatment with C60 and visible light. The cytotoxic effect of photo-excited C60 was comparable with that induced by hydrogen peroxide, as both agents caused 50% decrease of cell viability at twenty-four hours.[37] C60 also shows significant activity for treatment of arthritis. C60 inhibited the stress-induced production of matrix-degrading enzymes, down-regulation of matrix production, and death and premature senescence in human cartilage cells. In rabbits with osteoarthritis, treatment with water-soluble C60 significantly reduced articular cartilage degeneration, whereas control knee joints not treated with C60 showed progression of cartilage degeneration with time. This inhibitory effect was dose dependent and was superior to that of hyaluronic acid. However, combined treatment with C60 and hyaluronic acid yielded a more significant reduction in cartilage degeneration compared with either treatment alone.[38]

As unique nanoparticles, fullerenes have attracted much attention due to their physical, chemical, and biological properties. Various fullerenes with -OH, -NH$_2$, -COOH, and peptide modifications have been developed. In cancer therapy, fullerene derivatives have shown high efficiency and low toxicity. They scavenge reactive oxygen species, inhibit lipid peroxidation, and act as antioxidants. They also have antimicrobial activity and inhibit the human immunodeficiency virus.[39]

If exposed to light, fullerenes can produce singlet oxygen in high quantum yields. This action, together with direct electron transfer from an excited state of fullerene and DNA bases, can be used to cleave DNA. In addition, fullerenes have been used as a carrier for gene and drug delivery systems.[40]

Although pristine C60 demonstrated no antimicrobial activity, fullerenols chemically modified exhibited good antimicrobial activity against Propionibacterium acnes, Staphylococcus epidermidis, Candida albicans, and Malassezia furfur. In particular, C60(OH)$_{44}$ exhibited a strong and wide-ranging antimicrobial activity comparable to that of catechin. This C60 compound exhibits antimicrobial activity via inhibition of microbial cell growth and not via bactericidal activity.[41] Carbon 60 also provides defense against UVA-induced skin damage.[42]

These vast, possible medical applications of Carbon 60 are extraordinary, given its nonexistent, side effect profile. This should be researched further and can be utilized in many different clinical settings. My interpretation of Ramtha drawing a parallel that C60 looks like a Blu Room is that it could be related to its geometry and light-giving properties. C60 is a potent electron donor. I postulate that the healing properties described above are related to the molecules' electrical properties.

Molecules are able to give electrons, but some are even able to give protons. For example, fisetin, a molecule of the flavonoid family which occurs in fruits and vegetables, has been shown to be a senolytic, which means that it removes aging cells. Fisetin protects the brain, improves memory, and may help delay aging. It helps control blood sugar and may have properties against neck cancer. It protects the liver and the heart. This is due to its powerful anti-inflammatory, antioxidant, and immune-supporting properties. Fisetin has been shown to bind to quadruplex DNA and give off a proton. It is also a photosensitizer. The molecule has a total of three hydroxyl rings with the chemical formula $C_{15}H_{10}O_6$. It is these hydroxyl rings that have been shown to be electron donors and responsible for its beneficial, biological effects.[43] The ability of the substance to have beneficial effects in the body is dependent on its energy transfer capacity or high light value. It is the electrical capacity that will upregulate health genes and downregulate disease-promoting genes. The greater the electrical capacity, the greater the molecules' healing abilities.

CHAPTER 12
TORSION PHYSICS, THE DENSITY OF TIME, AND MIND

MIT-trained physicist Dr. Claude Swanson wrote the most comprehensive book to date on subtle energy, called *Life force, the Scientific Basis: Breakthrough Physics of Energy Medicine, Healing, Chi, and Quantum Consciousness*. In the fall of 2018, JZ Knight allowed me to invite Dr. Swanson for a weekend to visit and experience the Shiva Blu Room in Yelm, Washington. I had the opportunity to ask him many questions, and he was able to provide scientific guidance that directed me to research the torsion and biophysics aspect of Light Medicine as presented herein. The torsion science presented in this chapter—and much more information—can be found in his excellent book.

Dr. Swanson, through his meticulous research, described the physics of torsion and the density of time and how it relates to the phenomenon created by subtle energy in application to healing. In this chapter, I will correlate torsion physics as presented by Dr. Swanson to Ramtha's teaching about Light Medicine and what it means for the individual and our understanding of healing with the mind.

In the previous chapter, we have discussed the meaning of Ramtha's statement, "You are a conglomerate of a neighbor-hood of diversified light whose harmony is you." We are beginning to understand that biophysicists know we are biophotonic light creating an interference hologram that is our body. Our bodies exhibit quantum properties that are transmitted by our quantum computer brain to the whole of the body instantly.

We want to understand further Ramtha's statement: "Even if you are astute that all biology, their atomic structures, particles, chemistry, mathematics, and understand spin-ratio value, at the end how does one determine a particle's veracity? By its light." This brings us to the physics of torsion and how it relates to mind.

Dr. Nikolai Kozyrev, a Russian astrophysicist, wrote in 1953 that he discovered a new force in physics which he called the density of time. His research grew out of his study of binary star systems and his profound ideas about the nature of cause and effect, including the origin of time. His experiments showed signals traveling faster than the speed of light that can change mass and time. Dr. Kozyrev concluded that the rate at which time passes can be altered. Accompanying this change in time passage would be a twisting effect in space he called torsion, which interacts with the spin of particles.[1] Every elementary particle, such as electrons and protons, have spin, as do the subatomic particles called quarks, which comprise electrons, protons, and neutrons.

The basic constituents of matter include the fundamental fermions (quarks, leptons, antiquarks, and antileptons), which generally are "matter particles" and "antimatter particles," as well as the fundamental bosons (gauge bosons and the Higgs boson), which generally are "force particles" that mediate interactions among fermions.[2]

All these subatomic particles also have a certain spin and an axis of spin. The subatomic particles in superstring theory are thought to be comprised of strings of light. In physics it is known that all matter to its smallest component, which is really a mathematical construct, has spin. Physics also knows that this spin of each particle can encode one bit of information. The spin of a particle changes in a moment and therefore its information has the capacity to also change.

Dr. Kozyrev realized that time density would imply that space must have a twisting property. He postulated that if time is asymmetric, then so is space. Every particle with mass, such as electrons, protons, and neutrons, has spin. Every time such a particle accelerates, it must produce a twisting effect in space because of its spin. When entropy, which is the amount of chaos in a system, changes, it involves accelerations of particles and therefore affects this twisting property of space/time in the vacuum state from which the particles arise.[3]

Whenever a charged particle produces electromagnetic waves or photons, it also creates torsion waves. These effects occur in the vacuum and alter the fabric of space/time. When an irreversible process increases entropy or chaos in a system in one location, it also radiates torsion or time density. This will be absorbed at the point of measurement. At the point of absorption, negative entropy or order is produced which balances the entropy increase at the source. This ensures that the entropy of the entire universe does not increase. Kozyrev described that the flow of time compensates for any entropy increase.[4]

Torsion can be stored in an object and transferred from one object to another. Torsion behaves similarly to an electrical charge, but it is not conserved. It decays slowly over time. The storage time varies from tens of seconds to many months, depending on various factors. The torsion waves encode the information of the object, and this information as a torsion field can be altered and transferred to other objects.[5] When we change these properties of electrons, we can change the information of mass itself.

This specific fact is important in order to understand the DNA changes discussed in the next chapter between JZ Knight and Ramtha. Torsion fields are able to dissolve and reconfigure matter itself. Torsion waves bend light. When an electron changes levels, it emits a photon of light and it also creates a torsion wave.

In some torsion generating devices, the photons are removed, leaving only a torsion wave. Just as torsion of subtle energy affects light, it also affects virtually every other force known to physics. Experiments have shown that fast-spinning tires can be used to create a pure torsion field, and this has also been shown to deflect a laser beam. Torsion affects gravity, mass, time, and many other physical properties.[6] Torsion has two polarities: left- and right-handed spin. Forms of this energy appear to decrease entropy or chaos in a system, slow down the flow of time, and promote order and coherence within the system. As we have previously discussed, increased coherence in the biophoton field correlates with healing in the body.

Torsion waves can slow down the flow of time, which means in the body can cause the effect of slowing down aging and even age reversal induced by mind, since we know that torsion waves can flow forwards and backwards in time. When we increase the power of the torsion field through observation and focus, the particle matter that encodes the human body—which is a conglomerate of subatomic particles that are spinning in space—can be reorganized by changing the spin ratio of matter towards the state of health. Since torsion is controlled by mind, this can be done by a trained Observer, by technical equipment that can harness and accentuate torsion fields, or by biomolecules that have a high energy spin that are ingested into the human body.

Torsion has many different effects that were found in research and outlined in Dr. Swanson's book.[7]

Torsion alters water properties, water bond angles, and bond lengths. Water surface tension is affected by torsion. The water's ability to dissolve other substances is affected, and even the water's pH is changed. Torsion affects electromagnetism, creates magnetic effects in nonmetals, generates torsion waves, bends light, and affects electrostatic charges and magnetism. Torsion affects gravity and creates levitation phenomena. The weight of an object can either be increased or decreased due to torsion. The rate of time passage can be slowed down or sped up; therefore torsion is integral to time travel as well as to the nonlocal abilities of mind that can travel backwards and forwards in time. Nuclear decay rates are also affected.

Torsion generates heat during healing, and in experiments, anomalous temperature fluctuation in laboratory-controlled conditions have been recorded.[8]

During Ramtha's focus disciplines of C&E®, Blue Body® Healing, the Neighborhood Walk®, and others, a large amount of heat in the body is generated.[9] This is because intentional focus directly produces torsion fields and alters space/time. As we will see in documented studies, these disciplines manifest changes in gravitational fields.

Dark matter and dark energy effects in space were described in Kozyrev's work as areas charged with left-handed torsion.[10] In the writings of physicist David Bohm, potentials of the quantum field that have been manifested into material reality represent the explicate order. The implicate order are possibilities that have not yet been collapsed into physical reality by an Observer. This may be represented in dark matter.

In Ramtha's model of reality, dark matter begins in the light spectrum above ultraviolet-blue light into the X-ray, gamma ray, and Infinite Unknown bands. Infinite Unknown represents zero-point energy. This dark matter represents our future, and as we access streams of consciousness in higher frequency levels, we can manifest these realities.

When we generate torsion fields, we can access the higher dimensional reality that is enfolded in dark matter. Human beings have infinite possibilities in the manifestation of reality through accessing higher streams of consciousness. By increasing the torsion field's power, which is consciously manipulated during the discipline of C&E®, students affect time, gravity, and mass.

In Ramtha's school, students focusing during disciplines have even been photographed as they become translucent, as captured in Figure 2.

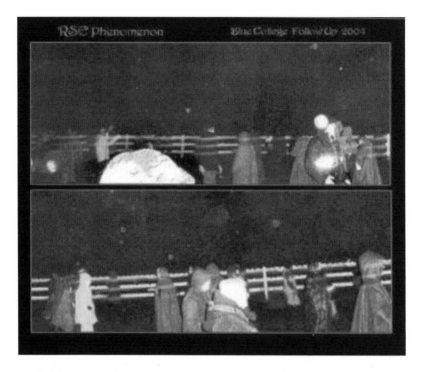

Figure 2: RSE students becoming invisible. Ramtha's School of Enlightenment – Blue College Follow-Up. © JZ Knight, 2004.[11]

In 2005, a group of students from Ramtha's School of Enlightenment were monitored for ambient field augmentation data during a closed advanced training event. The results of this study were published by the American Institute of Physics.[12] Sensors for monitoring magnetic field augmentation were placed in the main teaching hall and remained stationary for ten days while monitoring the ambient magnetic field, specifically during group activities. Figure 3 represents the baseline geomagnetic data in the hall. Figure 4 represents significant changes in geomagnetic spike, that in timing specifically correlated with the discipline of teleportation. The pattern changes in the geomagnetic data begin and end when the disciplines actually begin and end.

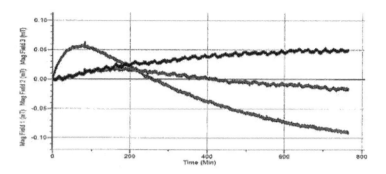

Figure 3: Daylong Geomagnetic Baseline. American Institute of Physics, 2005.[13]

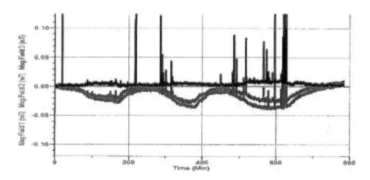

Figure 4: Daylong Geomagnetic Experimental File. American Institute of Physics, 2005.[14]

Gravitational force state was obtained with the use of a force plate. Individual advanced students were chosen to participate in the collection of this data by sitting directly on the force plate while practicing specific disciplines simultaneously with the entire group.

The baseline data represents the standard deadweight before or after experimental data baseline. This is demonstrated in Figure 5.

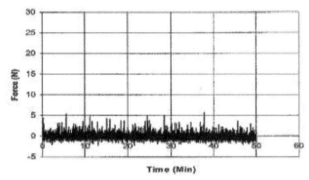

Figure 5: Controlled Laboratory Gravitational Force Dead Weight Baseline Data – Raw Data. American Institute of Physics, 2005.[15]

Figure 6 is representative of the collective, controlled experimental data file demonstrating significant gravitational force augmentation compared to the before and after control deadweight baselines. Experimental participants focused internally on activities of their choosing while sitting virtually motionless on top of the force plate platform. The first 5-plus minutes of the experimental file below is nearly identical to the control deadweight baseline shown in Figure 5 above. However, once the ambient field augmentation effects begin to be observed, the experimental data ranges between 13 to 25 N as depicted in Figure 6.

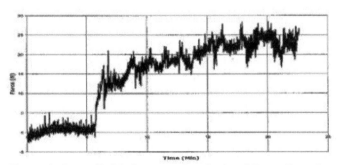

Figure 6: Controlled Laboratory Gravitational Force Experimental Data – Raw Data. American Institute of Physics, 2005.[16]

With a background knowledge of torsion physics, we can now explain the fluctuation in geomagnetic data as well as gravitational force experimental data. Since torsion fields are affected by conscious observation, the deeper the focus, the greater the effects on geomagnetic data and gravitational force experimental data.

In 1996 and 1997, a team of eighteen researchers studied JZ Knight, Ramtha, and the school's students. Shown in Table 2 below is the geomagnetic data measured during the channeling of Ramtha, which indicates effects in the Earth's magnetic field.

Eight standardized physiological, psychological, and behavioral tests were administered repeatedly on JZ and six long-time students. The scientific conference, entitled *In Search of Self: The Role of Consciousness in the Construction of Reality*, held in Yelm, Washington, in 1997, examined the results of the research.

"JZ, I don't know what you are, but whatever you are it is clear you are not a fraud," said team leader Dr. Stanley Krippner, psychologist and leading parapsychology researcher in the U.S.A. Following the conference, Dr. Krippner and Dr. Ian Wickramasekera published a paper in 1998 entitled "The Ramtha Phenomenon: Psychological, Phenomenological, and Geomagnetic Data" in *The Journal of the American Society for Psychical Research,* Volume 92. However, they did not include the physiological data. This was published in a subsequent paper: "Sympathetic Reactivity During Meditation," by Joan H. Hageman, Ph.D., Stanley Krippner, Ph.D., and Ian Wickramasekera II, Psy.D. in *Subtle Energies & Energy Medicine*, Volume 19, Number 2.[17]

Compared to the general population, the study participants measured high in Absorption (openness to experience) and Dissociation (the frequency and intensity of dissociating from one's environment). A third factor is described as mental Boundaries. People with thin boundaries:

> ➤ tend to be open, sensitive, and vulnerable
> ➤ experience "twilight" states of consciousness easily
> ➤ do not repress uncomfortable material
> ➤ do not isolate thought from feeling

In contrast, thick boundaried people are adaptive, well organized, punctual, reliable, responsible, and efficient; however, they may become rigid and unable to change. The conclusion of this paper "Sympathetic Reactivity During Meditation" states: "Lastly, our key findings highlight the practicality in clarifying the potentialities of meditation styles [C&E®] that emphasize the positive use of personality characteristics (e.g., absorption as a modest correlate of hypnotizability, dissociation, permeable boundaries) for individuals who have a greater ability to cognitively focus in addressing health concerns."

"Analyses revealed meditators [the RSE students] were characterized by thin boundaries, high absorption, high dissociation, and minimal self-perceived stress. They displayed significantly increased: electrodermal reactivity during meditation and recovery, heart rate during meditation, and bilateral hand temperatures during recovery. These outcomes are consistent with research demonstrating positive correlation between high hypnotizability and electrodermal reactivity, sympathetic increase with accelerated breathing meditations, and are inconsistent with decreased sympathetic activation in most passive meditation studies."[18]

As we discussed above, torsion fields create an increase in temperature, changes in gravitational fields, changes in water properties, and other effects. All of these can also affect the biophotonic coherent field and create a healing effect as well as a reversal in aging by bending space/time. Many students at RSE have had healing experiences when engaging in the disciplines.

CHANGES IN EARTH'S MAGNETIC FIELD COMPONENTS AS FUNCTION OF TIME

Time	Reference 1st magnetom.	H milligauss 2nd magnetom.	V milligauss 3rd magnetom.	Observed activity
15.20	0.45	0.16	-0.22	
15.25	0.41	0.17	-0.20	
15.27	0.39	0.20	-0.20	
15.28	0.37	0.20	-0.20	music starts
15.29	0.32	0.22	-0.20	
15.30	0.30	0.21	-0.21	
15.31	0.33	0.20	-0.22	
15.34	0.37	0.17	-0.28	
15.35	0.42	0.16	-0.28	
15.36	0.47	0.15	-0.29	hand clapping
15.37	0.50	0.14	-0.29	
15.39	0.53	0.13	-0.29	Ramtha arrives
15.41	0.58	0.13	-0.28	
15.43	0.55	0.14	-0.24	
15.45	no data	no data	no data	car enters, leaves
15.46	0.55	0.17	-0.22	
15.48	0.52	0.20	-0.20	
15.49	0.48	0.23	-0.21	
15.50	0.46	0.24	-0.22	
15.51	0.39	0.30	-0.22	
15.52	0.45	0.24	-0.23	group stands
15.54	0.44	0.23	-0.23	
15.55	0.46	0.23	-0.23	
15.56	0.40	0.28	-0.25	
15.57	0.50	0.21	-0.26	
16.00	0.55	0.20	-0.26	
16.02	0.58	0.20	-0.21	
16.10	0.52	0.24	-0.16	
16.12	0.50	0.26	-0.16	
16.15	0.50	0.26	-0.14	
16.17	0.49	0.26	-0.14	
16.20	0.42	0.25	-0.14	
16.22	0.35	0.31	-0.15	
16.23	0.44	0.25	-0.16	
16.26	0.51	0.20	-0.16	Ramtha leaves
16.29	0.55	0.19	-0.14	
16.36	0.39	0.32	-0.15	
16.40	0.31	0.32	-0.21	
16.44	0.32	0.26	-0.25	
16.45	0.35	0.28	-0.27	
16.49	0.49	0.15	-0.31	

Geomagnetic Aspects

Table 2: "The Ramtha Phenomena: Psychological, Phenomenological, and Geomagnetic Data." *Journal of the American Society for Psychical Research,* Volume 92, 1998.[19]

Dr. J. Gordon Melton, an American religious scholar and founding director of the Institute for the Study of American Religion, was brought in to study Ramtha's School and assess the authenticity of the training. His conclusions appear in the book *Finding Enlightenment, Ramtha's School of Ancient Wisdom*, published in 1998: "Melton was tasked with determining whether or not the charges of fraud were valid, and after two years of studying the training, participating in the training, living in JZ's house, and speaking at length with students and JZ's personal staff, he found nothing in the phenomenon to suggest anything fraudulent. He would eventually ask JZ's permission to write a book about the school based on what he had seen and heard: She [JZ] had developed a noteworthy religious (sic) community, and I wanted to be the one to document it."[20]

In an interview with *SuperConsciousness Magazine* in the fall of 2010, Dr. Melton's thoughts regarding the training at Ramtha's School of Enlightenment were documented: "Yet, the first thing that came to mind was that in his decades of studying religious and spiritual practices" he stated, "how rare it was for students or devotees to consistently report the experiencing of the extraordinary: Healings, teleportation, levitation, clairvoyance. During the course of his professional career, less than 1% ever reported experiencing such phenomena, yet at Ramtha's School, it was almost 100%."[21]

This is important as accessing these abilities is innate in every human being and can have profound implications for the knowledge of self-healing, age reversal, and certainly our understanding of medical science itself. The most significant example of such rejuvenation and healing is JZ Knight, who is 74 years in biological age at the time of this writing, and physically appears clearly younger. Ramtha has taught that when we are present in a Now, the body does not age. Understanding torsion physics, we can now also explain the profound physiological changes that occur during channeling as well as the healing documentation of JZ Knight's medical history. This research will be presented in the following chapter as it pertains to our new modality of healing—Light Medicine.

As we discussed, torsion was described by Dr. Kozyrev as the density of time. In Ramtha's audience, time warping phenomena are frequently experienced by participants. A moment with Ramtha can seem like infinite Now experienced. While in audience with Ramtha, frequently participants have little memory of what was said and yet the experience changed their lives. In this enhanced state of Now, the capturing of memory seems impaired. When you move to parallel timelines and live in the Now, what is there to remember in the past, and which past of your choosing are you remembering when you actively know how to create a future Now? Past and future are subject to observation.

During the ambient and geomagnetic field measurements taken in 2005, the data file recording stream pushed nine hours into the future when Ramtha entered the hall. Several students were witness to this phenomenon. Ramtha had taught that evening that the future has already happened and the measurement was a manifestation of his teaching.

This was exactly what occurred with the measurements of Krippner's physiological research, as will be discussed in the next chapter.

JZ Knight, in a 2008 interview with Danielle Graham for *SuperConsciousness Magazine*, spoke about her experience of time:

"JZ: Time is still a mystery, not only for scientists, but for each of us too.

"Let's start with time relative to science. These new questions about the existence of time really began to be raised in the beginning of quantum physics, because at that base level, observation causes the energy to stop. Measurement is equal to time. To be able to measure the momentum of a particle, it had to have time, so time was generated by momentum, or the collapsing of energy into particles. And we are all familiar with that. In our struggle to define time, if we define it in terms of momentum, then I am very agreeable with that. Momentum, meaning action—

"SC: Time is an action; it's a verb, not a noun . . .

"JZ: Exactly. Nouns have no time. Verbs are the action of the realization of that 'no time.' In talking to Ramtha many, many years ago about time, he threw me for a loop when he said, 'You can cease time by understanding there is no time and that all elements, all potentials, all worlds, all things exist simultaneously.' There is no arrow going backwards or forwards. It all exists in the moment. In my simple understanding of what I have seen out of my body and what I have experienced in my long life, that is absolutely correct.

"When I am in focus, I am in a no-time space. I am absolutely present to a concept that actually isn't born until I finish focusing on it. The moment that I release the focus, its action bubbles up from the quantum field. It is in momentum. What I focused on is getting built, and the building of that idea we call time. Our experience, our moving into the experience of our focus, is a time-related element.

"Now in focus, I am not even aware my heart is beating. I am not aware my body is functioning. I am aware that I am in a present Now, which opens the doors of perception to all levels, and all levels reveal themselves in a Now. My body is in action, but 'I,' the being inhabiting the body, is in inaction. And as I am creating, the body is getting revved up to experience it. When we talk about creation, we are talking about creation as a companion with time, the creation of an idea, of a concept that is being built. And our experience of our creation takes time to experience. Every part of our body gets to experience that.

"We are a processing machine of a long string of pearls. I like to use that because when we are talking about the future, the future is an infinite string of pearls. Just imagine them coming out of the top of your head and going in every single direction. And the clasp that reaches my midbrain, my infrared, is the clasp of potentials that is relative to what I am desiring, relative to what I am working upon, and that each pearl is a ball of light that opens up in my brain and begins the process of creation. The future holds an infinite amount of potentials for all of us. And I see them as pearls, as strings, necklaces going into infinity and that the ones that make it to my midbrain to process are a line of potentials that are related to one another. And so I bring them in, I observe them, I open them up in a 'no time.' The moment that they are being observed, they move into time. It is the creative machine, and time is an explanation for our creativeness. Just imagine our brain and our body as the machine that processes potentials into time. That's how I see it."[22]

This no space/time or vacuum state, the absolute Now, the omnipotent I Am, is the state of being that Ramtha is. Ramtha has explained that the spiritual being he is manipulates the body and brain of JZ Knight and that he is not in the body but above it. In the Now, he bends light into form with his mind. Ramtha teaches that the human body is a projection of two sets of bands that are the whirling light surrounding the body. These bands represent the spiritual being that we are. In photographs taken at different events, this torsion effect of these spinning bands has been captured.

Figure 7: Ramtha explaining torsion phenomenon. © JZ Knight, February 2, 2012. Photo credit: Melissa Peizer.[23]

When the photo above (Figure 7) was captured in 2012, Ramtha was explaining the torsion field he had created in the photograph shown below (Figure 8) that was being shown on the screen behind him (Figure 7). A spinning vortex is clearly visible in both photos.

Figure 8: Ramtha Torsion Effect. © JZ Knight, April 24, 2011. Photo credit: Melissa Peizer.[24]

Torsion travels through most physical media without loss. The group velocity of torsion waves is reportedly more than 1 billion times greater than the speed of light.[25] Dr. William A. Tiller, professor emeritus of materials science and engineering at Stanford University, showed that all equations of conventional physics hold true in their current form when torsion energy is present.[26] As the concentration of torsion increases, it modifies the equations. Torsion opens our normal three-dimensional, plus time universe into a higher dimensional space allowing access to other dimensions and parallel universes. Torsion affects all forces in the universe: electromagnetism, gravity, quantum mechanics, relativity, and nuclear forces.

Einstein discussed in his theory of relativity that events take place in the space/time continuum, which allows both space and time to be distorted and stretched by gravitational and other forces. Torsion is adding additional bending and twisting of space.[27]

The Russian physicists referred to earlier stated that all psychic phenomena can be duplicated with torsion and therefore the energies are identical. Torsion is controlled by consciousness and energy; therefore torsion is controlled by the mind of the Observer. As mind is able to affect torsion fields and thereby access other dimensions, now we can have information transfer between parallel universes. Particles exist in infinite possibilities simultaneously now. That means the same particle mass of our body and our physical reality in this instance is present in infinite parallel universes and infinite times, infinite places. According to our observation, we can change the spin of our particle mass. We can have any ability, knowledge, physical structure, and any reality that we desire, and we can occupy any place in time and space.

Abilities like remote-viewing, sending-and-receiving—which is reading someone's mind—accessing future potentials, modifying the past to affect the future, developing remote mind, out-of-body experiences, self-healing, age reversal, the changing of one's mind, are all disciplines taught at Ramtha's School of Enlightenment.

When we reexamine Ramtha's statement about understanding the spin ratio value and the determination of a particle's veracity that is affected by its light, we can now explain more through torsion physics. Since torsion fields are generated by classical spin, when a torsion field interacts with an object, only its spin state will change.

All substances are made of metaphysical or mathematical subatomic particles which have spin. All substances have patterns of spin and the pattern is connected to the chemical and physical activity of the substance. It encodes the information of the molecule. This pattern can be altered by a torsion field. As previously discussed, torsion fields are endowed with memory. An object with a torsion field causes the polarization of the vacuum energy surrounding it. The spin patterns can persist in objects from seconds to months, depending on whether the spin is stored in the electron or the nucleus. Spin can persist in space for a time after the initial object is removed.[28]

This explains how structured water that has been affected by intense focus is changed. The molecular bindings of water molecules and spin of subatomic particles have been altered. Ramtha often gives a focused blessing while holding water in a glass prior to starting gatherings with his students.[29] The students then drink the words they repeat. As we can now understand, the particle spin and the torsion field of that water have been changed. The water now holds healing properties encoded with the information of the blessing spoken. The information of the water has been reorganized to match the intent of the Observer.

As Ramtha has said: "All of these transmissions are through light, and every word has a light representation. That is the reason a master speaks in certain ways."

It is the observed word in a Now that collapses a new wave function of quantum particles and creates a torsion field with the new information, changing the matter of all reality instantaneously.

Ramtha's model of reality, called the eight-spatial diagram, is based upon the light spectrum. According to Ramtha, "Consciousness and energy are inextricably combined."[30] We have learned in the physics of torsion that the torsion waves are information and that the density of space/time is twisted. Understanding the light spectrum as we are rising through Hertzian, infrared, visible light, ultraviolet blue, X-ray, gamma ray, and Infinite Unknown, the density of time, or the density of subtle energy, changes proportionally with the rise in frequency. This means the information of the torsion field is encoding a higher level of consciousness and energy as described in the model below. Each level of the visible-light spectrum has its own consciousness inextricably combined with its corresponding energy, which encodes the torsion field of information into all particle mass.

Below is Ramtha's depiction of the consciousness encoded in each level of the visible-light spectrum:

Figure 9: Ramtha's Model of Reality Based upon the Light Spectrum. © JZ Knight.[31]

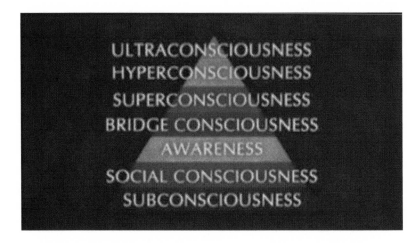

Figure 10: Ramtha's Model of Reality – Levels of Consciousness Associated with the Visible Light Spectrum. © JZ Knight.[32]

In Ramtha's model of reality, he describes two sets of bands that surround the human body. As defined in *Ramtha, A Beginner's Guide to Creating Reality:* "The bands are the two sets of seven frequencies that surround the human body and hold it together. Each of the seven frequency layers of each band corresponds to the seven seals of seven levels of consciousness in the human body. The bands are the auric field that allow the processes of binary and analogical mind.

"Binary mind means two minds. It is the mind produced by accessing the knowledge of the human personality and the physical body without accessing our deep subconscious mind. Binary mind relies solely on the knowledge, perception, and thought processes of the neocortex and the first three seals. The fourth, fifth, sixth, and seventh seals remain closed in this state of mind."

"Analogical mind means one mind. It is the result of the alignment of primary consciousness and secondary consciousness, the Observer and the personality. The fourth, fifth, sixth, and seventh seals of the body are opened in this state of mind." When the mind becomes analogical, "the bands spin in opposite directions, like a wheel within a wheel, creating a powerful vortex that allows the thoughts held in the frontal lobe to coagulate and manifest."[33]

In this manner, torsion physics is applied to the field surrounding the human body. Physicists know that torsion waves are controlled by the conscious mind. As the Observer enters a state of focus and absolute Now—in other words, analogical mind—torsion waves and subtle energy are increased.

Torsion change is related to the light level of information or the consciousness value of the energy being focused upon. Electron spin or nuclear spin, with its generation of torsion waves, is also related to the level of consciousness and frequency value created through the mind of the Observer. Not only does this explain all psychic phenomena—like the effects on electromagnetic fields, the loss of gravitation, the healing ability of students—but the higher the frequency reached, the higher the consciousness. This is where time is altered. In fact, as we discussed when accessing the vacuum state of the quantum field, there is no time; there is only Now. Therefore the body ceases to age because the aspect of time is so rapidly approaching no time when consciousness is increased. The corresponding energy of that consciousness is so high that the body doesn't require food, which has been shown with many chi gong masters who no longer need to eat. Tesla duplicated this effect by utilizing electrical energy to feed the body, and as we have seen in previous chapters, ATP energy production in the physical body can be turned on by all modes of energy, including high-level consciousness and energy.

Quantum physics understands that the Observer and the observed cannot be separated. Ramtha describes this as "consciousness and energy are inextricably combined," and that is what constitutes the nature of reality.

At all moments, what we think is what we observe, and that action of mind is what creates the collapse of the wave function of probability in the quantum field as reality. The more unlimited our thought process is, the greater the streams of consciousness we are able to access. In the Now, all time is, and all levels of consciousness can be accessed. This means the mass of the physical body, according to conscious observation, will be altered because the electron spin of the mass of the body is altered. If this alteration and observation are one of healing, the body can be healed by the mind. The body can be healed by frequency, such as applied in the Blu Room. And the body can be healed by compounds that store high-level electron spin, torsion field energy, according to the observation of the individual ingesting the substance.

This is also where the placebo effect of the mind comes in. Imagine an Observer that is ingesting a high light value compound and they doubt its effectiveness. Instantaneously this particle's spin and torsion field of the substance have been altered and rendered ineffective. The laws of creation, "Thy will be done," are always in effect.

The Count of Saint-Germain was said to have given to certain individuals a rejuvenating substance that would restore their youth and even create immortality. Such a substance would be an electron donor with a high consciousness and encoded electron spin and torsion field creating rejuvenation in physical structures. As we now understand, a being that can stream high-level consciousness can take any substance, any liquid, and turn it into an elixir of immortality.

The bands, as taught by Ramtha, are spinning and whirling around the body, in and through the seven seals of the body, and are encoding the information of each respective level of consciousness. This lays the foundation to understand when Ramtha says, "You are a conglomerate of a neighborhood of diversified light whose harmony is you." Biophysics calls this the biophoton field.

This biophoton field is in turn coupled directly into DNA through the chromatin. Patterns of spin encode information. Solid objects contain trillions and trillions of particles. Each spin can theoretically hold a bit of information. This indicates that even a small object is a potential reservoir for extraordinary amounts of information.[34] Mind affects the direction of spin axes and veracity of spin, which keep changing moment by moment according to the law of our thoughts. Hence, it is the mind that heals the body.

CHAPTER 13

JZ KNIGHT AND RAMTHA
PROOF OF THE EXTRAORDINARY

This chapter is a compilation of true miracles manifested in the body of a remarkable being, the great American channel, JZ Knight. I have had the privilege to study this extraordinary mystery in depth since I became JZ Knight's personal physician in early 2018. I have had access to all the historical data and medical testing that has been done over several decades and have myself ordered medical testing for specific conditions and was able to review the progress of my patient. I was instructed by JZ Knight to monitor her healing journey. For example, she would tell me that she will heal her kidneys and that I was to repeat the kidney function tests in three months. As the follow-up report came in, her prediction that she would heal herself manifested. This happened multiple times, as I have documented in this chapter.

JZ Knight has long been a shining example of the power of the mind to create DNA change and healing in the body. She has inspired thousands of people around the world for decades and never wavered in her search for truth and answers to the great questions science has asked for centuries. Her life is a demonstration of what we have discussed so far in this book regarding a new paradigm of health and longevity—Light Medicine.

The medical and scientific findings described here refer to two separate entities, JZ Knight (the channel) and Ramtha (an enlightened being). Channeling means that the consciousness of JZ leaves the body completely and allows the consciousness of

Ramtha to take over all bodily movements and functions. I have been, and remain profoundly and respectfully, moved as a scientist, physician, and student of Ramtha's School of Enlightenment to contemplate what is before me—the expression of God in a human body, the greatest potential for every human being. The genuine abundance of proof for those who have the eyes to see and are not blinded by their unfounded judgment is overwhelming.

That JZ Knight has great psychic abilities and sees the future are facts that I have experienced firsthand many times. She has used this gift to help and heal many people. She can see future timelines. She has contacted me about certain individuals and advised them to undergo medical testing and treatment to prevent devastating health issues from occurring. Because we heeded the warning, I know that lives were spared.

What it is like to have such a visionary in our life is a blessing for our whole community. JZ expresses love for so many people who in her mind she knows and is acutely aware of but without necessarily having had any personal contact. I have frequently seen patients who were suddenly gifted certain interventions by her that were specifically needed at that time. I have talked to her on the phone and she would tell me of a solution to a medical problem, and several days later a new patient would come into my office with that specific issue, and I would know about it in advance. In light of so much adversity and prejudice from the world that she has been subjected to, I have never seen anything else but unconditional love for all. After studying her life story in depth, she remains a beautiful mystery to me.

With her permission, JZ Knight's medical history and testing over the last 23 years will be discussed at length in these pages. These findings are referred to as miracles because in the current, scientific understanding of our time, there is no viable explanation of how such phenomena can occur in the physiology of a human body—not once, but many times over many years.

In this case study we see a manipulation and change of DNA at will, both by JZ, in verifiably healing her own body, and by Ramtha, who manipulates the DNA of the body and instantaneously manifests enormous changes, many of which are beyond current models of scientific, medical explanation. The contemplation of how this is possible can take anyone on a journey to decipher the signature of a unique, singular consciousness upon a physical body and open wide the doors of hope for a new model of medical science, as we are outlining in this book.

This case report is an important study in the context of Light Medicine and the understanding of how consciousness can interact with the body. We now know that mind controls the body because mind is matter. After our review of Light Medicine and torsion physics, we can now scientifically entertain the possibility of an all-powerful, all-present being having total control over the physical body with the ability to morph and heal it instantaneously at will.

Scientific Testing of JZ Knight and Ramtha

In a 2010 exclusive interview for *SuperConsciousness Magazine*, JZ stated that she became Ramtha's first student and provided information regarding her channeling experience:

"After two years of guiding JZ through new knowledge and experiences, Ramtha taught her to leave her body, telling her, 'This is what you are going to experience at the moment of death. You are going to die, but it won't hurt, and it will only be a little short while, and then you are going to come back.' Once she learned to relax, 'All of a sudden I was chasing that light at the end of the tunnel and this wind was whizzing by me. The moment I hit that light so bright, I was up against a light wall. I remember Ramtha talking to me; it was really beautiful and loving, and he said, 'Now you are your true self at this moment. This moment is who you really are, and you have left your body behind.'"[1]

This process was scientifically investigated in 1997 when 18 scholars—including scientists, psychologists, sociologists, and religious experts from diverse institutions and universities—undertook rigorous testing of JZ Knight and Ramtha over a period of one and a half years.

These tests and experiments included skin temperature, heart rate, blood volume pulse, and electrodermal responses. The findings were summarized in the article, "The Ramtha Phenomenon: Psychological, Phenomenological, and Geomagnetic Data" published in *The Journal of the American Society for Psychical Research*.[2] The research team categorically ruled out that the channeling phenomena was a fraud in part because the physiological changes in the body were impossible to fake. For example, when JZ left her body and Ramtha took over the body, the heart rate was recorded to drop to 40 beats per minute and then race up to 180 beats per minute. Eight standardized physiological, psychological, and behavioral tests were collected from JZ Knight before, during, and after channeling Ramtha.

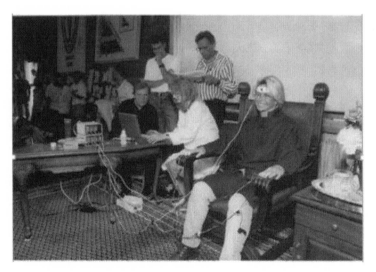

Figure 11: JZ Knight and Ramtha Testing, Yelm, WA.
© JZ Knight, 1996.[3]

These physiological measurements of autonomic activity included the electromyograph of the frontalis muscle, electromyograph of the trapezius muscles, left-side skin temperature, right-side skin temperature, heart rate, blood volume pulse, left electrodermal response, and right electrodermal response. The results of the physiological tests showed that when JZ Knight is channeling Ramtha, her muscle tension, pulse, and galvanic skin response increase while skin temperature and blood volume both decrease.[4] The scientists affirmed that Ms. Knight could not have voluntarily changed or faked all eight of these measurements. The results were presented at the scientific conference, entitled *In Search of Self: The Role of Consciousness in the Construction of Reality*, held in Yelm, Washington, in February 1997.[5]

The report states: "The psychological and behavioral testing included Absorption Subscale, Dissociative Experiences Scale, Boundary Questionnaire, Phenomenological Study, Stanford Gold Standard for hypnotic ability, and Mean Eye Roll Sign. JZ Knight also participated in a number of psychological tests, along with a number of the RSE students, including the Stanford test for hypnotic ability, the gold standard measure of hypnotizability. 'Knight and the students tested extremely high in their hypnotic abilities,' said Dr. Stanley Krippner, a former divisional president of the American Parapsychological Association and psychology professor at Saybrook Institute. Krippner explained that that was a significant finding because the relationship between hypnotic ability and bipolar personality (schizophrenia) and other mental disorders is counterbalancing—when one goes up, the other goes down. Krippner said, 'She got validation that she's not a fraud and she's not mentally ill.'"

It is important to note that the magnitude of the testing results at Ramtha's School of Enlightenment was higher than previously observed in other similar groups by the researchers. JZ Knight's individual results demonstrated a reliable capacity for mind/body interaction.[6] Dr. Krippner reported: "When we were testing JZ, [we] were quite astonished because the needles on the polygraph that were graphing all of the psycho-physiological responses literally jumped from one part of the page to the other part of the page when Ramtha entered the picture. We had never seen such a dramatic change . . . She's not faking it because when we hooked her up to test her physiological responses, we got results which could not have been manipulated."[7]

SuperConsciousness Magazine also spoke with Dr. Ian. Wickramasekera II, past president of the Association for Applied Psychophysiology and Biofeedback, who was originally involved with the collection and analysis of the test data obtained from both JZ and advanced students who participated in the study. He noted that the psychophysiological tests given everyone showed rare and paradoxical results. "It is remarkable to witness dramatically elevated psycho-physiological responses while in a state of complete relaxation." He went on to explain that meditation usually produces the classic relaxation response, thus to observe such a heightened brain activity response while the body remains inactive had rarely been observed before and only from reclusive, advanced adepts.[8]

JZ Knight's Medical Transformation

In 2005, JZ experienced a well-documented medical transformation by utilizing the Neighborhood Walk®, a discipline she created—as described in Part 1—that raises consciousness and energy to intentionally modify the brain's neuronet. Preestablished patterns of thinking that are no longer desired are replaced with new ones of our own choosing. This technique is exclusively taught at Ramtha's School of Enlightenment.

JZ had chronic hypothyroidism for nine years, which was supplemented with Armour Thyroid. This condition was completely reversed to normal function. JZ also had a chronic history of hypertriglyceridemia with abnormal numbers up to 584. Most people who have triglyceride levels greater than 300 are considered a cardiovascular risk and need pharmacologic intervention to bring those numbers down. JZ was able to change her numbers through a shift in consciousness with no significant alteration in her lifestyle. On 10/17/05, her triglycerides were documented in the normal range at 148. This change is substantial and unusual in that it was achieved without medication management. Other medical conditions like allergic rhinitis symptoms and COPD symptoms from chronic smoking were reversed through JZ's self-healing ability. The changes were well documented by her primary care provider, Kathy May, FNP.

DNA Testing of JZ Knight and Ramtha

In 2015, JZ's personal chiropractic physician, Dr. Matthew Martinez, took cheek swab DNA samples from JZ Knight. Two days later he took cheek swab DNA samples while Ramtha was in control of the body. The samples were sent to laboratories for analysis. The results are provided in Tables 3 through 6.

As recorded in Table 4, DNA lab results showed significant differences, the most astonishing one being that Ramtha had a Y chromosome, indicating a male body. This evidence would indicate that Ramtha is able to manipulate DNA at will and transform the female XX chromosomes to a male XY chromosome.

Report Date: 1/15/2015

■■■■ is accredited certified by AABB, CAP, ACluo-International, ISO/TEC 17025, CLIA, MYSDOH & ASCLD/LAB-International

Locus		SAMPLE 1		SAMPLE 2	
Case: 7786421 Name		) Knight		R Knight	
Race Date Collected: Test No:		Caucasian 1/7/2015 357622-19		Unknown 1/7/2015 357622-22	
Locus		Allele Sizes		Allele Sizes	
D8S1179	0.50	14		14	18
D7S820	1.43	7	9	9	10
CSF1PO	1.33	12		12	17
D3S1358	2.50	16		14	17
TH01	1.32	9	11	9	9.4
D13S317	1.39	13	15	17	
D16S539	1.91	17	19	19	
D2S1338	0.50	11	16	9	13
D19M433	0.50	10	14	8	11
vWA	0.50	18		15	16
TPOX	1.13	10	13	10	14
D18S51	2.20	9	12	9	12
D5S818	0.50	11	14	11	13.3
FGA	0.50	19	22	19	21
Amelogenin		X		X	Y
DNA SEQ		TACTGATCG		ACCAGCTGC	

Interpretation:

The DNA from sample 1 was compared with sample 2. Based on testing results obtained from the analysis of the DNA loci listed, the probability of relatedness is 42.3%. The likelihood that sample 1 is not the biological relative of sample 2 is 1.42 to 1. This probability of relatedness was calculated by comparing to untested, unrelated, random individuals of the Caucasian population (assumes prior probability equals 0.51).

Subscribed and sworn before me on January, 15, 2015   I, the undersigned, verify that the interpretation of the Results is correct as reported.

Table 3: DNA Test Report Samples 1 – JZ Knight and Ramtha, January 15, 2015.[9]

174

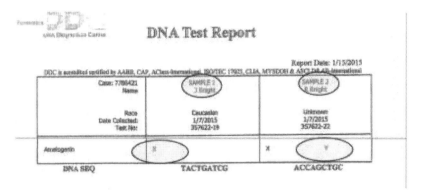

Table 4: DNA Test Report Samples 2 – JZ Knight and Ramtha, January 15, 2015.[10]

Case: 7786421 Name		SAMPLE 1 J Knight		SAMPLE 2 R Knight	
Locus		Allele Sizes		Allele Sizes	
D8S1179	0.50	14		14	16
D7S820	1.43	7	9	9	10
CSF1PO	1.33	12		12	17
D3S1358	2.59	16		14	12
TH01	1.32	9	11	9	9.4
D13S317	1.39	13	15	17	
D16S539	1.91	17	19	19	
D2S1338	0.50	11	16	9	13
D19A433	0.50	10	14	8	11
VWA	0.50	18		15	16
TPOX	1.13	10	13	10	14
D18S51	2.20	9	12	9	12
D5S818	0.50	11	14	11	13.3
FGA	0.50	19	22	19	21

Table 5: DNA Test Report Samples 3 – JZ Knight and Ramtha, January 15, 2015.[11]

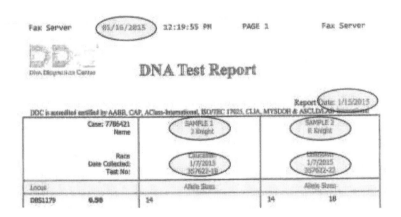

Table 6: DNA Test Report Samples 4 – JZ Knight and Ramtha, January 15, 2015.[12]

As shown above, fourteen STR alleles were profiled showing two distinct individuals (Table 6). The likelihood that one sample (JZ) was not from the biological relative of the other sample (Ramtha) was calculated to be 1.42 to 1, meaning there was a probability of relatedness of only 42.3%.

This would indicate that Ramtha does have the ability to instantaneously change the genome of the body that he takes over.

These findings are particularly significant considering physiological changes that have been proven to occur with the 1996 scientific testing. Understanding that it is possible for a spiritual being to produce a human physiologic response that would be considered impossible, according to medical standards, should provide an inquiry in our scientific understanding as to how consciousness interacts with the matter of the physical body. How truly malleable is the human genome and genetic code when manipulated by a powerful consciousness? In understanding torsion physics and looking back at the photographs of Ramtha showing the distortion of the torsion field around him, we now have the physics to explain how such a profound change is possible. The DNA testing results not only demonstrate that JZ and Ramtha are different entities but also—in the context of this entire medical history—that an unlimited, singular consciousness has unlimited ability to manipulate the genetic code.

Clearly the phenomenon of JZ and Ramtha, that has been extraordinarily well documented through objective, scientific testing over decades, shows a consistency of miraculous transformation.

Examination of Heart and Kidney Function

In 2010, JZ had an echocardiogram that showed left ventricular hypertrophy as well as reduced diastolic compliance, which means that the heart muscle is thickened and has a problem relaxing. The heart showed borderline left atrial enlargement. Ejection fraction, which is a measure of how well the heart pumps, was preserved at 68%.

These findings can be seen in patients with longstanding, uncontrolled high blood pressure. When blood pressure values remain uncontrolled, heart disease can progress to diastolic congestive heart failure due to stiffening of the heart muscle and impaired relaxation, which is essential for normal cardiac filling to maintain adequate cardiac output.

JZ has a history of intermittent, uncontrolled hypertension for which she has been taking blood pressure medication. The body has been shown during channeling sessions to maintain heart rates of 180 beats per minute for many hours without evidence of cardiac heart failure or cardiac arrest. This was well researched and documented in the 1996 testing discussed earlier. Yet in a more recent cardiac exam, JZ has none of the signs of medically expected heart disease and aging progression. In fact, she has a reversal of structurally documented heart disease. JZ has applied her personal-healing focus work and, since its inception, used the Blu Room regularly multiple times a week.

A repeat echocardiogram in June 2018 shows left ventricular hypertrophy without indication of reduced diastolic compliance and no evidence of borderline left atrial enlargement but instead normal atrial sizes. There is a new development of moderate mitral annular calcification without any clinical significance or compromise in mitral valve function. In other words, her ejection fraction remains normal at 66%.

In a normal case of longstanding high blood pressure or sustained extremely high heart rates, as well as due to the aging process, progression and worsening over time of the heart findings would be medically expected. JZ had been previously told that she has an "athlete's heart." In extreme athletes, the heart muscle is thickened due to the significant exertion the heart has to undergo. This interpretation of her condition is comparable, even though her "athlete's heart" is due to the extreme stress on the heart of beating a documented 180 beats per minute for many hours at a time during channeling sessions without cardiac arrest, a feat that is medically impossible.

While extreme athletes can maintain heart rates of 180 beats a minute during strenuous exercises for periods of time, the idea that a 74-year-old woman who lives a sedentary lifestyle could do so without evidence of congestive heart failure, lack of perfusion of the heart muscle wall, or cardiac arrest, is medically inexplicable.

ECHOCARDIOGRAM
JUDITH KNIGHT
DATE OF SERVICE: 11/30/2010

FINAL IMPRESSION:

1. Moderate concentric left ventricular hypertrophy with well-preserved left ventricular size and systolic function, ejection fraction 68%. There is reduced diastolic compliance.
2. Borderline left atrial enlargement.
3. Normal cardiac valves.
4. Normal right heart.[13]

Judith Darlene Knight
ECHO Complete
Study Date: 6/6/18

CONCLUSION:

The left ventricle is normal in size and function. Moderately increased left ventricular wall thickness. Normal aortic root size.
No hemodynamically significant valve disease. Normal atrial sizes.[14]

JZ also had hypertensive nephropathy with stage 3 chronic kidney disease, indicating kidney damage from high blood pressure, documented since before 2014 on several blood tests and with elevated creatinine numbers of 1.12 and calculated glomerular filtration rate (GFR) as low as 48. The GFR is normally greater than 60, and a number of 48 already shows progressive kidney damage, in particular when it has been documented for many years.

Through healing focus, JZ's kidneys were completely healed and she had normal kidney function on her blood test on 6/20/18 with a creatinine of 0.95 and GFR of >60.

Date	12/1/2014	4/6/2016	11/3/2017	6/20/2018
Creatinine	1.05	1.12	1.12	0.95
BUN	14	14	12	14
GFR	52	51	48	>60

Table 7: JZ Knight – Chronological Renal Function Test Results.[15]

On February 12, 2018, JZ had a heart CT scan to noninvasively evaluate for coronary atherosclerosis. The results indicated she had a coronary calcium score of 670, with severe disease in the right coronary artery, 90th percentile for her age.

This finding is highly concerning because the right coronary artery supplies blood flow to the entire back wall of the heart. Further evaluation with stress testing or heart catheterization would normally be recommended, in particular if JZ had shown any symptoms like chest pain, which she did not.

It is significant to consider again the findings of 1996 which do show in the transitioning from JZ to Ramtha that the heart rate dropped to 40 beats per minute and then raced to 180 beats per minute moments later. Medically, it is well known that blockages in coronary arteries can cause demand ischemia of the heart muscle during stress. Demand ischemia means a critical lack of blood flow during increased blood flow requirement, as occurs during exercise, which can lead to heart attacks. This means that the heart muscle pumping at 180 beats a minute is requiring increased oxygen, which the blood flow through the blocked artery cannot provide. Under normal circumstances this leads to massive heart attack, given that the right coronary artery supplies the blood for the back wall of the heart. The lack of oxygenation to the heart muscle in turn can lead to potentially fatal heart arrhythmia.

The physiology of channeling is a miraculous occurrence in a young and healthy heart, for no normal human heart can sustain many hours of heart rates measuring 180 bpm. Considering that JZ's heart has clearly been diseased, the miraculous nature of her channeling Ramtha is extraordinary.

After learning of the calcifications in her coronary arteries, JZ opted to focus and dissolve the calcifications.

Of note, JZ had a cardiac arrest in 2015 during anesthesia for a surgical procedure from which she was successfully resuscitated. JZ had no further follow-up with a cardiologist;

however, this history was very concerning for a possible correlation with the blocked right heart artery.

After it was found that JZ had critical carotid artery stenosis and surgery was recommended, a preoperative evaluation of her heart with a stress test was advised. The purpose of this test is for patients to evaluate their risk of having a heart attack under anesthesia. The pretest's probability for cardiac ischemia was very high considering the high calcification score on the CT scan. Until this testing, JZ led a sedentary lifestyle due to chronic knee pain, and she showed no cardiac symptoms of angina.

In October 2018, prior to undergoing carotid surgery, JZ had a nuclear medicine stress test for preoperative clearance. Due to her knee arthritis, JZ was unable to exercise, so the test had to be performed chemically. The result showed no evidence of blockage of the coronary artery. Under severe stress, the back wall of the heart with the previously blocked artery was getting normal blood supply, indicating resolution of the blockage through her focus.

Given the severity of the calcium score earlier in the year, and documented below, this represents a medical miracle.

CT Coronary Artery Calcium Score 2/12/18
CCS 670 with severe disease in RCA, 90th percentile for age.

JUDITH KNIGHT
Nuclear Medicine Stress test 10/31/18

ECG positive for inferolateral ischemia.
Myocardial perfusion images negative for ischemia or prior infarction.

LVEF 57% by gated SPECT is within normal limit.[16]

JZ Knight's Brain – A Complete Mystery

JZ is a true, genius mind, Blu Room inventor, author, visionary, President of JZK, Inc., and much more. Given her long list of accomplishments, it is a surprise to learn about the findings of her brain anatomy.

In November of 2010, a screening MR brain angiogram was ordered, which showed multiple abnormalities in the blood supply to the brain, in particular the left brain.

This test indicated that both internal carotid arteries had less than 40% plaque occlusion, meaning that the blood flow was about 60% of normal in 2010 through those main front arteries. Inside the brain, the left middle cerebral artery had a worrisome 60% occlusion, and this artery supplies blood to the entire middle part of the left hemisphere. The posterior cerebral artery, supplying blood flow to the back part of the hemispheres, had less than 50% blockage, and the left vertebral artery supplying blood to the lower cerebellum already had 50% blockage.

Usually with such findings, a patient has follow-up, and certain interventions occur to reduce the risk of progression of a disease, like blood pressure control, cholesterol lowering measures, and smoking cessation. With a 60% blockage in the left middle cerebral artery, some people may already have symptoms of neurological deficits that may affect motor coordination, memory, and concentration. Usually patients are carefully followed up on and monitored.

However, JZ never had any follow-up monitoring done. In fact, she did not even know that she had these findings in 2010, as her then primary care provider never shared the results with her. The majority of her cerebrovascular disease was on the left side of her brain. From 2010 to 2018 she had no follow-up testing on the blood flow of her brain or her carotid arteries and remained overall asymptomatic.

The normal blood supply to a brain occurs through four major arteries, the right and left internal carotid arteries, and the right and left vertebral arteries. These four arteries allow the blood flow through the neck into the brain. Within the brain, these four arteries converge in the circle of Willis, which the arteries that supply the two hemispheres and midbrain, as well as cerebellum, spring from. These arteries are called anterior, middle, and posterior cerebral arteries. They supply the blood for the front, middle, and back brain areas.

The left side of the brain is responsible for controlling the right side of the body. It also performs tasks that have to do with logic, such as in science and mathematics. On the other hand, the right hemisphere coordinates the left side of the body and performs tasks that have to do with creativity and the arts.

MR Angiogram 2010
Judith Knight
MRA HEAD W/O CONTRAST
DATE OF EXAM: 11/30/2010
INDICATION: ANEURYSM SCREENING

TECHNIQUE: Three-dimensional time-of-flight noncontrast-enhanced MR angiogram of the circle of Willis was obtained. Multiplanar MIP images were obtained for evaluation.
COMPARISON: None.

FINDINGS: No evidence of vascular malformation is identified. There is atherosclerotic luminal irregularity of bilateral cavernous internal carotid arteries (less than 40% luminal stenosis), proximal M2 segment of the left middle cerebral artery (approximately 60% luminal stenosis), proximal left side posterior cerebral artery (less than 50% luminal stenosis) as well as distal left vertebral artery (measures 6 mm in length with approximately 50% luminal stenosis). The visualized brain parenchyma is unremarkable. No aneurysmal dilatation seen.

IMPRESSION: Multiple foci of atherosclerotic luminal irregularity and stenosis involving the circle of Willis vessels as described, all measure less than 60% luminal stenosis. No hemodynamic significant stenosis or aneurysmal dilatation.[17]

Only in 2017 did JZ have a CT scan done of her chest for a concern about possible pneumonia by her naturopath. The results showed calcifications of her carotid arteries.

She then went to a cardiologist in February 2018. At the time, smoking cessation and cholesterol lowering were recommended. JZ mindfully focused on dissolving the artery blockages with support of the Blu Room and supplements.

On September 21, 2018, JZ had a bilateral carotid ultrasound, which showed 70-95% critical right internal carotid stenosis secondary to bulky plaque and 50-69% left internal carotid artery stenosis. She had retrograde flow of the left vertebral artery suggesting subclavian steal syndrome. The right vertebral artery was normal.

These results meant that of the four arteries going to the brain, one did not have any blood supply, the other had around 30% blood supply, one was flowing backwards, stealing blood supply to the brain because of a calcified artery in the arm, and only one out of four was normal, the right vertebral artery. This poses a severe medical concern and would put anyone at dangerous risk for strokes. Usually patients who have such disease of the brain also have vascular disease of the small vessels. This is called small vessel ischemic disease and leads to a vascular form of dementia. The brain is so impaired, due to the lack of oxygen to the neurons, that patients have memory loss, behavior problems, and an overall decline in neurological function, which can be severe and is usually progressive. JZ had none of those symptoms.

Doctors intervene medically when patients complain of problems or there is a finding that looks dangerous and needs an intervention like surgery. The medical providers who saw her did not address the MRA report from 2010, so no further scan was performed.

On the 2010 MRA of JZ's brain, all occlusions were only on the left side. In her neck, both internal carotid arteries were affected.

The fact that in 8 years the right internal carotid went from less than 40% occluded to 75-95% critical stenosis, and the left internal carotid went from <40% to 50-69% stenosis, and left vertebral artery went from 50% blockage to flowing retrograde due to subclavian steal, poses the following question:

Provided that blocked arteries may progress similarly in time if there were a 50% increase in occlusion on the right internal carotid artery, imagine what the increase in blockage in the left middle cerebral artery was in that time frame. No follow-up MRA was performed for ten years to check the intracranial blood supply; however, one can only logically extrapolate the progression over time. If the left middle cerebral artery has an occlusion of greater than 90%, how is it possible that someone with such low blood supply to critical areas of the brain is able to not only function without stroke-like symptoms but function at an extraordinary high level, making genius inventions like the Blu Room, continuing to channel Ramtha, and leading several organizations?

The left middle cerebral artery provides blood to a large part of the left side of the brain and divides into smaller artery branches. Based on where the blockage occurs in the artery or in the branches, the effects will vary. Damage most often can cause changes in movement and sensation, attention, memory, judgement, perception, speech, and vision. Problems will show up on the right side of the body.

If the left middle cerebral artery has a substantial blockage, there could be stroke-like symptoms. Based on where the stroke from the blocked artery occurred, the amount of loss may be spread evenly over the entire right side of the body, or it may be worse further away from the trunk of the body. A stroke victim may have changes in sensation, including numbness and inability to feel pain. A patient may neglect their right side. They may not remember how to brush their teeth. Attention can be severely impaired, and focusing on a thought or reading a full article can be impossible. Reading, writing, mathematics, memory impairment, coordination, all can be impaired with lack of blood flow to the middle cerebral artery.

In November 2020, JZ underwent a brain MRI and MR angiogram, for the first time visualizing the extent of intracranial atherosclerosis. The results were astonishing to me as a physician, showing extensive atherosclerosis but comparatively very mild changes of brain tissue. Despite severe blood vessel occlusions in major brain arteries, JZ never had a stroke. The report indicated mild chronic vascular ischemic changes, which is caused by lack of blood flow, but the findings were disproportionally mild given the severity of occlusions and lack of blood flow to so many brain areas.

The MRA reveals many severe narrowings of all major arteries to JZ's brain. The brain arteries are divided in front, middle, and back sections that provide blood flow to both hemispheres. The MRA also reveals that the left side of the back brain circulation is completely gone. The front, middle, and back arterial sections are all moderately to severely occluded.

JZ Knight literally dies every time she channels Ramtha. Her consciousness completely leaves her body, as would occur in a death experience. There is no greater love anyone can exhibit than to lay down their life for others.

In the thousands of hours JZ has channeled Ramtha over the past five decades, she has spent approximately half her life outside of her body—in elsewhere. She lives outside of time. What kind of neurological wiring does it require to be such a unique human being? This MRI/ MRA report to me is the most extraordinary additional proof that someone who walks with God in such a dedicated and extraordinary manner can physiologically operate the human body beyond our current scientific understanding.

I cannot explain to you how JZ Knight exhibits such genius with so little blood flow to her brain. I can, however, tell you that she is a miracle beyond current scientific understanding.

Ana Maria Mihalcea, MD
AM Medical LL
715 E Yelm Ave, Suite 5
Yelm, WA 98597
Phone: (360)960-8538

KNIGHT, JUDITH
F 74 yrs
Exam Date: Nov 13, 2020

MRI BRAIN MR ANGIOGRAPHY HEAD WITHOUT IV CONTRAST

EXAM: MRI of the brain without contrast, MRA of the head without contrast

COMPARISON: Brain MRI of November 30, 2010

FINDINGS:

MRI Brain: There is no restricted diffusion to indicated acute or subacute ischemia. There is no acute hemorrhage or mass. Mild bilateral periventricular and to a lesser extent subcortical T2 hyperintense lesions are present, nonspecific, but probably sequela of small vessel ischemic disease, chronic. Mild peripheral volume loss. No hydrocephalous. There is no midline shift. There are no extra- axial fluid collections. The pituitary gland is normal. The vascular flow voids are unremarkable. The dural venous sinuses and deep cerebral veins are patent.

The paranasal sinuses are well aerated. The mastoids are clear. The skull base and calvarium are normal. The craniocervical junction is normal. The orbits are unremarkable.

MRA Head: Motion artifact degrades many images. Given limitations of the study, the left vertebral artery essentially terminates in the left PICA. There is interval occlusion of the left V4 segment with a stump of the distal left V4 segment and the basilar artery connection.

Multisegment irregular stenosis of the proximal and distal intracranial arterial segments of the anterior and posterior circulations are present, most consistent with intracranial atherosclerosis, including moderate to severe right V4. Severe multifocal right M1 moderate distal left M1, severe left M2, moderate right M2, severe multifocal left pericallosal, severe distal right pericallosal, moderate cavernous left ICA, moderate cervical left ICA, moderate right A1, mild to moderate proximal basilar, moderate multifocal PCA stenosis.

There is a focal fusiform dilation of the right M1 segment, likely related to relative sparing of intracranial atherosclerotic disease/post stenotic dilation rather than a fusiform aneurysm. CTA can further evaluate.

The distal segments are difficult to evaluate and small distal branch high-grade stenosis or occlusions cannot be excluded. No intracranial saccular aneurysms are identified given resolution of CTA (less sensitive in detecting aneurysms smaller than 2mm).

IMPRESSION:

MRI Brain:
1. No evidence of acute intracranial hemorrhage, infarction, or mass.
2. Mild chronic microvascular ischemic changes
3. Volume loss
4. Mild chronic inflammatory paranasal sinus disease.

MRA Head:
1. Compared to November 30, 2010, marked progression of multifocal stenoses of the anterior and posterior circulation as listed above, most compatible with intracranial atherosclerotic disease. Multifocal high-grade stenoses are now present.
2. Likely interval occlusion of the distal left V4 segment.
3. There is a focal fusiform dilation of the right M1 segment, likely related to relative sparing of intracranial atherosclerotic disease/post stenotic dilation rather than a fusiform aneurysm. CTA can further evaluate.
4. Small distal occlusions or high-grade stenoses are difficult to confirm or exclude given resolution and limited filed of view of MRA.
5. No saccular intracranial aneurysms identified.

Figure 12: MRI and MRA Results – JZ Knight, November 13, 2020.[18]

Channeling Physiology and JZ Knight's Brain Changes

During the physiological testing (results published in 1997), indicating when JZ left her body and Ramtha took the body over, her heart rate hit a low of 40 beats a minute and then raced to 180 bpm.[19] JZ has channeled many times during the last 40 years. Considering the 2020 MRI and MRA brain blood supply findings, physiologically understanding the brain and its function under the stress of JZ channeling Ramtha is significant, because it should be impossible for a human being with such severe artery occlusion to function under such cardiovascular stress. Ramtha would hold lectures for twelve hours at a time without any type of script or notes. How is it possible to utilize a significantly diseased brain under a physiologic extreme stress situation while there is no substantial blood flow to both hemispheres? Under such conditions a stroke for a normal human would be occurring. However, while channeling Ramtha, JZ Knight's body and brain show no symptoms of any type of cognitive or neurological dysfunction. That too is in the realm of the miraculous and medically unexplainable. Again, by returning to our torsion physics background, we are able to offer a scientific explanation for such a phenomenon.

In explaining about her brain, JZ says that it is a physical reflection of having moved neighborhoods so many times, meaning she consciously changed neurological occupation in areas of her brain. She describes how the old, unused neuronets now literally have "lights out" in the specific areas, hence no blood flow is needed. JZ reports that her psychic abilities have only increased, despite the lack of blood flow.

JZ Knight's Arthritic Knee

During a personal conversation in 2020, JZ gave me some background understanding about her history of knee pain that provided an additional dimension of understanding to her medical history. She described that in a previous lifetime during the 1700s she lived in a Catholic convent. She was pressed into service to God and was made to scrub floors on her knees continually. Because of this, she developed an open wound that later progressed into gangrene. She died from complications of the gangrene as a young woman in her twenties. Being pressed into service, instead of being allowed to freely commit herself to her love for God, caused resentment.

JZ explained to me how physical symptoms are carried over in between lifetimes and are recorded in our soul. Attitudes that are carried over to the next lifetime affect the mental and physical body and can manifest in physical difficulties in the next reincarnation. Who we are as spiritual beings leaves imprints that we sometimes express medically in inexplicable ways. Odd scars, moles, and curious inflammation are not always of a solely physical nature but may be a bleed-through from other lifetimes manifested into the current time. This phenomenon has been researched by Dr. Ian Stevenson, a psychiatrist from the University of Virginia, who studied children who remembered their past lives. Dr. Stevenson was able to show a direct correlation between how a person died in a prior life and their birthmarks now in this current life in hundreds of cases that he meticulously documented.[20]

Ramtha has previously taught about soul bruises— attitudes carried over lifetimes that have manifested as physical maladies. The key to healing these often inexplicable, nagging vulnerabilities is to address the very soulful bruise that created them. Often these bruises are the most challenging, emotional propensities that the individual is struggling to overcome in their current life. When successfully addressed, the physical issues often resolve as the soul pain eases.

This very topic addresses the multidimensionality of healing and the need of a spiritual being to heal across time. In JZ's case, the physical vulnerability of her knee later in life manifested as significant arthritic degeneration.

JZ describes that as a little girl in her current life, she had severe knee pain and often cried at night because of it. Her mother thought she had growing pains and would treat her with aspirin.

Many years later, in 2015, JZ once again manifested significant problems with her right knee. At the time, she underwent arthroscopic partial medical meniscectomy and partial lateral meniscectomy and chondroplasty of the medical and lateral femoral condyle. Two weeks after the procedure, JZ describes how she traveled to South Korea for a World Tour event. In the rented house was a door leading outside that she had not used before. The first night after dinner she went outside for a walk. Stepping outside the door, JZ fell into free space and landed on the cement patio on her freshly operated knee. The pain was excruciating, and the knee swelled up immediately to an unbendable size causing extreme difficulty to put any weight on that leg. Ignoring the swelling and pain, JZ prepared herself to channel Ramtha the next day, after receiving treatment by her personal chiropractor. When Ramtha came into the body, there was no longer any swelling or pain, with full mobility demonstrated as he taught his students for several hours. When back in her body, JZ again suffered from the injury. However, Ramtha taught the entire weeklong event and demonstrated no physical impact when present in JZ's body. Witnessed by her staff and the large South Korean audience, this should prompt one to ask how such a miracle could be possible.

December 28, 2015,
MRI of Right knee
Judith Knight

IMPRESSION:
1. Marked progression of cartilage loss pertaining to the weight-bearing portion of the medial and lateral compartment, most especially in the lateral compartment compared to April 3, 2015.
2. Extensive curvilinear tear free edges tears involving both medial and lateral menisci.
3. Somewhat lax appearance of the medial most fibers of the anterior cruciate ligament, suggests partial tear.
4. Moderate joint effusion with associated synovitis.
5. Mild lateral subluxation of the patella. Correlate clinically for any evidence of patellar tracking disorder.
6. Probable ganglion cyst versus parameniscal cyst along the posterior lateral aspect of the medial femoral condyle.[21]

These findings from JZ's MRI show significant de-generative arthritis as well as meniscus tears. This is a very painful condition associated with significant inflammation. The fact that there is a moderate joint effusion means that the knee is quite significantly swollen.

Treatment for such severe conditions can be steroid injections, removal of the fluid from the joint, injected medications that might help with cartilage regrowth, and other modalities like stem cell injections. Knee replacement may be recommended by orthopedic surgeons. During multiple occasions in which Ramtha has used the body, he has walked normally without any pain, limping, or other impairment. This indicates again that Ramtha is able to manipulate the DNA in the body at will to change the anatomy of the knee instantaneously and heal it. Upon return of the body to JZ's consciousness, the symptoms of knee problems would reoccur. For several years, JZ continued to focus on healing her knee. She opted to have no further medical treatment.

As of May 2020, JZ reports that her knee is healed.

In Conclusion

The multitude of evidence in different, objective, scientific testing modalities—from physiology data to laboratory data to DNA testing to radiologic scans, ultrasound, and cardiac stress testing—this body of evidence clearly documents genuine, miraculous phenomena over a span of decades.

This case study provides substantial evidence of how consciousness manipulates DNA at will. It presents the rapid, dynamic changes that occur when Ramtha's consciousness uses the body, the significant healing abilities of JZ Knight's consciousness upon her body, and the mystery of her body's anatomy. Looking at the unique physiology of Ramtha and JZ over the span of decades reveals many miracles.

Dr. Krippner stated at the conference *In Search of Self: The Role of Consciousness in the Construction of Reality* held in Yelm, Washington, in February 1997:

"Let me mention some of the other implications of this, because there are very practical payoffs. As many of you know, medical costs keep going up. What you might not know is perhaps 50% of the people who go to physicians wouldn't have to go to physicians at all if they practiced self-care more assiduously. Part of self-care is diet, exercise, meditation, voluntary control, and self-regulation. One of the things that interests me most about the Ramtha School is that people are learning how to self-regulate their bodily processes. I think that this has implications for preventing and overcoming ailments. Then of course they go beyond that and go into the Consciousness & Energy® training to learn how to heal others. There are many, many implications of what we have done that could be of tremendous importance in terms of the medical system and people's ability to practice more assiduously self-care and prevention."[22]

Twenty-three years later, I could not agree more with Dr. Krippner. We have discussed the data and medical evidence that not only convey an extraordinary phenomenon but also poses the question: Who are we, really? If a body can be manipulated by a divine being in this manner—and this knowledge lies in everyone and is everyone's possibility—what does this mean for the future of medicine?

PART III

LIGHT MEDICINE

THE APPLICATION OF SCIENCE AND SPIRIT IN OUR LIVES

CHAPTER 14
CHRONIC INFECTIONS AND DISEASE

Is it possible to rejuvenate you? Do you think YOU can reverse diseases that are causing your aging? In contemplating how integrative approaches to health affect the light in our cells and assist in their rejuvenation, my own conclusion is: "Yes! You can."

I look at this question from the perspective of one cell. This cell is like a house that needs repair. The more energy, electricity, or light we have to perform the repairs, the faster and more efficient the renovation process can happen. Vitamins and nutrients are the building blocks that allow that reconstruction to take place by affecting DNA to transcribe healthier information. Making sure hormones are functioning properly is allowing the communication between neighborhoods of cells to occur. The detoxification of heavy metals that interferes with the proper functioning of our DNA and vital enzymes is an important step in helping cells become more youthful. Information carriers, such as peptides and exosomes, can also provide messages to reverse illness. In the following chapters, I explain integrative medical treatments that have proven successful in my practice. By enhancing the light in our cells, these methods are able to assist in the process of healing.

Immune Dysfunction in the Emergence of Illness

Chronic inflammation and oxidative stress have been well established as causes of accelerated aging. Our immune system has a key role in the aging process. Immunosenescence, which is the aging of the immune system, causes increased vulnerability to chronic infections as well as an inability to contain latent infections in the body and prevent them from reactivating.

Scientists have proposed that measuring specific aspects of immune function is a good marker for biological age and even a predictor for longevity. Oxidative stress affects all cells. This includes the regulatory systems in the body, such as the endocrine system with its hormone regulation and the nervous system with its overarching control mechanisms of information processing. The consequence of a weakened immune system, and therefore premature aging, is the emergence and affliction of the body with infections by pathogens. We live in a symbiotic relationship with a world of microbes, viruses, bacteria, and fungi. However, when the balanced relationship of immune function that keeps these infections at bay is altered, the body can become overwhelmed by the effects of pathogenic presence.

Recently there has been a reemergence in discussing the infectious etiology of many chronic diseases. Infectious microbes are involved in the etiology of cardiovascular disease, cancer, and respiratory diseases. A possible relationship in the alteration of gut microbiomes to type 2 diabetes and obesity has been discussed, as seen in people who are sharing a household having similar chronic diseases.

Around forty million people die from noncommunicable diseases each year. These diseases, which are cardiovascular diseases, cancer, chronic respiratory diseases, and diabetes are responsible for almost 70% of all deaths worldwide. The research team from the *Humans & the Microbiome* program of the Canadian Institute for Advanced Research (CIFAR) has provided information that the so-called "noncommunicable" diseases can possibly be passed on from person to person via the microbiome. Microbial colonization of the human body, including bacteria, fungi, and viruses, is central to transmission of these diseases. Obesity, inflammatory bowel diseases, type 2 diabetes, and cardiovascular disease show significant changes in the microbiome compared to the healthy body. Such changed microbiome compositions lead to the development of diseases when they are transferred to an originally healthy mouse in a laboratory experiment. If the gut microbiome from an obese mouse is transferred to a healthy animal, it will also become overweight. The scientists found evidence that animals that live together show the microbiome and external appearance to be the same.[1]

There have also been many publications that show that even cancer development is related to pathogens like fungal, viral, and bacterial chronic infections. Microbial imbalance has been found in colon, liver, and pancreatic ductal adeno-carcinoma (PDA). The fungal microbiome has also been associated with cancer development. Fungi migrate from the gut lumen to the pancreas, and this is implicated in the development of pancreatic cancer. Pancreatic tumors in humans and mouse models of this cancer displayed a 3,000-fold increase in fungi compared to normal pancreatic tissue. Removal of the mycobiome protected against tumor growth. When the mycobiome was reintroduced with certain fungal microbes, this accelerated the development of cancer.[2]

One in six cancers has been shown to be caused by preventable infections. A study estimated that of 12.7 million new cases of cancer that occurred worldwide in 2008, about 2 million were caused by infectious diseases. The infections that cause cancer include helicobacter pylori (the bacteria that cause stomach ulcers), hepatitis B and C (viruses that cause inflammation of the liver), and human papilloma viruses (sexually transmitted viruses that cause several cancers, notably cervical cancer in women).

In women, cancers of the cervix were estimated to account for about half of infection-related cancers, and in men, liver and gastric cancers accounted for more than 80%. Treating these infections preventatively may be an effective way to reduce the number of global cancer deaths. Understanding, treating, and reversing immune dysfunction and senescence is therefore critical to disease prevention as well as a longevity approach.

The following pathogens were associated with the development of cancer: Helicobacter pylori (stomach), hepatitis B and C (liver), human papilloma virus (cervix, penis, and other sites), Epstein-Barr virus (lymphomas and nose/throat), human T-cell lymphotropic virus type I (T-cell leukemia and lymphoma), human herpesvirus type 8 (Kaposi's sarcoma), Chinese and South Asian liver flukes (gallbladder and bile duct), and Schistosoma trematode worms (bladder).[3]

There is emerging literature that discusses using antimicrobials, antiviral, and antifungal drugs to treat cancer-causing microbes.

Antimicrobial agents can benefit cancer patients by killing microorganisms that can activate cancer, inducing genes, and by protecting from recurring immunosuppression-induced infection and their direct ability to inhibit cell growth and cell damaging effects. Different mechanisms are involved in the cancer growth inhibiting effects of antibiotics. These include targeting gene translation initiation factors and degrading cancer inducing proteins by binding to proteins involved in their folding. They also interfere with the growth of blood vessels needed for a tumor to survive and metastasize and impair the function of mitochondria, causing cancer cell death. Antimicrobials could potentially decrease some side effects of currently used therapies against cancer. These include inhibition of inflammatory cytokine release and the enhancement of cytotoxic activities by conventional chemotherapy drugs.[4]

Italian Oncologist Dr. Tullio Simoncini, in his book *Cancer is a Fungus*, describes his theory of how a fungal infection initiates the development of cancers and then spreads to the whole organism. The growth of the fungal colonies, together with the reaction of the tissue that tries to defend itself against the invasion, causes the tumor. Dr. Simoncini explains that in his view there is only one cause of cancer: candida, which causes different reactions in the body tissue. These in turn cause the different types of tumors. He discusses sodium bicarbonate in a solution of 5% or 8.4% as a remedy capable of making the tumors disappear when the sodium bicarbonate is brought into direct contact with the tissue. He does so by bringing a special catheter into the arteries that go to different organs, or by using conventional endoscopic methods. He has reported favorable results in treating cancer.[5]

In our Light Medicine approach, we are proposing a reference framework that could encompass all scientific findings and allow for their understanding in a broader context. As we previously discussed, the loss of light or electrical cellular capacity creates the fertile ground for cellular dysfunction, which in turn causes the immune dysfunction that can allow for pathogen emergence. We still maintain that the original cause of disease occurs with the loss of light and are now describing downstream effects in the body that have been proposed as primary mechanisms in the scientific literature but, in my view, are consequences.

Atherosclerosis, another prevalent chronic disease, has also been described as a chronic inflammatory disease. Pathophysiological similarities between chronic infections and atherosclerosis triggered interest in a clinical association between these conditions. Various infectious microbes have been linked to atherosclerotic vascular disease in epidemiological studies. Studies in animal models have identified immune pathways involved in the development of atherosclerosis. Various bacteria and viruses have been shown to have a direct effect on the vascular endothelium as well as an indirect effect by systemic release of inflammatory messenger molecules, both of which contribute to accelerated atherosclerosis.

Infectious agents that have been linked to atherosclerotic disease include, but are not limited to, Chlamydia pneumoniae, Porphyromonas gingivalis, helicobacter pylori, influenza A virus, hepatitis C virus, cytomegalovirus (CMV), and human immunodeficiency virus (HIV). As stated, there is evidence supporting the role of the immune system in developing hardening of the arteries. Structural similarities exist between oxidized low-density lipoprotein cholesterol (ox-LDL) and bacterial cell wall polysaccharide. This could indicate why the immune system would create inflammation against both molecules: cholesterol, and the bacterial cell wall poly-saccharide.

Infections have been implicated in the initiation, progression, and rupture of atherosclerotic plaque where numerous studies have shown the presence of bacterial and viral microorganisms. Pathogens may be harbored in a dormant state or proliferate in cells, such as macrophages, creating a chronic, inflammatory environment. Most implicated organisms are intracellular microbes which exert their effects from within the cell, evading the body's immune mechanisms.[6]

Chronic fatigue syndrome has been an emerging disease that affects many and has been linked to viral infections.[7] The pathogenesis of chronic fatigue syndrome is likely multifactorial, and various microbial and viral infections are considered to be the possible trigger factors. The illness has been frequently accompanied with various viral infections, and studies have been conducted in association with Epstein–Barr virus, cytomegalovirus, human herpesvirus (HHV) 6, HHV-7, HHV-8, human parvovirus B19 (B19V), enteroviruses, lentivirus, and bacteria as mycoplasma, Lyme disease causing borrelia, Q fever causing Coxiella burnetii, and other pathogens.[8]

Judy Mikovits, Ph.D., detected retrovirus xenotropic murine leukemia virus-related (XMRV) in blood cells of patients with chronic fatigue syndrome (CFS).[9] She found that at least 30% of our vaccines are contaminated with gamma retroviruses. This contamination is associated with autism and chronic fatigue syndrome, as well as Parkinson's, Lou Gehrig's disease, and Alzheimer's. Dr. Mikovits says that 6% of the U.S. population is harboring a retrovirus in their bodies that can develop into an acquired immune deficiency. They can become activated during times of stress to produce symptoms of chronic fatigue syndrome (CFS), which include muscle and joint pain and persistent fatigue.

Dr. Mikovits explains that the retroviruses mentioned do not directly cause diseases by themselves but may do so when a weakening of our immune defenses is present. In such circumstances, the viruses create inflammatory processes that disrupt the immune system.[10]

These viruses are thought to be most likely introduced into humans through contaminated vaccines and biological products, including genetically modified organisms (GMOs) or food. Others include human blood products needed for transfusions, the milk of cows, and human breast milk. These retroviruses can be passed between family members through body fluids, which is a similar finding to the changes in gut microbiome in families discussed earlier. Dr. Mikovits' research team found that 67% of chronic fatigue syndrome patients had XMRV. Other researchers found that 86.5% of these patients had evidence of infection by a broader group of retroviruses that were linked to laboratory mice.

Dr. Mikovits and her team also found that 3.7% of a healthy patient group showed evidence of XMRV infection. Further research by other scientists indicated that 6.8% of a healthy control population were infected with additional murine leukemia viruses. It is estimated that eleven to twenty-one million individuals in the United States were potentially exposed to these viruses.[11]

Retroviruses carry their genetic blueprint in the form of RNA. Retroviruses are named for an enzyme known as reverse transcriptase, which transcribes RNA into DNA. This represents a reversal of the usual direction of cellular gene transcription, from DNA into RNA. The action of reverse transcriptase makes it possible for genetic material from a retrovirus to become permanently incorporated into the DNA genome of an infected cell.

Retroviruses may cause cancer via mutation of genes that promote malignant transformation called oncogenes.[12]

A retrovirus known as human T-cell lymphotropic virus type 1 (HTLV-1) causes a form of cancer called adult T-cell leukemia. It can also cause a neurodegenerative condition known as HTLV-1-associated myelopathy (spinal cord inflammation) and spastic paraparesis (paralysis of the lower limbs). As many as twenty million people worldwide are thought to be infected with HTLVs, but only a small percentage of infected individuals actually develop the disease.[13]

Viruses are intracellular parasites that use the host cell for replication of the viral genome. An infection is characterized by the release of new virus particles, often upon the destruction of the host cell. The virus can live latently in our cells and, at times of great stress and immune system compromise, be reactivated. There are many viruses known to cause latent infections. They include herpes simplex virus, varicella zoster virus, Epstein–Barr virus, human cytomegalovirus, human herpesvirus 6, human herpesvirus 7, Kaposi's sarcoma-associated herpesvirus, JC and BK virus from the human polyomavirus family, parvovirus, and adenovirus.

The varicella zoster virus causes chickenpox and can reactivate from its latent state to produce a disease in adults called shingles. The incidence of zoster in the U.S.A. is approximately 5–6.5 per 1,000 individuals per year at 60 years of age, increasing to 8–11 per 1,000 at 70 years of age. The incidence may increase due to diminishing immune function with aging, and this immunodeficiency may be a vital predisposing factor for the development of zoster.

Epstein–Barr virus (EBV) is present mainly in B lymphocytes and epithelial cells. EBV is a cancer inducing herpesvirus that persistently infects over 95% of the human population. These viruses may cause many nonspecific symptoms in patients experiencing a decline in their vitality and health status.[14] Considering these infectious latent agents in the body as a cause for disease, I apply a strategy to address them in treatment plans by enhancing immune function and utilizing antimicrobial and antiviral agents as an important cornerstone in my practice. These considerations may bring treating clinicians closer to addressing nonspecific symptoms that often adversely impact the quality of life of many patients but are not detected on routine medical examinations.

Professor Luc Montagnier is a French virologist and recipient of the 2008 Nobel Prize for the discovery of the human immunodeficiency virus (HIV). "He found water carrying only the electromagnetic signature of a DNA sequence can make a replica of the sequence out of simple building blocks."[15]

HIV is an RNA virus, normally detected in the bloodstream of people infected with HIV. The viral RNA is not responsible for the electromagnetic signal. However, reverse transcriptase creates a complementary strand DNA sequence. These DNA electromagnetic signals are detected in patients previously treated by antiretroviral therapy while having no detectable viral DNA copies in their blood.[16]

Dr. Montagnier and his team have demonstrated that highly reproducible electromagnetic signals can be detected from biological samples. The signals are responsible for a biological function, for example, bacterial and viral infection. The scientists have linked the source of the signals to specific gene sequences of the bacteria and viruses. These signals and their associated function appear to survive in "nanostructures" even after the DNA solutions are highly diluted, to the point where no molecule of the original DNA is present.

DNA has molecular vibrations in a wide range of frequencies, from below 1 cm^{-1} (radiofrequency) to 4,000 cm^{-1} (far infrared) ranging from 200 nm to 800 nm. This can be detected and modified by externally applied electromagnetic fields. Water can hold the memory of such specific vibrations, especially when the DNA molecule has been diluted away.[17,18]

This means that water in humans can carry the electromagnetic frequency signature of viruses and this electromagnetic memory can have biological effects. As we have discussed in the chapter on torsion fields, every living thing has an electromagnetic frequency signature, and the memory of that is carried in the torsion waves produced. We are electromagnetic frequency beings, and the information of a virus, bacteria, fungus, and other pathogens have the ability to affect the human body and create a vast array of symptoms and diseases.

Dr. Montagnier's group showed that water nanostructures and their electromagnetic resonance can perpetuate DNA information for numerous bacteria like Borrelia burgdorferi, the agent of Lyme disease. One single complete mycoplasma cell is sufficient to generate the whole infection of lymphocytes.

The induced water nanostructures were assessed in their potency by re-creating from them the DNA sequence. They were then put into a test tube. All ingredients to synthesize the DNA were given to the medium. From the electromagnetic frequency nanostructure of the water, the bacterial DNA was subsequently able to be re-created.[19] This is very much likened to the principle of homeopathy, where extreme dilutions of a compound in a water solution still have the clinical effects of the original molecule.

These research findings have been performed earlier in Russia and are explained by the holographic linguistic-wave genome theory outlined by Professor Gariaev from the Institute of Linguistics of wave genetics in Moscow, Russia. DNA acts as a biological, holographic computer which generates electromagnetic and acoustic waves carrying four-dimensional, epigenetic information used by organisms for their biological self-organization in space and time.[20]

This has phenomenal implications in the future of medicine as described in this book. First, the human body can be infected with bacterial and viral agents through a frequency signal alone. However, this would also indicate that treatments targeting specific pathogens with neutralizing frequencies—similar to the earlier Rife machines—could have a significant role in the future treatment of infectious and chronic diseases.

As stated, the Blu Room is utilizing ultraviolet-blue light that has been shown to disinfect bacteria and viruses. This could be a mechanism in which Blu Room technology, with its specific frequency of UV light, may be beneficial in reversal of chronic diseases.

Pathogens in the body are reactivated by stress. The Blu Room has been shown to reduce stress. This may also be a means of prevention of chronic illness. Studies have revealed that narrow-band UVB light has effective antimicrobial action, for example, against oral bacteria like the ubiquitous streptococcus species.[21,22]

Ultraviolet LEDs have also been shown to have antiviral activity. For example, they decreased viral Influenza A RNA in infected cells. UV LEDs inhibited host cell replication and transcription of viral RNA. In particular, it has been demonstrated that 280 and 310 nm UV LEDs inactivated highly pathogenic avian Influenza A virus H5N1 subtype.[23] This shows tremendous promise for a new model of medicine in combating pathogens based on UV light technologies.

Treatment of Chronic Diseases with Antimicrobial Agents

Recently, the COVID-19 pandemic has made the well-known antimalarial agents chloroquine (CQ) and hydroxyl-chloroquine (HCQ) famous. Scientific evidence supports the use of CQ and HCQ in the treatment of cancer because of their ability to sensitize tumor cells to a variety of drugs, potentiating therapeutic activity. CQ and HCQ exert effects both on cancer cells and on the tumor microenvironment. They inhibit the natural mechanism of the cell that removes dysfunctional components and affect the toll-like receptor 9, which is a cellular DNA receptor of the innate immune system and has been used in breast cancer as a treatment target. CQ also affects the tumor suppressor gene p53 and the regulator of the angiogenesis pathway in cancer cells. In solid tumors, chloroquine was shown to affect the tumor vasculature, cancer-associated fibroblasts, and the immune system.[24] The UV spectroscopy maximum for hydroxychloroquine is at 343 nm, in the ultraviolet range.[25]

Of interest also is fenbendazole, used as a dog dewormer, that has been shown to have antitumor effects. In a study where mice were supplemented by both vitamins and fenbendazole, significant inhibition of tumor growth was found.[26] Mass spectroscopy of fenbendazole has the highest peaks at 267 nm, 299 nm, and 266 nm.[27]

Itraconazole, another common antifungal drug in widespread clinical use, has antiangiogenic activity and can inhibit the hedgehog (Hh) signaling pathway. This is a highly conserved, evolutionary pathway of signal transmission from the cell membrane to the nucleus. Deregulation of the Hh signaling pathway is associated with developmental anomalies and cancer—including basal cell and small-cell lung carcinomas—as well as medulloblastoma, pancreatic, breast, colon, and ovarian carcinomas.[28]

Itraconazole may also induce cancer cell growth arrest. Clinical trials have shown that patients with prostate, lung, and basal cell carcinoma have benefited from treatment with itraconazole. There are additional reports of positive activity in leukemia, ovarian, breast, and pancreatic cancers. Itraconazole may synergize with a range of other drugs to enhance the anticancer effect.[29] The UV spectra of itraconazole is at a wavelength of 268 nm.[30]

If certain molecular side chains of drugs have frequency emissions in the ultraviolet range, could the antipathogenic mechanism of action be related to their frequency signature? UV has long been found to have antipathogenic properties. All molecules give off their own light signature. This remains to be studied further.

These antiviral, antibacterial, and antifungal compounds, used in combination therapy with nutritional optimization and nutraceuticals that induce cancer cell death, may greatly enhance the antitumor activity of combination cocktails.

Based on the understanding that there are clear causative relationships between pathogens and the emergence of chronic diseases, new treatment pathways can be explored, such as the application of UV light and therapy using antimicrobial agents.

A link to dental infections and root canals causing chronic diseases has also been documented. In fact, there are scientists considering these infections as causation for severe disease like cancer. Spontaneous remissions of advanced cancer have been documented after the removal of root canals. For example, diffuse large B-cell lymphoma of the maxillary bone was resolved without chemotherapy or radiation after biopsy and treatment with antibiotics for an infected root canal.[31]

Considering the theory that all chronic diseases could be caused by infections, strengthening the immune system is of prime importance in prevention and treatment of chronic diseases. Vitamin C, D3, and other vitamins crucial to a functioning immune system could thereby be used to treat and potentially prevent many ailments.

In a futuristic society that understands health prevention, CRISPR gene editing could be used to correct the human gene defect that prohibits humans to synthetize ascorbic acid out of glucose. By correcting this gene defect, we could ensure the adequate function of our immune system that according to need could produce vitamin C in large quantities and heal all diseases from atherosclerosis, obesity, high cholesterol, chronic fatigue, to cancer. Ensuring that we take adequate amounts of vitamin D and zinc are also important preventative and treatment considerations.

In addition, antimicrobial, antiviral, and antifungal treatments need to have further studies in their effects of treating all diseases.

Many questions remain in this area. However, there appears to be substantial cumulative evidence that many chronic illnesses are associated with chronic infections. I am of the opinion that with the introduction of Light Medicine, optimization in nutritionally boosting the immune system would be a safer way to ensure health than potentially dangerous vaccines.

CHAPTER 15
DISEASES RELATED TO ELECTROPOLLUTION

Today we are living in a world that is dependent on the use of Wi-Fi and other electromagnetic exposures for communication technology. How might this impact the well-being of the human body?

Dr. Aleksandr Samuilovich Presman, in his 1970 book, *Electromagnetic Fields and Life*, identified several significant effects from the interaction of electromagnetic fields with living organisms. By carrying information, electromagnetic fields have communication roles that are used by living organisms as information messengers from the environment to the organism, within the organism, and between organisms.

These fields are involved in life's vital processes in that they facilitate "pattern formation, organization, and growth control." Presman postulated that "if living organisms possess the ability to utilize electromagnetic fields and electricity, there must exist physical structures within the cells that facilitate the sensing, transducing, storing, and transmitting of this form of energy."[1]

With the rollout of 5G, some consumers have become more aware of the potential adverse health effects of such advanced technologies. Scientists have shown that Wi-Fi leads to cell death (apoptosis) and oxidative stress, which is the mechanism that increases our rate of aging and development of chronic diseases, including cancer and neurodegenerative diseases like dementia. The male testes have been affected by its adverse effect on the endocrine system and lowered production of testosterone, causing low sperm count and thereby impaired male fertility. Cellular DNA damage, which increases the risk of cancer, has also been documented.[2] DNA has a high absorbance of electromagnetic frequencies (EMFs). There are studies showing that DNA, when it absorbs EMFs, undergoes structural changes. Neuropsychiatric changes have been documented with electroencephalogram (EEG) changes. The mechanism is thought to act via voltage-gated, calcium-channel activation. Pulsed EMF, which is Wi-Fi, has been shown to be more biologically active and thereby more harmful to organisms than non-pulsed EMF. The adverse health effects are cumulative. Studies stating that EMF is harmless have been shown to be flawed. In children, EMF exposure is linked to increased incidence of cancers and neurodevelopmental diseases, including autism.[3]

Weak EMF can cause nonthermal effects in body cells, tissues, and organs. Electromagnetic fields can be dangerous, not only because of the risk of cancer but also other health problems, including electromagnetic hypersensitivity (EHS). Electromagnetic hypersensitivity symptoms occur after exposure of people to electromagnetic fields. This can manifest in the body as acute and chronic inflammation occurring in the skin, nervous, respiratory, cardiovascular, and musculoskeletal system.[4]

The phenomenon of electromagnetic hypersensitivity in the skin is associated with mastocytosis. The tissue biopsies taken from skin lesions of patients with EHS indicated infiltration of layers of the epidermis with mastocytes and allergic reaction mediators such as histamine, chymase, and tryptase. The number of people suffering from EHS is growing, and many are describing themselves as functionally impaired. They show nonspecific symptoms upon exposure to low doses of electromagnetic radiation. Such reactions are often associated with intolerances to many chemical and environmental compounds.[5]

We must become aware as a society of the multitude of effects of electromagnetic frequency upon our bodies in regard to who we are as electromagnetic beings of light. The health effects mentioned do not even include the mind control component or psychotronic warfare in which behaviors and modes of thinking can be altered via electromagnetic signals. All of this needs to be reevaluated in terms of future freedoms that we desire to live as enlightened, healthy, and unlimited being.

CHAPTER 16
ENVIRONMENTAL HEALTH AND CHELATION THERAPY

Multiple studies have demonstrated that the functioning of our bodies can be adversely impacted by environmental toxins. These come in many forms and can have many detrimental effects on the body. One category of environmental toxins is heavy metals that have accumulated in our environment and food supply. These are interfering with mitochondrial function and cellular energy production, in essence diminishing the light or electrical capacity of the organism. This leads to accelerated aging and the onslaught of the chronic disease process.

There are many heavy metals that can have an adverse health impact. Examples are lead, arsenic, mercury, cadmium, chromium, cobalt, and others, such as nickel, tin, and vanadium. Copper is an essential heavy metal that is utilized in the body; however, in excess, it can cause problems. Elevated cobalt levels are seen more frequently now due to artificial joint replacements and the leaking of metal from those devices. In this chapter we will be focusing mostly on lead, mercury, and cadmium—no amount of those heavy metals is safe, despite artificial ranges of "normal" given by regulating agencies.

Gadolinium, which is utilized as contrast material for MRI radiologic procedures, can cause long-term health impacts, including nephrogenic systemic fibrosis. Gadolinium has been shown to be deposited and retained in the brain, and safety concerns have been raised regarding use of this substance.[1]

Heavy metals occur in different mediums. Mercury is found in fish—especially tuna, sea bass, halibut, and marlin—

and in dental care, like amalgams. It is in preventative medical practices, such as thimerosal in vaccines, as well as in industrial and occupational operations.

Cadmium is in cigarettes, with trace amounts in leafy vegetables, potatoes, crustaceans, and drinking water. Toxic jewelry is another potential source of exposure to heavy metals. In jewelry for children, the levels of cadmium were found to be between 15 to 7,000 times higher than the threshold for cadmium given by the Public Health Agency of Canada.[2]

Aluminum is in pharmaceutical and personal care products, like deodorants, drinking water, and cooking ware.

Arsenic occurs in rice, insecticides, herbicides, fungicides, ceramics, and shellfish. In fact, pesticides with high arsenic content that were extensively utilized after World War II are what made our soils so filled with arsenic.

Recently in the news it was reported that high levels of arsenic found in baby cereal made with rice could cause a drop in children's IQ. Over 170 baby foods were tested by a nonprofit group who found that 95% of the samples contained heavy metals like lead, arsenic, cadmium, or mercury. The rice-based cereal was identified as the top source of arsenic in the infants' diets. And the projection is that newborns and children up to two years old would lose a total of more than eleven million IQ points from the exposure to arsenic and lead in food.[3]

An article featured in the *Huffington Post* in 2017 made reference to arsenic being toxic. It has been associated with lung, skin, and bladder cancers. There are many different forms of arsenics. Inorganic arsenic is the most toxic and dangerous; therefore rice intake should be done in moderation.[4]

Before 1979, gasoline contained lead, and millions of tons of lead were distributed into our air and inhaled by people. Lead is in soil, bone broth, collagen, paint, lead-contaminated food, as well as drinking water. Lead paint is used in manufacturing processes, plumbing, pottery, and certain ceramics.

On the FDA Web site, we find information that lead is in our food, food wares, and dietary supplements. Lead occurs in what we consume because of its presence in the environment. It can enter the food supply by settling into the soil where it can then be absorbed by plants. There have even been high amounts of heavy metal contamination found in Ayurvedic health supplements.[5] Lead that is deposited on plants cannot be completely removed through the washing process, and the lead in plants or water may be reabsorbed by the animals that we eat. This heavy metal is prolific in our modern environment.

Lead poisoning is also a major threat in America's shooting ranges. An article appearing in *The Seattle Times* discussed the high risk of the exposure to lead through vapors that are released when engaging firearms. There have been studies conducted through L&I that looked at thousands of blood test results for lead through the Washington State Adult Blood Lead Epidemiology and Surveillance program. Results showed fifty-nine employees at nine gun ranges with lead levels of 25 micrograms or higher in the blood, and that is thought to be an underestimation. The lead was creating symptoms of nausea and fatigue, organ damage, mental impairment, low testosterone levels, erectile dysfunction, and many other health problems. Lead vapors are released due to the bullet having a lead core that the shooter then inhales as a vapor upon firing.[6]

Lead is prevalent in lipstick—used by millions of women. The Campaign for Safe Cosmetics and the FDA did research on the lead content in these cosmetics. Lipsticks contain 61% of lead with levels ranging up to .65 parts per million. No amount of lead is safe, regardless of the acceptable levels given by regulatory agencies.

These lead-contaminated products included such famous name brands as L'Oréal, CoverGirl, and Dior. The FDA found that the highest lead levels were made by the following manufacturers: Procter & Gamble, L'Oréal, Maybelline, and Revlon.

The FDA did another study in 2010 and found lead in 400 lipsticks at levels up to 7.19 parts per million. Five of the ten most lead-contaminated products in the FDA studies are made by L'Oréal U.S.A.[7]

The heavy metal concentrations of 32 lip products belonging to a California woman were analyzed. In addition to lead, aluminum, chromium, manganese, and cadmium were found.[8] Lead is not safe in any amount and can be toxic neurologically in small doses. It has been linked to learning difficulties, language deficiencies, behavioral problems, reduced fertility in men and women, hormonal disruption, menstrual irregularities, delayed onset of puberty in girls, and delayed development of testes in boys.

Lead is in purses, belts, and shoes and can be absorbed through the skin. In 2009, legal action was taken against major retailers for selling purses and other accessories with high levels of lead. Sixteen out of twenty-one stores visited had significantly high lead contents in purses.[9]

Lead is found in drinking water. The acidic chemicals added to water in municipalities magnifies the uptake of lead into the body. On top of that, 98% of homes have lead in their plumbing from lead and copper pipes. Even chrome-plated faucets are made of brass that contain up to 8% lead.[10]

Examples of other means of lead exposure include the fire of the Notre Dame Cathedral, during which 400 tons of lead tile burned. In the surrounding Paris area, lead levels were up to 1,300 times higher than the French safety guidelines. The lead spread across central Paris, settling in schools, parks, and other public places, with more than 6,000 children younger than age six living within a half mile of these locations.[11]

Reuters published a map outlining the lead concentration in soil samples in the United States. It has been found that thousands of U.S. towns have lead poisoning worse than Flint, Michigan.[12] All of these examples illustrate the ubiquitous nature of toxic heavy metals and their demonstrated adverse impacts on our health.

The problem is that the half-life of lead is extremely long. Lead, once ingested or inhaled, is absorbed into the bones, where its half-life is thirty years. People born before 1979 should be evaluated for heavy metals if they have chronic diseases like atherosclerosis, as during that time lead was in our gasoline and the population became exposed by inhaling it at the gas pump. Absorption of this substance is cumulative.

Cadmium is stored in the kidneys, liver, and lungs, and can be toxic. The half-life of cadmium is also thirty years in these organ systems.

Mercury is stored in the kidneys and the brain. The half-life is one to two weeks, but it is also a very toxic metal.

Low-level exposures to heavy metals are associated with long-term effects. Most studies look at one single toxicant. Yet many people are exposed to multiple toxic substances that bioaccumulate and have a synergistic effect. This synergy has to be taken into account, as well as the individual sensitivity and vulnerability of the patient.

We do not have good studies in which the effects of multiple toxic heavy metals are well-studied in the biological system. The levels for exposures given by regulatory agencies have not yet considered that humans bioaccumulate metals. Reference ranges exist that are given by labs for what is considered normal, but no level is safe based upon the effects that occur on a cellular level.

Over the last two decades, data indicates that the blood lead levels in children are increasing. The CDC released a report that showed the average child blood lead levels were going down from 2007-08 to 2013 but then increased again in different percentiles in 2015-2016.[13]

The adverse health effects caused by lead and the mechanisms of disease progressions are mediated through oxidative stress. Oxidative stress is one of the mechanisms by which we are aging. Reactive oxygen species produced through the effects of lead are causing DNA and cellular damage.[14]

Lead reduces the production of nitric oxide, and nitric oxide is imperative for vascular health. Lead increases inflammation. It adversely affects the endothelial cell function that is the lining of the blood vessels in the arteries and interferes with calcium signaling. Calcium signaling is an important mechanism in how cells are functioning.

Lead burden leads to hormonal dysregulation. Exposure to lead may affect libido, semen quality by declining sperm count, motility, viability, integrity, elevation in morphological abnormalities, and sperm DNA integrity. These effects can cause reduced fertility potential and chances of miscarriages and preterm birth. Lead impairs hormonal synthesis and regulation in both sexes. Lead exposure can affect female reproduction by impairing menstruations, reducing fertility potential, and delaying conception time. It also alters hormonal production and circulation, affecting pregnancy and its outcome. At present, the safe dose for lead cannot be advocated, as more and more data have been generated in recent years which indicate the toxic potential of lead, at a low level, to human reproduction that was previously thought not to have such effect. Hence, use of lead should be stopped/avoided or restricted to safeguard human reproduction.[15] Lead and other heavy metals cause kidney dysfunction.[16]

The symptoms of lead in the body burden are fatigue, irritability, hearing loss, reduced IQ (particularly in children), infertility, high blood pressure, heart disease, changes in the electrical system in the heart leading to electrocardiogram changes, chronic kidney disease, peripheral neuropathy affecting the nerves in the feet and hands, joint pain, muscle pain, gout, and gastrointestinal symptoms like nausea and constipation.[17]

Elevated blood lead levels increase antisocial and criminal behavior.[18] Lead causes cataracts, emotional instability, cognitive decline, seizures, coma, and death at high levels.

Mercury toxicity is very important to consider in our current age, as it can cause harm to the human body at very low doses. The International Academy of Oral Medicine and Toxicology has excellent information regarding dental amalgam fillings, which are known to have elemental or metallic mercury in them. There are different forms of mercury. Fish contain mainly methyl mercury. Vaccines contain ethyl mercury, and those are metabolized differently. Silver fillings contain about 50% mercury.

The problem is that mercury vapor from amalgam dental fillings is off-gassing continuously, causing low-level intoxication of the person who has these amalgams. The mercury is then absorbed, retained in the body, and acts as a neurotoxin, causing brain damage. The vapor production is increased through chewing, teeth grinding, and the consumption of hot liquids.

The accumulation of mercury causes symptoms like emotional instability, loss of appetite, weakness, skin changes, cardiovascular problems, cognitive and neurological impairments, memory loss, decrease in mental function, delusions, delirium, hallucinations, dermatologic skin conditions, endocrine disruption, the enlargement of the thyroid, abnormal responses to stimulation, fatigue, headaches, hearing loss, immune system impairment, lack of sleep, nerve response changes, decreased coordination, muscle atrophy, and twitching.

The manifestations in the mouth can cause gingivitis, metallic taste, lichen planus—which can develop into cancerous lesions—and salivation problems. There are psychological issues, mood swings, anger, depression, irritability, nervousness, kidney problems, respiratory problems, excessive shyness and social withdrawal, tremors, and weight loss.[19]

As a clinician, it is important to consider ongoing mercury exposure from amalgams and other sources when consulting with patients having these symptoms. The treatment of the mercury body burden—as well as all heavy metal burdens—is, first, the removal of the toxic source, in this case the removal of the amalgams. The process of removal needs to be done very specifically and by professional individuals who are well trained in the safe removal of these amalgams; otherwise more toxicity to the body can occur.

Tobacco has heavy metals in its leaves, and that is affecting smokers. A study from Greece showed that tobacco smoke has radioactive nucleotide radium, and polonium. Other radioactive isotopes were found in the leaves of tobacco and were a thousand times higher than in the leaves of trees around Chernobyl at the time of the nuclear accident. Consequently, for people who smoke about thirty cigarettes a day, their natural radionuclides are at 251 microsieverts a year, whereas 0.199 was measured from Chernobyl fallout in tree leaves. Scientists are warning that cancer deaths among smokers are due to the radioactive content of tobacco leaves, and not just the nicotine and tar.[20] In smokers, I often see high levels of cesium in provoked heavy metal urine testing at my office.

How are toxic metals affecting our epigenetics? Epigenetics is the inheritable changes that occur in gene expression, but it's not about changing the DNA sequence. Heavy metals can induce DNA methylation, which is a biological process by which methyl groups are added to the DNA molecule. This methylation process can change the activity of a DNA segment without changing the sequence and can suppress gene transcription. In addition, heavy metals can induce histone changes, which is a protein modification that affects the folding of DNA. This alters subsequent microRNA production.

MicroRNA is what governs about 60% of the human genome. Through these different mechanisms, the genetic expression can be changed. It's been shown that organic toxins, as well as metals like cadmium, arsenic, nickel, chromium, methylmercury, and lead have their adverse effects by changing epigenetics, DNA methylation, and causing changes in microRNA transcription. Heavy metals are altering how our genetic material is read, and through these epigenetic changes, disease is created. Already there is information describing how babies in utero are affected by chemicals found in plastics, heavy metals, solvents, and other chemicals.[21]

Lead exposure can cause multigenerational epigenetic changes.[22] Epigenetic changes, such as DNA methylation, are chemical modifications that change how DNA is expressed without altering the genetic code. In one particular study, researchers measured lead levels and methylation at over 450,000 DNA locations, or loci, from current blood and neonatal dried blood spots from both the mother and child of 35 mother-infant pairs. The researchers found that mothers whose own neonatal blood spots showed high lead levels, correlated with DNA methylation changes at 564 loci in their children's neonatal blood. These results suggest that lead exposure during pregnancy affects the DNA methylation status of the fetal germ cells. In turn, this leads to altered DNA methylation in grandchildren's neonatal dried blood spots.[23]

The exposure to heavy metals leads to oxidative stress. Heavy metals increase inflammation. They cause hormonal disruption, which also changes gene expression, increases the risk of disease, and accelerates the aging process. It has been shown that DNA methylation, the change in the histone folding, and the changes in microRNA expression are leading to many different diseases, including cancer, Alzheimer's disease, diabetes, atherosclerosis, gait imbalance, immune deficiencies, rheumatoid arthritis, multiple sclerosis, and systemic lupus. The toxicologic effects of heavy metals are relevant in epigenetic regulation as gene transcription in some cases is silenced or activated for other genes. This can lead to disease-causing genes to be transcribed and disease-preventing genes to be downregulated.[24]

The medical effects of heavy metal total body burden, how it causes chronic diseases, and how addressing this body burden and detoxifying the body as a treatment for chronic diseases are very important.

Studies have shown that elevated blood lead levels cause high blood pressure in perimenopausal and postmenopausal women. In one study, 2,165 women age forty to fifty-nine years were found to have elevated blood lead levels. This was correlated with an increase of their systolic and diastolic blood pressure.[25]

Lead not only induces high blood pressure but also acts upon multiple sites in the cardiovascular system. There are direct effects on the excitability of the electrical system in the heart as well as the contractility of the heart muscle. Lead leads to alterations of compliance of the vascular smooth muscle tissue. This impairs the ability of the smooth muscle to adapt to different volumes of blood that are being pumped through the vascular system. Lead also affects the brain areas that are responsible for neurological blood pressure regulation.

Kidneys play a major part in controlling blood pressure through the renin-angiotensin system. Since lead is toxic to the kidneys, this is another pathway in how high blood pressure is caused.

A low-level environmental exposure to lead has been associated with chronic kidney diseases. Low-level lead body burden accelerates kidney toxicity and chronic kidney failure in patients who are not diabetic. A comparison study of 108 patients who were treated with chelation—and a control group that was not treated with chelation therapy—showed that the chelation group had a less rapid decline of kidney function as measured in the glomerular filtration rate. This indicates that the lead that was not removed in the control group was progressing the kidney disease more rapidly.[26]

There is evidence that lead inhibits nitric oxide formation, and it has been shown that lead exposure is associated with significantly increased cardiovascular risk. In part this is related to oxidative stress. Oxidative stress creates free oxygen radicals that damage DNA. Reduced nitric oxide production causes endothelial cell dysfunction which are irregularities in the lining of blood vessels. Thirty men and thirty-two women who were exposed to lead had different nitric oxide metabolites measured in their blood. Their lead exposure had reduced nitric oxide production. This appears to be one of the significant mechanisms of how lead increases cardiovascular risk.[27]

A study published in *The Lancet Public Health* in 2018 shows that lead exposure in the United States is linked to over 400,000 premature deaths from all causes, of which 250,000 deaths occur from cardiovascular disease each year. The study analyzed data from the third National Health and Nutrition Examination Survey in which 14,289 people that were twenty years or older were followed over a prolonged period from 1988 to 2011. People who had high lead levels were at 37% greater risk of premature death from any cause. They had seventy times greater risk of cardiovascular death and double the risk of death from ischemic heart disease compared with people that had lower levels of lead in their blood. Low-level environmental lead exposure is an important, but largely overlooked, risk factor for cardiovascular disease mortality and is a silent killer in the United States.

Despite a 75% reduction in lead levels in blood since the 1970s, due to eliminating lead from gasoline, millions of tons of this toxic metal were expelled into our atmosphere. During that time people inhaled lead and bioaccumulated it in their bones.

After lead was taken out of gasoline, a substantial reduction in the compared blood levels was noted. Despite this, 38% of U.S. adults have a blood lead level of 2 micrograms per deciliter or greater. It is known that any level above 1 already increases the risk of death substantially. There is a 151-248% increase in death from stroke, 88-189% increase in death from heart attacks, and a 25% increased overall death rate.

This is why lead is called "the silent killer."[28]

In the TACT trial (Trial to Assess Chelation Therapy), the effect of disodium ethylenediaminetetraacetic acid (EDTA) chelation on cardiovascular events in patients who had a previous heart attack was evaluated.

Conducted by a team of Dr. Gervasio Lamas, Chairman of Medicine and Cardiology, Columbia University, the study included 1,708 patients fifty years or older who had had a heart attack. The group received either forty infusions of chelation with or without vitamins, compared to a placebo group that didn't receive the EDTA chelation. This was a groundbreaking study, and the results were quite significant.

Two groups of people had beneficial effects: those who were nondiabetic and those who were diabetic. Patients with diabetes had a 41% reduction in cardiovascular endpoints, including heart attacks, strokes, and a 43% reduction in total mortality. The number of diabetics needed to treat over a period of five years was just seven. This means that seven people would have to be treated to prevent one adverse event. In nondiabetics, there was a 26% reduction in cardiovascular events. If compared to commonly used heart medicines, taking aspirin has a 25% reduction in cardiovascular events, but you have to treat between twenty-five and fifty patients for two years with aspirin to prevent one adverse event. Beta blockers have a 23% reduction in cardiovascular events, but you have to treat forty-two people over two years to prevent one adverse event. Cholesterol medications, like statins, have a 21% reduction in cardiovascular events, but you must treat thirty-three to sixty-five people over two years to prevent one adverse event. ACE (angiotensin converting enzyme) inhibitors, like the commonly used blood pressure medication lisinopril, have a 19% reduction in cardiovascular events, but you have to treat twenty-eight up to two hundred people to prevent one event.

Chelation with vitamins in nondiabetics had a 26% reduction of cardiovascular events—better than aspirin, beta blockers, statins, and ACE inhibitors. The chelation in diabetics had a 41% reduction of all cardiovascular events, 51% of myocardial infarction, and 43% of all-cause mortality.[29]

The results comparatively are extraordinary, yet chelation therapy continues to be marginalized and even condemned by many prominent medical institutions that are funded by Big Pharma through their foundations. The immune system is affected by heavy metals, and a correlation is indicated in the increased incidence of autoimmune diseases. In my integrative practice, addressing heavy metal total body burden is a corner-stone treatment approach for reversing cardiovascular disease.

There is a link between allergic diseases and heavy metal burden. Many are aware of nickel allergy that causes eczema. Studies show that heavy metals play a key role in the exacerbation of several autoimmune diseases through an alteration in immune cells, as the T helper cells type 1 and TH type 2 reactivity is changed.[30]

In a publication from Pakistan, one hundred rheumatoid arthritis patients were analyzed for cadmium, chromium, lead, and nickel, and their levels compared to healthy controls. It was found that these heavy metals were significantly elevated in the rheumatoid patients. The conclusion was that heavy metals may contribute towards the development of rheumatoid arthritis.[31]

A Korean study in macular degeneration showed that toxic heavy metals, like lead, mercury, and cadmium, negatively influence particularly late macular degeneration, while lead adversely affected early and late macular degeneration.[32]

Mercury has also been shown to increase inflammation and autoimmunity. There have been multiple pathways found in which autoimmunity and immune dysfunction is induced due to mercury heavy metal exposure.[33]

There is also a correlation between heavy metal exposure and metabolic health by altering the gut microbiome and the metabolites produced by it. The exposure to arsenic and cadmium is common and can cause metabolic health problems, including type 2 diabetes. Evidence suggests that type 2 diabetes could be occurring because the gut microbiome is altered along with the metabolites that it is producing. Arsenic and cadmium exposure cause significant changes to the gut microbiome. They are affecting bile acids, amino acids, and other elements that are associated with our metabolic health.

Scientists have discussed that the gut microbiota that normally live in the gastrointestinal tract are involved in the detoxification of arsenic, lead, mercury, and chemical entities. Given that heavy metals disrupt the gut microbiota through their toxic effect is very significant, this mechanism alone can cause many different adverse health effects.[34]

Chronic fatigue is associated with high heavy metal burden. A case study showed improved chronic fatigue symptoms after removal of mercury in a patient with increased mercury concentration. At the time, a toxic mineral assay from a hair sample was done. Hair testing is no longer recommended by leading authorities. However, in this case the individual developed chronic fatigue after ongoing mercury exposure. Symptoms included weakness, headache, poor memory, and concentration difficulty. The mercury concentrations in the body were assessed and then removed, and the patient's symptoms of chronic fatigue were lessened.[35]

A Chinese study evaluated mortality due to long-term, heavy metal pollution. The scientists looked at the heavy metals in environmental samples like water and food crops, as well as the whole blood of 1,152 residents in a specific area. There was a significant increase of mortality, in particular, death rates from cardiovascular disease as compared to areas that didn't have such high-level exposure.

Cadmium and lead were linked to a higher risk of dying from cancer for men and women. The long-term environmental exposure to cadmium and lead is associated not only with an increased risk of cardiovascular disease but with all types of cancer death rates. It did appear that zinc exposure might have provided weak protection against dying from cardiovascular disease.[36]

Quite a few heavy metals, such as arsenic, cadmium, chromium, lead, and nickel, have been linked to development of cancers. There are studies which have shown that workers who have been environmentally exposed to high levels of these heavy metals have a disruption in the tumor suppressor genes. Damage to the repair process in the cells and enzymatic activities are affected. The oxidative stress via the free oxygen radical species can damage DNA, and when gene mutations and DNA damage happen, cancers occur.

Arsenic is affecting cancer risk by leading to DNA damage, cell death, and cell damage through oxidative stress.

Multiple cancers have been associated with this mechanism, including prostate cancer, skin cancers, leukemia, and liver cancer.[37]

Heavy metal burden has also been linked to Alzheimer's disease and neuroinflammation.

In Alzheimer's dementia, heavy metal burden affects accumulation of beta-amyloid and tau protein deposition and neurodegeneration. Therefore, metal chelation is a promising strategy for the management of Alzheimer's.[38]

Chelation of heavy metals does occur naturally in the body. There are three phases of detoxification of organic compounds. Phase 1 is oxidative activation via the cytochrome P450 enzymes. This step is inhibited by multiple heavy metals and organic toxins, like glyphosate.

Phase 2 conjugation occurs through multiple enzymes, like the glutathione S-transferases and others. Heavy metals inhibit this enzyme step of detoxification, which in turn prohibits the neutralization of reactive oxygen species which damage the cells.

Phase 3 is the unidirectional excretion of the toxin via the ATP dependent flux pumps. These pumps are energy dependent and require B vitamins, magnesium, manganese, iron, and CoQ10. The optimal detoxification requires a coordinated regulation of genes and the encoding for enzymes in all three phases.

Inflammation of the intestine's leaky gut syndrome or the liver impairs the detoxification process. It is important to keep the bowels moving to prevent the inhibition of detoxification processes and to minimize the reabsorption through the gut and liver of toxic heavy metals.

Glutathione is an intracellular antioxidant that is involved in the different phases of detoxification. Glutathione and the enzymes correlated with it are working to protect the cells, but at some point these heavy metals are binding to different pathways intracellularly and deactivating the ability of the cells to protect themselves against free-radical oxygen species.

The antioxidant properties that are protecting the cells become no longer available, and continuous cell damage occurs and leads to more rapid aging, disease development, endocrine disruption, and many other pathways in which these heavy metals cause illness.

Environmental health and heavy metal detoxification are important aspects that we need to consider for our longevity. If we have accumulated heavy metals in our body and there is disruption of health cell function, we must intervene in that mechanism in order to age-reverse a patient or help them heal from their disease.

This information sheds new light on what we should be aware of in our environment and how we could remove ourselves from damaging exposure, for example, by getting amalgams removed, decreasing the intake of fish with high mercury content, and decreasing the intake of high arsenic foods and other substances that can negatively affect us.

People are impacted in different ways, depending on their genetics, their propensity, their susceptibility, and/or their bioaccumulation, and each person individually is different in what they can tolerate.

Heavy metals chelation is important from a Light Medicine perspective, as heavy metals directly create mitochondrial dysfunction and interruptions in the electron transport chain, hence lowering the electrical capacity of the cell for repair.[39] If we want to increase the light in the body electric, we need to remove what is prohibiting the electrical system to function adequately. In my view and practice, all antiaging interventions are combined with detoxification measures like heavy metal chelation to allow improved ability for cellular regeneration. I use chelation therapy for a wide variety of medical diseases when high body burden of metals has been detected. In my practice, I have seen good, clinical outcomes in atherosclerosis reversal, renal dysfunction, autoimmune diseases with objective improvements in laboratory markers, and clinical improvement in symptoms.

CHAPTER 17
REVERSING ATHEROSCLEROSIS

Atherosclerosis is the deposition of fat, cholesterol, and calcium into the artery wall. The disease is progressive and leads to occlusion of the artery and decreased blood flow to organ tissues. This narrowing of the arteries can involve every artery in the body. If the plaque in the artery breaks off, it can cause an infarct downstream, triggering heart attacks and strokes. The general view is that high cholesterol causes this process and that lowering cholesterol can help prevent vascular disease. This idea has led to the widespread promotion of low or nonfat diets and cholesterol lowering pharmaceutical drugs for healthy individuals to presumably lower their risk of developing peripheral artery disease.

Some of the information that is presented here is different than what is presented in the mainstream—the idea that high cholesterol is the cause for atherosclerosis. There are many scientists who discuss a different view and approach which, in general, has been rejected and censored by the mainstream. However, if we want to have objective science, we must allow all hypotheses and evaluate all with an open mind. Atherosclerosis reversal goes again hand in hand with our comprehensive Light Medicine approach as the delivery of nutrients to every organ, and their proper perfusion is imperative for youthful function and regeneration.

Linus Pauling won the Nobel Prize in chemistry in 1954 for his research into the nature and application of chemical bonds to elucidate the structure of complex substances. He won the Nobel Peace Prize in 1963.

Pauling made significant contributions to medical science with what is now called orthomolecular medicine in discussing how nutrients and vitamins can be utilized in high doses as medicine. He was a pioneer in theories of atherosclerosis reversal and the role of vitamin C.

Thomas Levy, M.D., a board-certified cardiologist and author, has written groundbreaking books on the cause of atherosclerosis as vascular scurvy, which is extreme vitamin C deficiency. In his meticulous research on the topic as described in his book, *Stop America's #1 Killer! Proof that the Origin of ALL Coronary Heart Disease is a Clearly Reversible Arterial Scurvy,* he quoted excellent studies illustrating this cause that we will discuss below. Several studies have shown that the initial steps of atherosclerosis are related to depleted levels of the antioxidant system, such as glutathione deficiency.

These initial steps are also related to vitamin C deficiency as this molecule is needed for proper collagen matrix building. In my practice, I check everyone's urine vitamin C level. Low levels are very common, and adequate supplementation results in a wide variety of clinical improvements, from overall increased well-being to decreased pain and increased energy.

Heavy metal body burden that is increased through lead, cadmium, and arsenic have interactive effects and are depleting the antioxidants in the vascular wall. Mechanical turbulence is a risk factor for atherosclerosis in arteries like carotids, the coronary arteries, and causes mechanical stress on the vessel wall. Nitric oxide deficiency has been shown to be a factor in the progression of atherosclerosis. The overall synthesis of nitric oxide gets downregulated by several causes, including high heavy metal burdens in the body after age 40. Very high cholesterol—if the above conditions are first present—can contribute to atherosclerosis. Heavy metals inhibit nitric oxide production.

Dr. Walter Hartenbach was a university professor in Munich who described the fairy tale of bad cholesterol. He examined thousands of artery plaques and found that cholesterol is not the initial cause for atherosclerosis. He found pathological changes in artery tissues that are seen before the fatty streaks in the artery walls occur, something that happens before the cholesterol gets deposited into the vessel wall. The cholesterol itself is not the causing mechanism.[1]

In the United States, about 40 million people take statin drugs to lower cholesterol. Dr. Harumi Okuyama, of Nagoya City University in Japan, has written extensively about concerns that statins stimulate atherosclerosis and heart failure and the underlying mechanism. He described statins as mitochondrial toxins that impair mitochondrial function. Mitochondria are the powerhouse of the cell, and in the heart muscle there are about 5,000 mitochondria per cell. When we have a substance like a statin that inhibits mitochondrial functioning, it can then impair muscle function in the heart and blood vessels. Statin drugs deplete CoQ10 and another substance called Heme-A, and those are involved in ATP production. ATP is the energy currency of the cell. Without these coenzymes, the production of the ATP—which makes the energy in the heart muscle cells—is impaired, and this affects the functioning of the cells. Statins also inhibit the manufacturing of vitamin K2, which is a cofactor for matrix Gla-protein activation, a mechanism that protects the arteries from calcification.[2]

Statins inhibit the production of proteins that contain selenium, like glutathione peroxidase, which lowers oxidative stress. The impairment of these enzymes may increase the risk of congestive heart failure.

Oxidative stress from the accumulation of free radicals is a process by which our cells are aging. Dr. Okuyama raised many concerns regarding the widespread use of statins. Some practitioners use red yeast rice as an alternative in patients who get severe muscle aches with statins, but red yeast rice is lovastatin—monacolin K found in red yeast rice, which is exactly identical to lovastatin—and is thereby also a mitochondrial toxin.[3]

Dr. Levy refers to multiple studies in his book showing that cholesterol only adds to the development of atherosclerosis after this process has been initiated by degenerative changes in the artery wall because of vitamin C deficiency. The extensive evidence that Dr. Levy's research has provided has made vitamin C one of the most important cornerstones of nutritional optimization in chronic disease reversal. It truly is a panacea, as Dr. Levy has discussed. Vitamin C is part of activating the carnitine transporter that allows fat molecules to be transported out of a cell. This means vitamin C supplementation is essential to weight loss as well. Vitamin C neutralizes toxins, including heavy metals, as it acts as a chelator. When you don't have the vitamin C, these toxins cause an increase in cholesterol, because cholesterol is a molecule that neutralizes toxins.[4]

In 1978, studies had found that vitamin C deficiency alone would result in accelerated atherosclerosis. Cholesterol and triglycerides were found to be deposited into the aorta blood vessel wall, without even having cholesterol in the diet.[5]

Arteries have a basement membrane that is gel-like, made from a collagen matrix called the glycocalyx. Vitamin C is involved in keeping that gel in the proper state, but when vitamin C is deficient, the collagen in that gel cannot bind and it becomes watery and thereby vulnerable. When vitamin C in the arterial wall was depleted in areas of high mechanical stress, injury in the blood vessel wall was caused. Vitamin C deficiency is associated with wound healing difficulties.

Dr. Levy explains that when a blood vessel is scarred or injured, it requires even more vitamin C to repair itself and to maintain its integrity. Now the deposition of the plaque, which is made of cholesterol, is a mechanism to compensate for that weak wall because of vitamin C deficiency. There is a scarring, a thickening of the artery wall, and then there's leakage of blood into that plaque that then leads to further plaque progression and growth.

High blood pressure can initiate and promote this continued plaque buildup because it is overtaxing the collagen-depleted blood vessels, causing more injury. When there is injury upon injury, atherosclerosis progresses.

As we look at vitamin C from a Light Medicine perspective, we understand that the electron donor status of the molecule can regenerate the depleted ATP production of macrophages that are deposited as inflammatory debris in the vascular wall. The cause for its profound ability is its high electrical potential, therefore high light value.

Vitamin C deficiency has been linked to high blood pressure. It's been shown that a combined antioxidant supplementation, which included vitamin C, reduced high blood pressure. A placebo-controlled, double-blind study in 1996 showed that vitamin C was effective as a single therapy—no other blood pressure pills were included—in lowering the blood pressure of patients who had high blood pressure. A meta-analysis of 29 trials evaluating the effects of vitamin C on blood pressure confirmed this in 2012.[6] The lowering of blood pressure was correlated to blood plasma levels of vitamin C.[7]

Humans have a genetic defect due to mutations in the L-gulono-γ-lactone oxidase (GLO) gene which codes for the enzyme responsible for catalyzing the last step of vitamin C biosynthesis. Humans, guinea pigs, and some bat and bird species have lost the ability to make this important antioxidant that is crucial for collagen synthesis.[8]

We cannot make ascorbic acid out of glucose in our liver and therefore we must supplement it every day. Most diets are unable to supply the amount of vitamins and nutrients needed in larger quantities, and thus we are unable to get high enough doses of vitamin C in our diet and must supplement accordingly. People with chronic underlying conditions and smokers may need higher recommended doses. The absorption of vitamin C taken by mouth is between 20% and 40%. This rate is improved with liposomal vitamin C, and optimal with intravenous vitamin C. Because vitamin C is water soluble, it needs to be taken in every day.[9]

Dr. Levy describes an atherosclerosis study showing that cholesterol was taken up into the artery wall when the cholesterol was extremely high—over 250 total cholesterol—but when the cholesterol levels were lowered, the cholesterol was reabsorbed into the bloodstream. This indicates, along with other scientific evidence, that atherosclerosis is reversible.[10]

Vitamin C slows down the penetration of cholesterol that gets deposited into the blood vessel wall, while increasing the release of the cholesterol already in the blood vessel wall. Vitamin C is effective in slowing down the progression of atherosclerosis, as well as promoting the reversal of the disease. Lifestyle changes—exercise, nutrition, stress reduction—all these interventions are decreasing inflammation as preventative strategies and can contribute to the reversal of atherosclerosis.

A meta-analysis of thirteen randomized, controlled trials showed that vitamin C supplementation lowers serum low-density lipoprotein cholesterol and triglycerides. This was only an average dose of 500 mg vitamin C daily.[11] It is very important to understand that the beneficial effects are dose dependent, which is why Linus Pauling advocated much higher dosages in the range of 8000 mg to 10,000 mg daily. Understanding electrical properties, the higher the dose in the blood, the greater the electron donor capacity, hence ability for regeneration.

There are studies indicating that cholesterol serves as a neutralizer and a deactivator of toxic substances. They show that elevated cholesterol seems to be a marker of toxic exposure. For example, total heavy metal burden, through increased pesticide exposure, can increase cholesterol levels. Once the toxic exposure is eliminated—i.e., mercury amalgams get safely removed, root canals reversed, heavy metals chelated—the cholesterol levels can drop. Vitamin C can lower cholesterol because vitamin C is a toxin neutralizer, so you don't need to make as much cholesterol to help the body.

Inflammation is a major cause for progression of atherosclerosis. If the plaque destabilizes and a piece of that plaque breaks off, it causes an infarction downstream resulting in concerns, like heart attack. It has been shown that the plaques that break off and cause these complications have a large amount of inflammatory cells. Stable plaques which don't break off have lesser complications, less heart attacks, and less inflammation. Inflammation is a protecting reaction of the body by working to lessen the injury to the artery wall.

White blood cells are cells of the immune system and they need vitamin C to function. White blood cells have between 25 to 80 times higher levels of vitamin C than in the surrounding blood plasma. The artery walls are depleted in vitamin C, so it appears that the white blood cells are going to the artery wall to deposit their vitamin C because the artery wall is weakened, and it is attempting to keep the local levels of vitamin C from getting even lower.[12]

In 2001, a study found that patients with severe atherosclerosis in the legs had chronic inflammation and low vitamin C levels in the blood. Low vitamin C levels were directly related to the presence of inflammation and the severity of vascular disease. Vitamin C downregulates inflammation and thereby helps those with atherosclerosis.[13]

Toxins in our body can use up the vitamin C in the blood. As vitamin C neutralizes heavy metals—when there are high body burdens of heavy metals—vitamin C stores are used up faster. It has been shown that sicker patients require much higher levels of vitamin C because they use more.

At time of autopsy, when patients were evaluated in regard to their blood, microbial infections were found in the blood vessel walls, causing local inflammation. Patients with periodontitis, inflammation of gums, and root canals have been shown to have chronic infections in the jawbones. These patients have higher levels of inflammation in the body. These infections cause this chronic inflammation, which then causes a more accelerated atherosclerosis and need for higher doses of vitamin C. Heavy metals have been shown to be associated with atherosclerosis, and the mechanism is that heavy metals increase oxidative stress. They utilize the antioxidant system in the cell.

Heavy metals increase inflammation, interfere with calcium signaling, and cause endothelial cell dysfunction, which is the small lining of the blood vessel wall. Heavy metals increase blood pressure, induce kidney problems, and they change epigenetics.[14]

As previously discussed, it has been shown that low-level lead is a silent killer in the United States. Over several decades, as noted in 2006, death from all causes had increased by 25%. But for heart disease, cardiovascular mortality had increased by 55%, heart attack death rates by 89%, and stroke death rates by 151%. In the U.S., 38% of the adult population was at risk because of the levels of lead exposure.[15]

There are many studies regarding chelation therapy. Denmark pursued an interesting project in 1992. In providing socialized medicine, the government was spending a lot of money on coronary artery bypass grafts, so they tried chelation. On the waiting list were sixty-five people needing a bypass, yet only seven required the procedure after chelation therapy. Twenty-seven individuals were scheduled for amputation because they had severe artery disease in the legs, and only three needed the surgery. This study was conducted over six years and revealed the chelation treatment had saved the Danish government over $3 million dollars.[16]

In 1993, a meta-analysis was done on EDTA chelation for cardiovascular disease with 22,000 patients. Chelation therapy was helpful with cardiovascular disease in 88% of the patients who showed improvement through objective testing.[17]

The TACT trial, published in the *Journal of the American Medical Association*, was discussed in an earlier chapter. The trial involved chelation therapy for patients who had experienced prior heart attacks, and it showed that EDTA reduced the events—cardiovascular events—by 18%. When just oral vitamins were given, the reduction was 11%. When chelation was combined with vitamins, the reduction in events was 26%. The reduction in cardiovascular events was 41%, with 43% less mortality. Heart attacks were reduced by 51%.[18]

The relationship between vitamin K and peripheral artery disease has also been investigated in a very large study. In 36,629 patients, high-dose vitamin K was associated with a reduction of risk of peripheral artery disease, particularly in high blood pressure patients.[19]

Glutathione is part of the antioxidant system of detoxification. One study showed that supplementation with glutathione improved the dysfunction of the endothelial cell lining and did so by increasing the body's production of nitric oxide. Researchers were investigating patients who had a gene defect in the enzyme glutathione peroxidase that is involved in the production of glutathione. The patients with this defect had a significant thickening of the inner lining of the artery, resulting in more atherosclerosis in the carotid artery and in development of peripheral vascular disease.[20] An imbalance of this antioxidant, and others mentioned, is very much part of the process of developing atherosclerosis.[21]

When taking glutathione as a supplement, the liposomal form gets absorbed well, and at my clinic we give it intravenously after chelation or other vitamin infusions.

Dr. Broda Barnes, in 1976, wrote a book called *Solved: The Riddle of Heart Attacks*. In the book he compares the results from the Framingham studies of 5,000 patients between thirty-two and sixty years old—who had a rate of heart disease of about 150 per 1,000 patients over twenty years—with his cohort of 2,000 patients that he treated with desiccated thyroid hormone, which is equivalent today to Armour or Nature-Throid. The period was again over twenty years, yet the heart rate disease in Barnes' patients was only 2 per 1,000.[22]

One of the potential mechanisms for this outcome is that desiccated thyroid hormone contains all four thyroid hormones. We produce T4, and out of that we make the active form of T3. There is also T2, which appears to regulate the density of mitochondria in cells.

The idea is that when we are increasing mitochondrial density and are able to produce higher energy, we can make the cells function better, and that could be one way of being able to prevent heart disease and any other chronic disease, for that matter.

Evaluating thyroid hormone status in everyone is important and, where indicated and where needed, supplementing—with bioidentical hormones—desiccated thyroid. The ratio of T3 to reverse T3 should be greater than 20 to ensure that active hormones are being produced in the body and adequately transported into and used by the cells.

In summary, there is evidence that natural treatments, like high-dose vitamin C and detoxification with chelation therapy, as well as supplementation with other substances, such as liposomal glutathione and nitric oxide, can support atherosclerosis reversal and improve cardiovascular health. In my own practice at AM Medical, I have observed many patients demonstrate significant clinical improvements in well-being and functionality after following this approach. Objective markers, such as the lowering of cholesterol, improvement of arterial stiffness as measured by autonomic nervous system function testing, improved blood pressure, and other cardiovascular markers have all been observed in my treated patients.

CHAPTER 18
HYPERBARIC OXYGEN THERAPY

Oxygen is a versatile element essential for life. Therefore, could oxygen therapy in fact increase the light in your cells and thereby facilitate cellular repair? Studies suggest that it can. This occurs not just through the chemical but also oxygen's electrical properties. The chemical versatility of this fundamental component of life is attributed to two unpaired electrons.

The existence of unpaired electrons in a stable molecule is rare and unusual in nature and causes high chemical reactivity. The chemical reactions leading to this are either oxidation or reduction. Oxidation is a loss of electrons, while reduction is a gain of electrons. These reactions always occur in pairs. Highly reactive molecules can oxidize molecules that were previously stable and can lead to unstable molecules, such as free radicals, which in excess, in turn, can lead to accelerated aging.

A certain amount of oxidative function is necessary for proper health. For example, oxidative processes are used by the immune system to kill microorganisms. Appropriate tissue oxygenation is essential for healthy cellular functioning and is directly related to the energy production in cells. Mitochondrial energy production with high oxygen levels creates higher outputs of ATP than energy production in low oxygen states.

Hyperbaric oxygen therapy (HBOT) occurs in a hyperbaric pressurized chamber where the patient is breathing pure oxygen. The air pressure is increased about three times higher than normal air pressure. The amount of oxygen that's carried in the blood is increased, and that promotes healing and fights infections. For best results, the treatment needs to be repeatedly ongoing for a period of time.

There are many FDA-approved indications for HBOT, which include wound healing, burns, infections, and nonhealing wounds like diabetic foot ulcers, carbon monoxide poisoning, and severe anemia. HBOT has also been used for athletic performance enhancement. Many athletes use the oxygen therapy in the hyperbaric chamber to help their recovery times, their healing, and their overall mental acuity. It helps with cognitive performance enhancement. It has antiaging effects. It's been used in AIDS and HIV, in allergies, in dementia, arthritis, asthma, autism, and things like traumatic brain injury. It's been used as an adjunct in cancer therapy, for cerebral palsy, chronic fatigue syndrome, liver cirrhosis, depression, fibromyalgia, ulcers, heart disease, hepatitis, migraines, multiple sclerosis, Parkinson's disease, spinal cord injury, sports injuries, and strokes.[1]

The effects of HBOT on the brain has been researched. In strokes, there has been a decrease in the infarct size and improved recovery. Some studies show that hyperbaric oxygen promotes the differentiation of the stem cells into neurons. In traumatic brain injury, it has been used with beneficial effects. In autistic children, there are results of improved overall functioning, better social interaction, better eye contact, and improved sensory and cognitive awareness.[2]

In January of 2019, researchers found the first PET scan-documented case of improvement in the brain's metabolism in Alzheimer's disease with HBOT. A 58-year-old woman had five years of cognitive decline and then started to progress clinically very quickly. A SPECT tomography suggested Alzheimer's disease. She underwent forty HBOT sessions five days a week over sixty-six days, with a total treatment time of fifty minutes. After twenty-one treatments, the patient had increased energy and improved level of activity, better mood, improved ability to perform daily activities of living, and improvement in ability to do crossword puzzles. After forty treatments, she had increased memory and concentration, sleep, conversation, appetite, ability to use the computer, more good days than bad days, resolved anxiety, and decreased disorientation and frustration. There were some other neurological tests, like tremor and tandem gait and motor speed that were also improved. A repeat imaging study showed up to 38% improvement in brain metabolism.[3]

Higher oxygen levels improve the immune system and the ability of white blood cells to kill bacteria. Fracture recovery of bones is accelerated, wound healing is enhanced, and circulating stem cell numbers are increased. Inflammation is decreased with HBOT treatment. Angiogenesis is improved. Blood flow is improved. There is increased hormone production. Energy production is increased. Environmental toxin neutralization is enhanced with HBOT treatment and allergic symptoms improved. Pain reduction is often reported as well as relaxation of fatigued muscles with benefit for athletes.

How does voltage, oxygen, and pH work together? How, by increasing cellular voltage, is oxygen therapy a potential great adjunct in Light Medicine?

A normal cell operates at a pH, which is a marker for acidity and neutrality. The lower the pH, the more acidic the body is—the higher the pH, the more alkaline the body is—with normal being at around 7.35 up to 7.4. This is equivalent to about -20 millivolts. In order to maintain health, we want to have high oxygen tissue saturation, a pH in the alkaline range, and high cellular voltage. When pH drops, voltage drops and oxygen is lower. The body becomes acidic and hypoxic, and pathogens like bacteria and fungi and viruses can start proliferating in the body and cause diseases.

It is very important to maintain a neutral to alkaline environment, as well as to maintain oxygenation in the tissues. Acidity in the body causes accelerated aging. It is associated with all chronic diseases. There is increased free radical damage, aching muscles due to increased lactic acid in the muscles, and reduced stress resistance. When people are achy and tired, they are adversely emotionally affected. In the brain, low cellular voltage may cause brain fog, loss of motivation, as well as anxiety and depression.

In my office I use the WAVI brain EEG technology as a screening tool for brain performance that can quantify these effects objectively.

Mitochondria, the powerhouse of the cell, make ATP. ATP is our currency of energy. When we have oxygen for this cycle, we can make 38 ATPs for every fatty acid. If there is not enough oxygen, the energy production may take the anaerobic pathway and only produce two ATPs. Dr. Jerry Tennant, who has written several books regarding the subject of healing with voltage, correlates the energy production to your vehicle. Your body is like your car; instead of getting thirty-eight miles a gallon, you're only getting two miles a gallon.[4]

It is important for metabolism and for overall health, as well as issues like weight loss, to be on the oxidative side of this biochemical process. Addressing nutrient deficiencies is also very important, because without appropriate nutrients, we are not efficiently metabolizing our foods.

HBOT has been shown to have antiaging effects. The global gene expression in the human endothelial cells was analyzed in exposure to hyperbaric oxygen. The research revealed an upregulation of antioxidant, cytoprotective, and immediate early genes. This increase coincided with an increased resistance to oxidative stress.

The data indicates that HBOT can induce protection against oxidative insults in endothelial cells and may provide an easily administered treatment to help promote healthy aging.[5] HBOT increases circulating stem cells, and this is nitric oxide dependent. The population of CD34(+) stem cells in the peripheral circulation of humans doubled in response to a single exposure to 2.0 atmospheres absolute (ATA) O_2 for two hours. Over a course of twenty treatments, circulating stem cells increased eightfold and bone marrow nitric oxide concentration also increased.

Researchers concluded that HBOT mobilizes stem/ progenitor cells by stimulating nitric oxide synthesis.[6]

A study of HBOT in chronic fatigue syndrome (CFS) showed improvement in symptoms. Patients included in the study were diagnosed with CFS and received fifteen HBOT treatment sessions over a period of three consecutive weeks for five days per week. The outcome measures—Visual Analog Fatigue Scale, Fatigue Severity Scale, and Fatigue Quality of Life Score—were assessed before the treatment and after completion of the fifteen sessions. HBOT was well tolerated, with no complications. After treatment, patients' scores were found to have improved with respect to all scoring systems.[7]

The effects of HBOT on the immune system were evaluated in mice models for the autoimmune disease lupus. HBOT resulted in increased survival, decreased proteinuria, alterations in lymphocyte-subset redistribution, reduced anti-dsDNA antibody titers, and amelioration of immune-complex deposition, therefore attenuating disease severity.[8]

Three patients with rheumatoid arthritis, who were treated with hyperbaric oxygen for an unrelated diagnosis, improved with HBOT. Sleeping patterns improved and pain decreased. Patients were able to increase their activity level, and there was a decreased need for standard rheumatologic medications. This is an interesting alternative because rheumatoid arthritis is treated with significant immune suppressants that can have substantial side effects.[9]

In cancer therapy, treatment with hyperbaric oxygen is an important aspect because it has been proven that a common feature of all tumors is acidity caused by low oxygen. Tumor cells themselves have a way of maintaining their pH inside the cells but making all of the surrounding tissues acidic, which in turn is a low oxygen environment. This acidification of surrounding tissues breaks down base membranes, hence metastatic spread is accelerated.

HBOT can be used as an adjunct therapy to many treatment approaches for a wide variety of diseases as well as preventatively. The treatment is important in our Light Medicine model, as it has direct effects by increasing cellular voltage, thereby increasing the light within the organism. Most importantly, tissue oxygenation with HBOT, when safely administered, has no side effects.

CHAPTER 19
PEPTIDES

Peptide therapy is an integral part of a regenerative Light Medicine approach. Once a cell is nutritionally optimized, it can be given informational peptides that allow regeneration and rejuvenation of tissues to occur. Age reversal, optimized organ function, and healthy longevity can be achieved in using peptides. As we previously discussed, peptides also act as electron donors and therefore light givers. When used appropriately, they have no significant side effects, as these are substances that the body makes and is familiar with.

Peptides are short chain amino acids found in all living organisms, in every cell and tissue, that regulate biological activities. Thousands of peptides occur naturally in humans and animals. The function of a peptide depends on the amino acid sequence and shape. Peptides often act as hormones and biological messengers, like insulin and growth hormone. Peptides bind to specific cell receptors. They can be produced naturally in the body or synthetically in a laboratory and are classified according to how many amino acids are contained in them and how they are produced. Out of approximately 7,000 known peptides, there are 60 peptides that are FDA-approved for clinical use.

Peptides have added tremendously to my practice. Below are a few commonly used peptides and their clinical applications.

Epitalon is a synthetic pineal gland peptide derived from epithalamin which activates the telomerase enzyme and elongates telomeres, thereby having antiaging effects.[1] It increases secretion of melatonin. Epithalamin can be more beneficial than melatonin because the former not only produces direct antioxidant effects but is also able to stimulate the expression of the enzyme superoxide dismutase (SOD), which may improve health and lengthen life span. The pineal gland peptides enhance the antioxidant defense system, which can contribute to their geroprotective properties.[2] In clinical application, epitalon is a fabulous antiaging peptide.

Epitalon was studied on the function of pancreatic islets and regulation of blood glucose level in female rhesus monkeys of various ages. Epitalon corrected the age-related decrease in glucose tolerance and restored the dynamics of insulin level in response to glucose load.[3] In my office I have witnessed the insulin sensitizing effects of epitalon and have had excellent results in treating and successfully reversing type 2 diabetes.

Epitalon reduces lipid oxidation and radical oxygen species and has been shown in animal models to extend life span and decrease mortality by 52%.[4,5]

A study conducted on 266 people over age 60 demonstrated that treatment with epithalamin, produced a 1.6–1.8-fold reduction in mortality during the following 6 years. When combined with thymulin, a 2.5-fold reduction in mortality was observed, and a 4.1-fold reduction in mortality when combined with thymulin and administered on a yearly basis.[6,7,8] A study on patients with coronary artery disease over twelve years found improved physical endurance, circadian rhythm, and carbohydrate and lipid metabolism. Epithalamin was given twice a year. There was a 50% lower rate of cardiovascular mortality, a 50% lower rate of heart failure and serious respiratory disease, and a 28% lower rate of overall mortality.[9]

In patients with retinitis pigmentosa, epitalon produced a positive clinical effect in 90% of cases in the treated group.[10] Other beneficial effects often observed in my clinical practice are the overall improvement in well-being. Hypertension improves, and as discussed in the chapter to follow about the Mercy Blu Room program, beneficial clinical effects have been documented in my heart failure patients.

GHK Copper is a peptide used for collagen synthesis improvement for skin disorders. It helps with wrinkles and skin restoration. This peptide also has been shown to have significant beneficial effects to restore around 4,000 genes—which is 30% of the human genome—back to health.[11]

GHK Copper has beneficial effects for people with severe lung injuries or COPD. In my practice, I have observed clinical improvement in patients with severe emphysema—noting a decrease in shortness of breath and an increase in functional ability.

GHK suppressed RNA production in 70% of 54 human genes overexpressed in patients with an aggressive metastatic form of colon cancer. It possesses antioxidant, anti-inflammatory, anti-pain, and antianxiety effects.[12] GHK Copper is available as a subcutaneous injection for systemic effects, but it is also used as a peptide for cosmetic skin products and can be applied as a foam to regrow hair. In my practice, I use GHK Copper in combination with epitalon and thymosin alpha 1 for antiaging purposes as well as in adjunctive cancer treatment.

Mitochondrial-derived peptides (MDP) are encoded by functional, short open reading frames in the mtDNA. These include humanin, with strong cytoprotective actions, and MOTS-c, which regulates insulin sensitivity and metabolic homeostasis. MOTS-c might also be involved in the aging process. High levels of MOTS-c peptide have been associated with the gene in a Japanese population that has the extreme longevity of 125 years and exceptionally good health.

MOTS-c is a promising antiaging peptide.[13] In my view, peptides that enhance energy production in mitochondria are excellent targets for antiaging and longevity purposes and should be rigorously pursued in research and application for this purpose.

There are several neurocognitive peptides that are useful for patients with dementia, Alzheimer's disease, Parkinson's disease, brain trauma, strokes, neuroinflammation, anxiety, depression, and more.

Cerebrolysin has had success in Alzheimer's and vascular dementia. It acts both as a neurotropic as well as has effects on delaying progression of the disease. It has had broad applications particularly in Europe for this purpose.[14]

Dihexa has been shown to be about seven times more powerful than brain-derived nerve growth factor (BDNF), which indicates it would take 10 million times as much BDNF to get as much new synapse formation as Dihexa. It causes the brain to grow new dendrites and synapses and has applications in a wide spectrum of cognitive diseases like Alzheimer's dementia and Parkinsons, as well as for cognitive performance enhancement.[15] As a former geriatrician, I have witnessed patients with cognitive decline for many years. Clinical results with Dihexa, particularly when used in early-to-moderate cognitive impairment, as well as Parkinsons, have been excellent.

In order to cognitively enhance the patient, regardless of the specific pathology of their condition, it is important to balance neurotransmitters. Chronic emotional states, like anxiety, depression, and even attention deficit, can be addressed successfully in clinical practice with peptides.

Selank is a synthetic peptide derived by combining the sequence of tuftsin with another sequence to improve its stability. Selank has profound antianxiety properties and can be used to treat anxiety and depression. It also acts as a neurotrophic and enhances learning and memory. It has been used in Alzheimer's and Parkinson's diseases, but it can also be used for cognitive performance enhancement. In clinical practice, the effects are very rapid. Selank can be given as a subcutaneous injection or nasal spray. In a study with sixty-two patients with generalized anxiety disorder (GAD) and neurasthenia, the effect of selank was compared to that of medazepam. Neurasthenia means an abnormal lack of energy or physical weakness. The anxiolytic effects of both drugs were similar, but selank had also antiasthenic and psychostimulant effects. Selank prevented degradation of enkephalins through enkephalinase inhibition. Selank may be resetting this enzymatic pathway and helping to protect the body's natural anxiolytic peptides.

Selank has been the most commonly used peptide in my practice, given its ability to block fear, stress, and aggression in the brain. Patients report no side effects but a great relief from their chronic anxiety and increased mental clarity. Given that aging and inflammation are driven in part by chronic mental stress, the use of this peptide has helped significantly in my clinical antiaging approach to patients.[16] Selank is a synthetic analogue of the immunomodulatory peptide tuftsin.

Tuftsin was evaluated in a mouse model for multiple sclerosis (MS), in which an autoimmune encephalomyelitis was induced. During the progression of MS, microglia, the immunocompetent cells of the brain, become activated and accumulate around demyelinated lesions. Tuftsin improved MS symptoms and revealed that the timing of macrophage/ microglial activation is critical for the clinical outcome of MS. The study showed that the disease progression can potentially be manipulated favorably at early stages by altering the timing of microglial activation. This in turn alters the systemic immune response to favor upregulation of T helper cell 2 genes that promote recovery from MS.[17]

Semax is another neurotropic peptide that has been used in Parkinson's disease, dementia, attention deficit disorder, and PTSD. Semax also has antianxiety and antidepression properties while enhancing learning and improving memory. Semax also has shown benefit for optic nerve disorders.[18]

Pharmaceutical antidepressants can be challenging to tolerate due to their side effects like increasing the risk of suicide, headaches, insomnia, stomach upset, nausea, diarrhea, and weight gain. Targeted peptides have an excellent tolerance profile. Honokiol and magnolol are substances that have been extracted from magnolia bark. Honokiol has short-term antianxiety properties without significant side effects. With regular pharmaceutical drugs like anxiolytics, oftentimes there are profound habit-forming effects. Chemicals like Lorazepam,

Xanax, or Valium will resolve anxiety but also affect the relaxation of muscles and induce drowsiness that can lead to impaired reaction time, such as when driving. Honokiol modulates synaptic and extrasynaptic GABA receptors. Both magnolol and honokiol are effective natural anxiolytics, sedatives, and anticonvulsants without significant side effects.[19]

Brain age reversal is possible with a comprehensive program, which includes nutritional optimization, hormonal optimization, detoxification, peptides, and other modalities that can substantially enhance a human being's cognitive ability. In my practice, I also carefully assess cellular voltage and work with mitochondrial optimization accordingly to enhance the electrical brain capacity, or light, of the brain cells. We already have all the alternatives we would need to address the epidemic of mood disorders, cognitive impairment, and dementia. We are able to prevent the onset of these diseases because we are understanding what the mechanisms of development and risk factors are.

Another category of peptides that are agonists of growth-hormone-releasing hormone receptors have been shown to increase the number of endogenous cardiac stem cells after myocardial infarction and enhance the growth of new blood vessels from mesenchymal stem cells.[20,21] Histological evaluation of skin biopsies showed that wounds in mice treated with GHRH were characterized by increased abundance of fibroblasts during the early stages of wound healing and accelerated reformation of the covering epithelium at later stages. These results identify GHRH in promoting skin tissue wound healing and repair.[22] Below we will discuss the role of growth hormone in thymus gland rejuvenation and its potential contribution to longevity.

AOD 9604 is a growth hormone fragment utilized for osteoarthritis.

In a rabbit model of collagenase-induced osteoarthritis, the additive effects of intraarticular recombinant human growth hormone (GH) administration to hyaluronic acid (HA) were evaluated in mature New Zealand white rabbits. The results suggest that co-injection of intraarticular HA and recombinant human GH is more effective than HA injections alone in treatment of osteoarthritis.[23]

Pentadecapeptide BPC 157, composed of 15 amino acids, is a partial sequence of body protection compound (BPC) that is discovered in and isolated from human gastric juice. Experimentally it has been demonstrated to accelerate the healing of many different wounds, including transected rat Achilles tendon. A study was performed to investigate the potential mechanism of BPC 157 to enhance healing of injured tendons. The outgrowth of tendon fibroblasts from tendon explants cultured with or without BPC 157 was examined. Results showed that BPC 157 significantly accelerated the outgrowth of tendon explants.[24]

BPC 157 has been shown to be helpful for vascular diseases. In the treatment of colitis and ischemia reperfusion in rats using BPC 157, the peptide restored blood supply to the ischemic injured area and rapidly activated collateral blood flow. This effect involves the nitric oxide system.[25] BPC 157 has had protective effects against many medication side effects, like the dangerous electrophysiologic heart QTc prolongation induced by psychiatric drugs like haloperidol, olanzapine, quetiapine, and metoclopramide. Furthermore, high-dose celecoxib administration—a nonsteroidal pain medication—led to gastric, liver, and brain lesions and increased liver enzyme serum values. A significant prevention of these side effects was identified with BPC 157.[26,27] In my practice, many patients with osteoarthritis and chronic pain have reported improvement of pain symptoms and decrease in inflammatory symptoms with a combination peptide treatment of AOD 9604 and BPC 157.

In clinical practice, these peptides can also be combined with thymosin beta-4. Angiogenesis is an essential step in the repair process that occurs after injury. In one study, the angiogenic thymic peptide thymosin beta-4 enhanced wound healing in rats. Addition of thymosin beta-4 topically or intraperitoneally increased reepithelialization of wounds by 42% over saline controls at four days and by as much as 61% at seven days post-wounding.[28]

The thymus gland is a central lymphoid organ in development and maintenance of immunological competence. The thymus generates large numbers of functionally mature antigen specific T-cells, which then migrate to the peripheral lymphoid tissue to exert protection against different infective agents. The thymus enlarges until late puberty and then involutes, the lymphocytes and epithelial cells being nearly completely replaced with fat.[29]

This thymus gland involution has been shown to be one of the leading regulators of aging.[30] Age-related regression of the thymus is associated with a decline in naive T-cell output. This is thought to contribute to the reduction in T-cell diversity seen in older individuals and linked with increased susceptibility to infection, autoimmune disease, and cancer. Thymic involution is one of the most dramatic and ubiquitous changes seen in the aging immune system, and this may be a significant component in the cascade of the aging physiology and regulation of the biological clock.[31,32]

Hence, restoration of thymic function is thought to be associated with longevity. This was studied in a clinical trial investigating the use of growth hormone for restoration of tissue in the human thymus gland. A prospective randomized study examining the effects of growth hormone on the immune system of HIV-1-infected adults showed that GH treatment was associated with increased thymic mass and increased the number of circulating T-cells.[33]

In 2019, researchers conducted the Thymus Regeneration, Immunorestoration, and Insulin Mitigation (TRIIM) study, which included 9 healthy white male volunteers between the ages of 51 and 65. For one year, the participants consumed growth hormones alongside two common drugs—dehydroepiandrosterone (DHEA) and metformin. Researchers gathered blood samples and magnetic resonance imaging (MRI) of the thymus gland at baseline and after the trial period. Tests revealed a rejuvenated blood-cell count in all participants and regenerated thymus tissue in 7 patients, indicating immune system revitalization. On average, participants reversed their epigenetic age by 2.5 years. These results indicate the potential of the medication cocktail to rejuvenate the immune system, increase longevity, and decrease biological age.[34]

All four thymus hormones that we make as children are available as peptides. These include thymosin alpha 1, thymosin beta-4, thymalin, and thymogen. These thymus peptides provide the ability to downregulate inflammation in the body. This means we have natural control over a central mechanism of biological aging.

There are many more peptides that have significant, beneficial, clinical effects with a low side-effect profile. They are a revolutionary tool for treatment of broad areas of disease as well as disease prevention, which has the potential to change the entire medical landscape, as it can replace many pharmaceutical drugs that exhibit a high side-effect profile and toxicity. Peptides and their use in cancer patients will be discussed further in a later chapter. Peptides are crucial instruments in longevity and age reversal.

CHAPTER 20
EXOSOMES

Exosomes are a fascinating, future prospective treatment with broad potential clinical applications. I look forward to their future approval by the FDA, given their tremendous clinical possibilities as documented in research. Hopefully this therapy will become widely available. From the perspective of Light Medicine and antiaging, the idea of being able to infuse youthful information into an aging body is fascinating.

What are exosomes? They are small vesicles that are between 40 and 100 nanometers, a thousand times smaller than a regular cell. They are made from the inward budding of membranous vesicles, made from cell walls. All cells produce these exosomes, including stem cells.

Mesenchymal stem cell exosomes discussed here are specifically from perinatal stem cells. Exosomes contain information, which can be called "cargo." The difference between perinatal mesenchymal stem cells and the mesenchymal stem cells of an older person is that the cargo is significantly altered. All stem cells are called pericytes.

Exosomes are information-packed little vehicles that act like a virus in the sense that they are so small they cannot be seen by our immune system and destroyed. This little vesicle can go into a cell and change how the target cell is operating.

Exosomes have several advantages over using stem cells. After an infusion, mesenchymal stem cells (MSC) attach to blood vessels and excrete the exosomes into the bloodstream. These exosomes are loaded with the information of the perinatal stem cells that then travel and modify the healing process in the organism.

Infused stem cells are removed from the body's circulation as fast as within twelve to seventy-two hours by getting lodged in the lungs. This process is called first pass effect.

Mesenchymal stem cells may cause a rejection inflammatory reaction because they are recognized by our body as foreign, as they have a cell wall and DNA. Exosomes are not perceived as foreign, due to their extremely small size and lack of a cell wall. Therefore, they do not provoke a rejection reaction. Mesenchymal stem cells cannot cross the blood-brain barrier. If we want to affect the brain and regenerate patients neurologically and rejuvenate them, we need to utilize something that is smaller than cells. Exosomes are able to pass the blood-brain barrier.

Stem cells, by virtue of their culture process, can be damaged by their culture medium. The process of culture expansion needed before MSC transplantation is associated with cellular senescence, meaning aging of the stem cells. The culture medium is also kept at a high oxygen tension, which creates oxidative stress.[1]

There are over 857 unique gene products in exosomes and greater than 150 kinds of microRNA. There are more than 300 growth factors in perinatal exosomes but only half of those growth factors are in adult stem cells. Exosomes are used by all cells as communication messengers. They are even used by cancer cells in order to promote metastasis. Aging cells use exosomes to modify their environment, because they are infecting their neighborhood with age, and that signaling process called the "senescence secretory phenotype" can occur via exosomes.

Inside of the exosomes of mesenchymal stem cells are many different information molecules like tetraspanins (CD9, CD63, CD81, CD82), adhesion molecules (integrins), receptors (EGFR, MHC II, MHC I, CD86), lipid rafts (cholesterol, flotillin, sphingolipids, ceramide), genetic material (mRNA, miRNA, mitochondrial DNA), cytoskeletal proteins (actin, cofilin, tubulin), vesicular trafficking proteins (annexins, TSG101, alix), heat shock proteins (Hsp70, Hsp90), and enzymes (GAPDH, pyruvate kinase, AchE). These information molecules can create a broad range of effects in any target cell.[2]

Exosomes contain genetic materials, messenger RNA, microRNA, and mitochondrial DNA. MicroRNA (miRNA) can be transferred into a target cell and create rejuvenating effects. We can affect mitochondria because we can give youthful mitochondrial RNA (mtRNA) to rejuvenate aging mitochondria. The messenger RNA (mRNA) can be transcribed by the target cell and manufacture proteins that are youthful, according to the information that is perinatal and healthy. MicroRNA has enormous effect on the host genome transcription. It regulates 60% of our genome.

The miRNA expression in human serum from young (mean age 30 years) and old (mean age 64 years) individuals was studied using next generation sequencing technology and real-time quantitative PCR. Of the miRNAs that were found to be present in serum, three were significantly decreased in twenty older individuals compared to 20 younger individuals: miR-151a-5p, miR-181a-5p, and miR-1248. Consistent with data in humans, these miRNAs are also present at lower levels in the serum of elderly rhesus monkeys. In humans, miR-1248 was found to regulate the expression of messenger RNAs involved in inflammatory pathways, and miR-181a was found to correlate negatively with the proinflammatory cytokines IL-6 and TNFα and to correlate positively with the anti-inflammatory cytokines TGFβ and IL-10. These results suggest that circulating miRNAs may be a biological marker of aging and could also be important for regulating longevity.[3] By infusing perinatal exosomes that have higher levels of these miRNAs, we could manipulate and reverse the aging process.

Exosomes contain heat shock proteins (Hsp), and especially Hsp70 has been associated with longevity in humans. Heat shock proteins 70 (Hsp70) are involved in cellular maintenance and repair mechanisms and are anti-inflammatory proteins.[4]

As discussed, about 60% of our human genome is regulated by microRNA. DNA gets transcribed into RNA, and then RNA is the code to make proteins in ribosomes. MicroRNA is a regulator that determines what is being transcribed and what kind of a protein is being made. It has regulatory action and can either prevent or allow the transcription into a protein. In many different organisms it's been shown that microRNA expression changes with life span. These microRNAs appear to also modulate the life span, and you can predict longevity by the amounts of certain microRNA that are present in the cells. With age in humans, microRNA expression changes, and it's been shown in peripheral blood cells that many microRNA levels are declining and there is a loss of regulation of these microRNAs.[5]

Some of the microRNAs that are in these exosomes have to do with the extraordinary effects of neurological rejuvenation. Increasing evidence is demonstrating that the positive effects of cell-based therapy are mediated by exosomes released from the administered cells and that the microRNA cargo in these exosomes is largely responsible for the therapeutic effects. This evidence raises the possibility that isolated exosomes could be used alone as a neuro-restorative therapy. The potential of exosomes as a therapy for brain disorders is being actively investigated.

Exosomes have effects on endogenous neurovascular remodeling events and have been considered in brain repair and improvement of recovery after stroke, traumatic brain injury, and other diseases in which neuro-restoration could be a viable treatment strategy.[6] The miRNA transfer mediated by exosomes promoted neurological recovery after stroke. MiR-126 levels were reduced in patients' plasma with acute ischemic stroke as well as in rat plasma and brain tissue after ischemia. Compared with a control, systemic administration of exosomes sig-nificantly increased the expression of von Willebrand factor (an endothelia cell marker) and doublecortin (a neuroblast marker) and improved functional recovery in stroke rats.[7]

MicroRNAs are responsible for neuronal regrowth and remyelination. What has previously been thought to be impossible—to regrow a spinal cord, to regenerate brain damage—may no longer be impossible as this field expands.

MicroRNA-133 is specifically associated with increased neuronal plasticity and neurite remodeling, promoting neuron outgrowth, and improving functional recovery. MicroRNA-21 is associated with improved survival of intact neurons. It is neuroprotective in cases of ischemia.

There are more than 150 microRNAs in these exosomes, and they are able to give information to the target cells and create regeneration. It appears that one of the mechanisms by which these exosomes are therapeutically valuable for so many diseases is through microRNA.[8]

Key immune and growth factors are present in these exosomes. For example, bone morphogenetic protein 5 (BMP-5) stimulates bone growth. Growth/differentiation factor-15 (GDF-15) belongs to the transforming growth factor beta superfamily. Osteoprotegerin (OPG) stimulates bone growth and blocks osteoclast precursor formation. G-CSF (granulocyte colony stimulating factor) enhances immune function. SCF (stem cell factor) is shown to be responsible for stem cell and melanocyte growth. Transforming growth factor, beta 3 (TGF-ß3) is the most important anti-inflammatory protein. It converts inflammatory T-cells to anti-inflammatory regulatory T-cells. VEGF (vascular endothelial growth factor) stimulates the growth of blood vessels. Intercellular adhesion molecule-1 (ICAM-1) binds inflammatory ligands on white cells and more.[9]

The therapeutic effects of these exosomes can influence the target cell. Exosomes influence the phenotype. The phenotype is what we are epigenetically expressing. For example, if you are an aging man or woman with many medical problems, then that is your current phenotype expression. Perinatal exosomes are modulating that expression of age and reversing it to youth. The target cells are now under the control of the information of perinatal, exosomal microRNA.

Exosomes contribute to the cell fate decision. Is this cell locked in inflammation and aging, or is it about to die?

By giving exosomal microRNA as a therapy, we could potentially change that regulation and give the message to the cell to rejuvenate itself as well as to improve its overall function and longevity. The exosomes do promote regeneration profoundly. We discussed neuronal regeneration above, but this is applicable to all tissue types in all organs.

There's a profound immune modulation and anti-inflammatory effect due to the specific transmitters and messengers in exosomes. This makes exosomes useful in diseases of autoimmunity, like lupus, Sjogren's syndrome, connective tissue disease, and chronic Lyme disease. Anti-inflammatory properties are important for most disease states like osteoarthritis, rheumatoid arthritis, and chronic bowel diseases.[10] There is an antifibrotic effect. Fibrosis means scarring. For example, chronic kidney disease is progressing through scarring of the kidney tissue, and we are downregulating that aging process of organ scarring.

What tissue effects do the MSC exosomes have?

They have been shown to be protective on the heart. In studies conducted, artificial heart attacks have been given to mice and then exosomes were injected. The exosomes protected the heart muscle from dying and thereby prevented progression to heart failure from muscle damage.[11] Studies of exosomes document cartilage regeneration, repair of lung injury, reduction of kidney fibrosis, and reversal of type 2 diabetes, because the insulin resistance is downregulated and the destruction of the beta cells in the pancreas is reduced.

We can reverse the degeneration of neurons, astrocytes, and the synaptic loss in the hippocampus. The hippocampus is in charge of our memory and also has a large storage of stem cells in our brain. The axonal growth of neurons in the brain can be enhanced and our neurological function improved.

Studies that have looked at the target tissues that exosomes could affect involved the heart, the brain, the liver, the lung, the intestine, the skin, and wound healing. Extraordinary results of regeneration have been shown. The transforming growth factor (TGF) gene is the gene that the salamander uses to regenerate its amputated limbs, and this is one of the proteins that is present in MSC derived exosomes. Limb ischemia, which is caused by peripheral artery disease or atherosclerosis in the legs due to decreased blood flow, has also been improved by exosomes.[12] Skeletal muscle regrowth, spinal cord injury, and immune system dysfunction are all areas of benefit.

The advantages of exosomes as compared to stem cells are that they could be transfused intravenously and intranasally. Exosomes can go through the cribriform plate, which is above the nasal septum, and pass directly into the brain. They are unique in that they do cross the blood-brain barrier. They deliver microRNA and messenger RNA. They can do something called homing. This means these exosomes have been shown to be intelligent. They know exactly where the injury site is and go there to repair.

For example, there were studies where functional MRI scans were done after infusions of stem cells, compared to infusions of exosomes that, as already explained, are information taken from stem cells and concentrated. The stem cells didn't make it to the brain where the stroke was, but the exosomes showed up on the functional MRI scan in the area of the stroke.

The potency of exosomes is related to their youthful functionality. We don't want to infuse exosomes from an old person but instead infuse perinatal, mesenchymal stem cell exosomes which have the highest functional capacity. An interesting study analyzed the effects of young exosomes that were injected in aged mice. Researchers evaluated exosomes from mice that were twelve to eighteen months old, compared to exosomes of three-month-old mice. Several microRNAs were reduced in the old mice in the lungs and liver. When the younger exosomes were injected into the old mice and microRNA levels were measured, the previously low levels in the lungs and liver were much improved. The researchers also wanted to know if the genetic markers of aging were affected. The results were that the exosomes from the young mice could reverse the expression pattern of the aging-associated genes and molecules in the aged mice. The markers of aging were p16, a regulator of the cell cycle and a marker of senescence.

The mTOR (mammalian target of rapamycin) gene is a regulator of aging and longevity, and we want to downregulate it for antiaging purposes. If mTOR is upregulated, then all of the diseases of aging start occurring like arthritis, diabetes, heart disease, and cancer.

In this study, after young exosome infusion, the mTOR expression was downregulated, which goes along with reversing aging and prolonging life span. The reduced expression of insulin growth factor is associated with longevity, and it was decreased in this study. The other marker was the gene expression of telomerase. Telomerase is the enzyme that repairs telomeres—which are the protective capping structures on our DNA. The more telomerase activity, the greater the cellular ability to repair the telomeres. Longer telomeres and increased telomerase activity are associated with prolonged survival and healthy longevity.

All markers described above were affected towards longevity and youthfulness in the old mice. By utilizing exosomes for age reversal and rejuvenation purposes, these pathways are beneficially affected.[13]

One recent study published in August 2019, in *Cell Metabolism*, has found that exosomes contain an enzyme, extracellular nicotinamide phosphoribosyltransferase (eNAMPT), which declines in mice and in humans during the aging process. It promotes the production of NAD, or Nicotinamide, which is a major molecule in the energy metabolism of our cells. The increase of this enzyme counteracts aging and extends healthy life span. This is contained exclusively in the exosomes of mice and humans. Giving youthful exosomes can increase the levels of the eNAMPT enzyme. The aging mice that were infused with young exosomes, that had high eNAMPT levels, had better physical activity and improved cognitive abilities. This is another avenue toward antiaging pathways affected by utilization of exosomes.

The eNAMPT enzymes in the exosomes affected increased biosynthesis of NAD in the pancreas and the retina, leading to better vision and photoreceptor function in the mice. In the hippocampus, there was improvement of cognitive function and better learning. Life span was increased; aging slowed down. The sirtuin1 (SIRT1) gene, which is a gene prolonging longevity through slowing down aging by downregulating inflammation, was beneficially affected. In addition, sleep quality and physical activity improved.[14]

Aging results in a loss of functional capacity in a number of key organs. Exosomes can become a novel, cell-free, therapeutic intervention that can mitigate the undesirable effects of aging by enhancing tissue regeneration and improving the human health span.[15] MSC-derived exosomes are a possibility with extraordinary regenerative and age-reversing properties. Exosomes contain microRNAs, messenger RNAs, and growth factors. They "infect" the donor cells with youthful information and cause messenger RNA translation into new proteins which are healthy and functional. The antiaging and longevity effects lie in the expression of our genes. Exosomes are involved in posttranscriptional regulation, which is the control of gene expression at the RNA level, therefore between the transcription and the translation of the gene. It contributes substantially to gene expression regulation across human tissues.

Exosomes have profound regenerative abilities. This is modulated due to their cargo of microRNA, proteins, and growth factors. The regenerative abilities of exosomes have been studied in multiple organ systems. Factors that affect the secretion of exosomes are low oxygen states, high inflammatory states, stress in the tissues, as well as calcium levels inside the cells. This induces exosomes to be secreted by cells. For therapeutic and regenerative purposes, perinatal exosomes with youthful information, growth factors, and microRNA could be used.

In clinical studies, it's been shown that in cardiovascular disease, exosomes reduce the size of the infarct, enhance tissue repair, and increase new blood vessel growth. In acute kidney injury, tubular epithelial regeneration was achieved. This means in the areas of the kidneys that filter plasma into urine, cell death of those important cells was reduced and there was a substantial reduction in fibrosis, or scarring. This is important because the scarring is what causes chronic kidney disease to occur. Atrophy of the kidney tubules was also reduced. In the liver, there was regeneration of the liver cells, scarring of liver was reduced, and cell death of liver cells was diminished. In the lungs, swelling from injury was reduced and inflammation was downregulated. High blood pressure in the blood vessels of the lung was reduced, and the subsequent changes in the heart muscle, which lead to a thickening of the heart muscle, was improved. Overall, lung vascular remodeling was also improved.

In skin, the regenerative abilities of exosomes produced increase in skin growth, less death in skin cells, and an increase in the proliferation of those skin cells.[16] In stroke, which is one of the leading causes of death and disability, there have been beneficial effects of exosomes through the improvement of blood supply to the neurons, as well as beneficial effects to neuronal stem cells. These beneficial effects of the exosomes occur via the microRNA that's transported to the injury site, as well as the proteins and growth factors that are present in the exosomes.

Exosomes have been shown to mediate the plasticity of the synapses and axons, which are part of the neurons. They are regulating neurogenesis, the growth of new neurons. They are engaged in brain remodeling after strokes and are affecting stroke recovery by increasing communication between different cell groups. Exosomes also communicate with the immune system after stroke.[17]

Specifically in neurodegenerative diseases, there is a great focus on new targets of treatment. In Alzheimer's disease, Parkinson's disease, and stroke, many of these applications have been studied because the neurogenesis, the growth of new neurons, is impacted. The fact that exosomes are able to beneficially impact the growth of new neurons is very promising. In Alzheimer's disease, abnormal proteins are being produced, called beta-amyloid and tau proteins. These abnormal proteins impair the functioning of the neurons and cause symptoms of dementia. Exosomes have been shown to clear beta-amyloid deposition out of the cells, thereby improving the symptoms of Alzheimer's.[18]

Peripheral nerves, as well as neurons, spinal cord injury, and brain injuries in general, have been previously thought to be very difficult or impossible to regenerate. Because exosomes contain the cargo of microRNA that specifically enhances neuronal growth and neurogenesis, there are promising findings that affect peripheral nerves as well. This can be for peripheral nerve injury or clinical neuropathies.[19] In spinal cord injury, there are reports where exosomes are able to assist in motor recovery, meaning the ability after paralysis to regenerate adequate neuronal connections so that motion in the muscles is again possible. There is a decrease in neural inflammation.[20]

Exosomes can regulate systemic blood pressure. Experiments were done on rats that had normal blood pressure, in which their exosomes were isolated and infused into rats that had high blood pressure. The rats that had high blood pressure normalized their blood pressure after getting the exosome infusion from a healthy rat. Subsequently, the test was reversed and the exosomes from the high blood pressure rats were infused into the rats that did not have high blood pressure, and those rats developed high blood pressure. It is the cargo that appears to be mediating high blood pressure. With aging, structural changes of the thoracic aorta occur, which include thickening of the artery wall and decreased abundance of collagen. Those changes were reversed when normal-functioning, young exosomes were given to old mice.[21]

Exosomes can also alleviate diabetes. An infusion of exosomes produced a reduction in blood sugar levels, reversed insulin resistance, and was able to accelerate glucose metabolism. Exosomes restored the phosphorylation (tyrosine site) of the insulin receptor substrate 1 and protein kinase B in type 2 diabetes, promoted expression and membrane translocation of glucose transporter 4 in muscle, and increased storage of glycogen in the liver to maintain glucose homeostasis. Exosomes inhibited β-cell apoptosis to restore the pancreatic insulin-secreting function of type 2 diabetes.[22]

In heart attacks, exosome infusion reduces the scar size and improves heart pump function. This occurs by protecting the cells, by stimulating new vessel growth, by reducing scarring, and by modulating the immune system that is infiltrating the infarcted region. This effect is thought to be brought about by the microRNAs and proteins in the exosomes.[23]

In a study involving peripheral vascular disease, arteries of a limb were injured, whereby the infusion of exosomes improved new blood vessel growth and prevented muscle damage, the same as happened in the heart. This occurred by reregulating different gene pathways, many signaling and hormonal pathways, and by utilizing vascular endothelial growth factor signal, which is the signal to grow new blood vessels. The genes that were associated with that signaling cascade were the transforming growth factor beta 1. As mentioned, TGF beta 1 is the gene that helps the salamander regrow its limb after it is amputated. This is the same cascade that is being activated after exosome infusion to an injured area.[24]

In chronic alcoholism and binge drinking, chronic inflammation and dysfunction of vital cells of the brain occurs through the toxicity of alcohol. This applies to all other psychotropic drugs as well, including cocaine, opiates, marijuana, and methamphetamine. This abnormal inflammation in the brain is what makes it so difficult for people to stay abstinent, because the inflammation remains even after people have stopped drinking. Because there is inflammation and dysregulation of the immune cells in the brain, there's a high risk of relapse. After exosome infusion, the inflammation in the brain normalized, the alcohol intake was inhibited, and relapse was decreased by 80-90% over 3-5 weeks.[25]

Given how many people are affected by alcoholism, drug dependence, and addiction, these findings suggest a novel modality to enhance recovery rates and help those affected find a path to a healthier life.

There are studies that show that mesenchymal stem cells are utilized in treatment of osteoarthritis and cartilage regrowth. The paracrine effects of mesenchymal stem cells occur via the exosomes and the cargo. Exosomes can regrow the matrix of cartilage.[26]

In autoimmune diseases, there have been many studies that show the benefit of downregulating inflammation. In multiple sclerosis, lupus, chronic kidney disease, and scleroderma, there is an abnormality and dysregulation of the immune system. Exosomes have profound immune regulatory abilities. Exosomes suppress the activation and proliferation of T-cells and reduce production of inflammatory cytokines, while improving the T regulatory cell function and anti-inflammatory cytokine generation. Exosomes play a suppressive role on the proliferation, differentiation, and immunoglobulin secretion of B cells.[27,28]

We want to find solutions to all chronic diseases for human beings. It has been found that perinatal exosomes have the ability in animal models to improve these conditions, hence the next step is the evaluation of perinatal exosome treatments in human clinical trials.

As we look to our scientific future and understand the ability to modulate gene expression for the evolution and greater good of human life, the possibilities of utilizing the information vehicle of exosomes are without number. No longer are disease states fixed, and I firmly believe all aspects of human genetic expression can be augmented and enhanced if so desired.

CHAPTER 21
AGE REVERSAL, LONGEVITY, AND IMMORTALITY MEDICINE

Science has made significant progress in identifying pathways for age reversal and longevity. As we continue to progress, we will be able to extend healthy human life span with the ultimate goal of achieving immortality. Imagine a time when human beings no longer are limited by time in the exploration of the unknown but could continue learning, experiencing, and evolving. Who would we become in a thousand-year life span, and what frontiers of exploration might we engage?

It is important in the unlocking of longevity and immortality to understand how the aging process occurs. Senescence is the expression of cellular aging. If we are endeavoring to age-reverse people and prolong healthy life span, we must get to a place where we have enough control over the body to inhibit the aging process. Health and aging are governed by the mind. It is not possible to achieve true, healthy longevity and immortality without mindfully changing those attitudes that are causing the decline of the physical body and manifestation of disease. Regardless of what treatments and novel methods are utilized, if the mind is not corrected, all modalities will be undermined, and their usefulness diminished and reversed. A stagnated mind will bring about decay, no matter what is done to help the body.

In the understanding of Light Medicine, our overused emotional attitudes and habits provoke the loss of light in the organism. We have to replenish that light at a higher rate than we are spending it in order to ensure ongoing cellular rejuvenation.

We have the knowledge of how our genes operate and what is making our cells age. These areas appear complex but should be interesting to every human being alive today. Why? Because you want to know why and how you are able to live a longer and healthier life. It is a language that anyone can learn.

To explain senescence, imagine that as we are aging, our cells progress on a timeline. Their youth and ability to function diminishes over time, but for a long time that process of aging is still reversible. Then it appears there is a point of no return when a cell has become so old that it is now locked in an aging expression. In that aging expression the cells start producing many cytokines, which are messengers that cause inflammation in the body. Inflammation makes all the surrounding cells age, including stem cells. This is called the senescence secretory phenotype, which is the name for the expression of aging.[1]

We must control senescence for several reasons. Imagine a middle-aged patient who may already have many cells locked in senescence. If we nutritionally optimize them, some people experience a worsening of their symptoms. Why is that? Scientists believe that food and nutrition were now not only given to the healthy cells but also to the senescent cells, so they are producing more inflammation.

There are several different mechanisms involved in how senescence and aging occur. One of the accelerating steps to aging is the inability to sense nutrients, hence the development of insulin resistance. Aging has been shown to be related to metabolism. When insulin resistance occurs and blood sugar goes up, many complications and manifestations of chronic disease have already begun. Increased risk of cardiovascular disease is seen with impaired glucose intolerance.[2]

The fact that insulin levels are rising and insulin resistance is occurring indicates that the aging process is accelerated. This metabolic change in the cell causes a cascade: inflammation increases, telomeres are getting shorter, stem cells are getting exhausted, and DNA methylation and epigenetic aging occurs.

DNA methylation is how the environment is changing and aging the expression of the code of our genes.[3] We can measure DNA age with an epigenetic DNA methylation test. When there is too much DNA methylation, certain genes cannot be expressed in a healthy way.

If mitochondria don't produce enough energy molecules of ATP, cellular function is getting impaired and the disease process commences. If protein folding is impaired or if the transcription of genes is improper, these processes are considered hallmarks of aging.[4] The Light Medicine model explains the multitudes of genetic aging expression as a loss of light and the diminished respective electrical capacity of the human organism.

As previously mentioned, another key genetic regulator is called the mTOR gene. The mTOR gene is considered the controller of longevity and aging.[5] When downregulated, it controls all the hallmarks of aging and prevents them from occurring. It has been shown that the mTOR gene can be affected by a substance called rapamycin. Rapamycin was initially found to be produced by a bacterium on Easter Island. Rapamycin has been shown in multiple animal models to extend life span by inhibiting the mTOR gene and to prevent diseases of aging.[6]

Rapamycin is used in high doses as an immuno-suppressant that is given to people who have had kidney transplants. In high doses it does have side effects, because there are two genes of mTOR: mTOR1 and mTOR2. The mTOR2 gene activation can cause elevated cholesterol and elevated blood sugar. In longevity medicine we want only the beneficial effects of antiaging. We achieve this by using intermittent doses of rapamycin, giving a small amount every week. Rapamycin given in the elderly has been shown to improve immune function.[7]

Research has shown that rapamycin inhibits epigenetic aging in humans, as expressed in DNA methylation. Rapamycin has been given in dogs and improves their heart function. It makes them age extremely healthy and perform physically well into advanced age. Echocardiography suggested improvement in both diastolic and systolic age-related measures of heart function in the dogs that received rapamycin.[8] Rapamycin has been given in middle-aged mice. It extended life span and decreased the onset of diseases of aging.[9]

The mTOR gene controls energy production in mitochondria and the aging of stem cells. It controls metabolism of glucose. The mTOR gene works in conjunction with other genes, like forkhead box class O1 transcription factor (FOXO1), which regulates the expression of genes involved in cell cycle control, DNA damage repair, cell death, oxidative stress management, cell differentiation, glucose and lipid metabolism, inflammation, and innate and adaptive immune functions. MTOR also interacts with the family of sirtuin genes, which are molecules that are responsible for regulating cellular health, metabolic regulation, cardiovascular health, DNA expression, and healthy aging.

Intimately related in the process of aging is the immune system. As we transcend our teenage years and sexual hormones that are being produced, the thymus gland involutes and shrinks. The thymus gland functions like a biological clock and controls our T-cells and immune system. This important gland has been shown to regulate hormonal expression and produce all hormones manufactured by all other endocrine glands during growth of the child, including growth hormone.

The thymus gland produces four thymus peptides or hormones, all of which we have now isolated as peptides: thymosin alpha 1, thymulin, thymoglobulin, and thymosin beta-4. Some scientists have postulated that the regeneration of the thymus gland is key to unlocking longevity. When we use an age reversal and longevity treatment approach, if we specifically target the genes and hormones that are involved in the aging process, then we can systematically affect the aging process and reverse it.

At my clinic, we use thymus peptides that can improve the immune function of the body. Senescent cells have a mechanism of camouflage, so they are not seen by the immune system and are not efficiently removed. Thymosin alpha 1 removes the camouflage of these aging cells so that the immune system can see them and remove them, and that is called senolytic action. It has been shown that senolytics prolong life, due to their ability to remove senescent cells.

Thymus peptides are able to downregulate inflammation. All the mechanisms that cause aging in the cell can be downregulated.[10]

We can reduce oxidative stress because we can remove dysfunctional mitochondria and give antioxidants in appropriate dosages. There are other cytoprotective peptides that can unlock the locked senescent state and take it to a reversible state. When these peptides are given to patients, we can see a remarkable transformation of rejuvenation because we are able to reverse the aging processes.

I combine antiaging peptides like thymosins, epitalon, and GHK-Cu with rapamycin, rotate the regimens together with nutritional optimization, and use of other modalities as described in this book. Novel targets are emerging at a rapid pace, for example, dasatinib combined with quercetin.

Senolytics, including the combination of dasatinib and quercetin (D+Q), selectively eliminate senescent cells. They disable survival networks that defend them against cell death. D+Q reduced senescent cell burden in adipose tissue within eleven days.[11] Therefore, there are potent ways of accessing genes that are controlling our aging process. This makes it possible to achieve youthful longevity. Eventually, as we are able to control these genes with our mind in addition to these different substances, we can entertain immortality.

Caloric restriction has been well researched, and it does extend life span. It appears to affect the cells through similar pathways involving AMPK (5' AMP-activated protein kinase) and other genes.

Regulation of longevity depends on genetic and environmental factors. Caloric restriction, which is the limiting of food intake, is recognized in mammals as the best characterized and most reproducible strategy for extending life span. Four pathways have been implicated in mediating the caloric restriction effect. These are the insulin-like growth factor (IGF-1)/insulin signaling pathway, the sirtuin pathway, the adenosine monophosphate activated protein kinase (AMPK) pathway, and the target of rapamycin (TOR) pathway. The collective response of these pathways to caloric restriction is believed to promote cellular fitness and ultimately longevity. This occurs via activation of autophagy, stress defense mechanisms, and survival pathways while attenuating pro-inflammatory mediators and cellular growth.

Furthermore, there is evidence supporting life span extension can be achieved with pharmacologic agents that mimic the effects of caloric restriction, such as rapamycin, via mTOR signaling blockade, resveratrol, by activating SIRT1 activity, and metformin, which seems to be a robust stimulator of AMPK activity. As an aging suppressor, klotho is an important molecule in aging processes and its overexpression results in longevity.[12] The longevity pathways in humans have been identified and can be modulated by many different biomolecules.

A stem cell is a factory of growth factors, information transmitters, and messengers. A perinatal stem cell has almost three hundred of those kinds of growth factors and microRNA. Aging diminishes stem cell ability for regeneration. Stem cell exhaustion is dependent on mTOR function, and therefore mTOR inhibition has a regenerative purpose for stem cells as well.[13] Some of the peptides that have the ability to reverse senescence also work in stem cells.

There are studies in which it has been shown that regular cells can be reverse engineered back into stem cells by applying certain micromolecules to those cells. The 2012 Nobel Prize in physiology of medicine went to Dr. John B. Gurdon, and Dr. Shinya Yamanaka. Gurdon and Yamanaka's work showed that cells can be reprogrammed to become pluripotent, that is, capable of turning into any kind of cell in the body.[14] Previous discussions about the hypothesis of Light Medicine imply that high electrical light value in an organism, either as generated by mind or by substances of high electrical value, could theoretically promote this age reversal mechanism.

We can give certain clinically evaluated nutraceuticals, which increase one's own stem cell production by up to 100%. If those stem cells are being age-reversed in the body, they can perform their functioning for regeneration in a much better way. Stem-Kine is a food supplement that was given in eighteen healthy volunteers twice daily for a 2-week period. Significant increases in circulating CD133 and CD34 cells were observed at days 1, 2, 7, and 14 subsequent to initiation of administration, which correlated with increased hematopoietic progenitors.[15]

Senolytics are an important adjunct in antiaging strategy in that the removal of senescent cells from the body has been shown to increase longevity. Many biomolecules have been shown to have senolytic actions. One of the best natural senolytics is fisetin, which in mouse models prolongs life span by 25%. Of ten flavonoids tested, fisetin was the most potent.

Acute or intermittent treatment of aged mice with fisetin reduced senescence markers in multiple tissues, consistent with a hit-and-run senolytic mechanism. Hit-and-run means not ongoing treatment, but short term and infrequent. This is to avoid causing adverse reactions by inducing too much death of aging cells.

Fisetin reduced senescence in a subset of human fat cells and, as mentioned, administered to mice late in life restored tissue equilibrium, reduced age-related pathology, and extended life span.[16]

We have many possibilities in addressing the syndrome of aging. The earlier we are able to start preventative strategies, the greater control we have in slowing down the aging process and actively reversing it. No one is too old to start antiaging measures. We know that as soon as sex hormones become active in puberty, thymus involution and therefore aging already begin. Possibilities of extending human life span in a meaningful way and being able to prevent some of the most devastating diseases exist now for everyone. How far-reaching is that? Diseases of aging are not just diabetes, heart disease, cancer, osteoporosis, macular degeneration, or cataracts. All of those are mediated by the exact same genes, that if they start expressing dysfunction, then those diseases happen. In Light Medicine we are accessing the regulatory mechanism for *all* diseases of aging.

Is it possible to age-regress someone? Yes, because by understanding these mechanisms, adding hormonal and nutritional optimization and detoxification from environmental toxins, such as heavy metals, there is nothing that would inhibit us from becoming stronger, smarter, more agile, and living longer and better lives.

The mind component is key. Nikola Tesla talked about the century in which we are studying nonphysical phenomena, that we will make more progress than all the previous centuries combined. The understanding presented in this book, the integration of consciousness as it relates to cutting-edge science in antiaging, is this epic place of advancement. Understanding how consciousness is affecting our biological organism is paramount to success in our quest for highly functional longevity and, ultimately, youthful immortality.

CHAPTER 22
ALTERNATIVE CANCER TREATMENTS

In Part 1 of this book, I talked about my longstanding dream to help patients with cancer. That idealistic vision seemed lost to me for years. However, once I finally let go of my past and entered the grand adventure of a new practice based upon Light Medicine, I have been able to support my cancer patients with different modalities, some of which I outline in this chapter. Looking back at Ramtha's teaching from May 2018, he stated: "So many entities say, 'Well, my dreams never came true.' Truly? Perhaps the dreams are faded petals of another time rather than a future time that, without knowledge, one cannot perceive. A limited entity cannot perceive higher flows of consciousness. It is only when they are trained properly, which the forty-some years of the work was about. In preparing entities to understand more broadly their place as divine beings—and in that to be able to tap into the superconsciousness, even if it is in Fieldwork®, even if it is in C&E®, even if it is in any discipline that has been created to augment the knowledge into a performed experience—the experience gives rational truth. To that person it is only important—to that person, to that being—as they accept that ability that opens them up. And now these dreams, long ago, have a place in the future. How many of you understand that? Not all dreams have a place in this time but in future times that can be augmented, as it were—a new word that I learned—into now."

Just as Ramtha said, it took me new levels of knowledge and experience to realize my dream that so dearly wanted to help patients with cancer. I now know from my personal journey and the experience of my patients that the healing of cancer requires a profound transformation on the spiritual, emotional, and physical levels of our being.

Most of us have known or lost someone dear to us who has suffered the painful decline from cancer. We have also known those who have conquered this terrible disease. What did they realize?

There are many theories about the causation of cancer. Mainstream medicine discusses genetic predisposition. However, we know that genes do not really determine how we express our destiny but that epigenetics, the influence of the environment, plays a much larger role. Into epigenetics we need to factor in the idea of mind as a principal causative factor. Understanding that we are beings of light, recurrent negative emotions—such as hate, anger, resentment, depression, self-loathing—cause a hostile environment in the body, a disharmony that breaks down the energetic functioning of the body. As we discussed earlier, photon emission in cancer patients was detected months prior to the diagnosis of physical cancer. The loss of biophotonic light with this subsequent molecular change was associated with cancer development.[1]

Traumatic and stressful situations can be precursors of incidences in which people manifest severe illness including cancer. Depression is known to be a risk factor for the development of breast cancer.[2] Carcinogens interfere with the photorepair effect in the body and lead to a scrambling of light.

The alteration of energy metabolism, and thus changes in the electrical properties of tumor cells, provides a target for a nontoxic, therapeutic approach, which focuses in restoration of high ATP production and antioxidant utilization for the purpose of electron donation and thereby restoration of biophotonic light of these cells.

We can induce cancer cell death with combination therapies that target different metabolic cancer pathways, for example, glycolysis inhibitors, inhibition of cholesterol pathways, angiogenesis inhibitors, hormonal modulation, mitosis inhibitors, pH modulators, antipathogenic medications, immunotherapy, and more. Many of those compounds are electron donors and have high light value and as such are able to modulate gene pathways that inhibit cancer growth.

A Light Medicine model combination therapy includes nutritional supplementation and optimization, anti- and pro-oxidants, repurpose drugs, mindfulness techniques, and light therapy.

Many cancers have been shown to be related to infections by viruses and bacteria. The utilization of repurpose drugs—that target latent viral, bacterial, and fungal infections—is part of anticancer cocktails. Other repurpose drugs target the metabolism of cancer cells at multiple access points and thereby inhibit tumor growth and initiate cancer cell death. These drugs have been utilized for other indications and were then found to have anticancer properties. Commonly used drugs are aspirin, metformin, cimetidine, loratadine, melatonin, doxycycline, nonsteroidal anti-inflammatories and many more. It is of great interest that some of these repurpose drugs directly affect the pH in cancer cells. The more acidic the cell, the lower the transmembrane potential. By alkalinizing the environment of the cancer cells through hyperoxygenation, electron donation, and inhibiting the proton pump exchange, we are actively treating the electrical properties of the cell and restoring the transmembrane potential which will activate the appropriate genetic pathways that are related to autophagy and cancer cell death.

Dr. Otto Warburg, Nobel laureate in medicine, postulated that the respiratory process of malignant cells was impaired and that the transformation of a normal cell to malignant was due to defects in the aerobic respiratory pathways, which are directly responsible for the production of ATP energy units in the cell.[3,4]

Dr. Albert Szent-Györgyi, also a Nobel laureate in medicine, viewed cancer as originating from insufficient availability of oxygen. Oxygen has an inhibitory action on malignant cell proliferation by interfering with anaerobic respiration, which is fermentation and lactic acid production that subsequently leads to extreme acidification of the surrounding environment to the cancer.

Cancer cells have a very efficient mechanism in which they pump out the acidic hydrogen protons into the environment while themselves maintaining a stable pH. Environmental tumor acidity is responsible for metastatic spread and cell invasion by degrading basement membrane and increasing expression of matrix metalloproteinases, as well as affecting immune cell function and drug resistance.[5]

The failure to maintain high ATP production and high cell energy levels may be a consequence of inactivation of key enzymes, especially those related to the Krebs cycle. Mitochondria, the powerhouse of the cell, may develop suboptimal function with reduced transmembrane potential. Mitochondrial dysfunction has been associated with the development of all chronic diseases and the development of cancer. The correction of mitochondrial function has been recognized as a nontoxic target for cancer therapy. ATP production can be increased by any form of energy—including light, sound, DC electrical current, and electron donation from molecules.

An increased glucose utilization rate has been observed in malignant cells. This allows repurpose drugs—like the blood sugar lowering agent metformin or the blood sugar lowering natural compound berberine—to decrease energy that is aiding the process of survival of the cancer cells. Optimum blood sugar control is important in integrative cancer treatment.

From a bioelectric perspective, it has been shown that a characteristic feature of cancer cells is having cell membrane potentials that are lower than the cell membrane potential of healthy adult cells.[6]

Bioelectric control of tumor growth and metastasis have been researched for decades. Bioelectric signaling has emerged as an important control of cell growth and its role in driving cell migration and metastases in a variety of cancer types. The role of ion channels, pumps, exchanger activity, and ion flux—along with the importance of the membrane potential and the relationship between ion flux and membrane potential—is all correlated in explaining the electrical properties of the cell.[7]

Ion transport is implicated in these cell functions in many ways, from the classic mechanisms relating membrane potential to calcium homeostasis, to the control of pH, cell volume, growth factor release, and interaction with the extracellular matrix. In peptides and proteins, electrons and photons modulate the vibration of the chemical bonds. They thereby change the chemical molecular structure, which then in turn affects their functioning as enzymes and proteins in the cell.

Everything is controlled by electricity. Electron flux is synonymous with biophotonic emission because every time an electron changes state, a photon is being emitted. In the medical literature it is easy to lose context, as the information is so enormous and there are so many fields of research, but they are speaking about the same mechanism in many different ways.[8]

Simply stated, the lowering of ATP production equals the lowering of cellular electricity. This is the signal for the development of the genetic mutations that cause cancer. Therefore, the reversal of this energy deficit can be utilized in the treatment of cancer.

Metastases have been controlled by external electric fields, while tumor regression has been achieved by applying electrical fields. A study evaluating the effects of low-level direct current therapy on preclinical breast cancer showed a direct correlation between charge passed and absolute volume regression when the intratumor electrode was made either a positive or a negative charge. Tumor destruction for a given charge was significantly greater following anodic (positive) rather than cathodic (negative) charge treatment. During the course of these experiments, a highly reproducible toxic effect was discovered. A positive charge greater than 10.6 coulombs, or a negative charge greater than 21.6 coulombs, resulted in 100% cell mortality at 24-72 hours, while lower charges had no influence on cancer cell death.[9]

In an animal model with induced liver metastases, direct current was applied with one anode (positive charge) in the tumor center and four cathodes (negative charge) peripherally. After five weeks, the MRI showed a 1.6-fold tumor enlargement in the treatment group versus a 2.9-fold enlargement in the untreated control group, indicating a slower growth rate in tumors treated with direct current. The histopathologic analysis of the treated livers yielded a 21% complete response rate and a 78% partial response rate.[10]

Electrical currents have been shown to function as an antioxidant. Apart from utilizing them in cancer treatment, they also have profound effects in accelerating wound healing. Wound healing is significantly diminished in age, and studies have shown that applying an ultralow current device overcomes the restrictions of aging and produces healing.

We know about the aging and eventually cancer-producing effects of free radicals and the mechanism of antioxidants in neutralizing them. The steady flow of electrons in a relatively low concentration appears to act exactly as one would expect from any antioxidant.[11]

In understanding that decrease of electrical flow and decrease of photon density in the body via accelerated biophoton loss correlates with disease, we also need to understand that the immune system keeps the balance of harmony by suppressing the effects of latent pathogens in our body. When overall voltage in the cells is decreased, functioning is decreased in all cells and aging occurs, which also affects the immune system. This allows fungi, bacteria, and viruses that have previously been kept in check to multiply in the body. We have already discussed the correlation between chronic infections of pathogens and the incidence of disease and cancer progression.

It is known that environmental toxins bioaccumulate. This includes heavy metals like lead, cadmium, and arsenic, which in turn cause disruption in the ability of the body to function properly as represented in endocrine disruption, epigenetic changes, increased atherosclerosis leading to decreased blood flow, and decreased synthesis of nutrients like nitric oxide. From a Light Medicine perspective, our body is acting like an antenna. Heavy metals interfere with the harmony of the bioelectrical field, thereby increasing sensitivity to pathogens and harmful electromagnetic frequencies.

Nutritional deficiencies, such as a lack of vitamins, are involved in increasing the risk of cancer. This occurs, for example, by exacerbating immune deficiency due to lack of vitamins C and D, which are both needed for numerous immune system functions. Harmful electromagnetic frequencies from cell phones, or radiation from CT scans and MRIs, have been implicated in elevated cancer risk. It is not that there is one cause but that there are cumulative causes. For a patient to heal from this disease, all levels—the physical, emotional, mental, and spiritual—need to be addressed.

Suppressed Cancer Cures

In his book, *The Enzyme Treatment of Cancer,* published in 1911, John Beard, a biologist from the University of Edinburgh, introduced the enzyme treatment of cancer. Dr. Beard noted that the trophoblast of the placenta is invasive and acts like cancer until week sixteen of the pregnancy. He postulated that the development of the pancreas and its subsequent production of the pancreatic enzymes trypsin and chymotrypsin inhibited the ongoing invasion of the placenta into the mother's body. He then utilized these digestive enzymes in an injectable form to successfully treat cancer.

Dr. Beard's approach was furthered by Dr. William Donald Kelley, a dentist, who treated cancer with a nutritional approach and pancreatic enzymes. He was also successful. Dr. Nicholas Gonzalez studied the results of Dr. Kelley and found remarkable evidence of cancer remissions, which inspired Dr. Gonzalez to continue the work on pancreatic enzymes for the treatment of cancer. Unfortunately, Dr. Gonzalez met an untimely death, but his work lives on in his books featuring successful case reports of cancer remissions even in advanced stages.[12,13]

Dr. Max Gerson was a German physician who developed the Gerson nutritional approach to healing, which includes the juicing and consumption of large amounts of raw vegetables, as well as the body's detoxification through coffee enemas. He also achieved many cancer remissions.[14]

Dr. William Koch discovered a molecule in 1919, which he named glyoxylide. It cured cancer within days without harming normal cells. When this substance was injected subcutaneously, within twenty-four hours a focal reaction took place accompanied by fever. This reaction lasted anywhere from six to forty-eight hours during which the cancer completely disappeared. Stomach, liver, and rectal cancers responded the fastest. Dr. Koch was never given the research facilities and the cooperation of the medical profession that he asked for to investigate his molecule, so his solution was never pursued. In 2015, scientists were able to resynthesize the chemical structure $O=C=C=O$. The molecule was synthesized in the process of experimenting with glyoxal. Koch's molecule is now called ethylenedione.

In 1937, Dr. Albert Szent-Gyorgyi had also worked on methylglyoxal, which is chemically a keto aldehyde that showed significant anticancer effects.[15] A methylglyoxal-based anticancer formulation was developed, and a three-phase study of treating a total number of 86 cancer patients was carried out. Most of the cancer patients benefited greatly and a significant number became free of the disease. Contrary to the effect of existing anticancer drugs, this methylglyoxal-based formulation is devoid of any toxic effect and is reasonably effective against a wide variety of cancers.[16]

The addition of creatine showed to enhance the anticancer effect of methylglyoxal. This was researched at the Department of Biophysics in Kolkata, India. Methylglyoxal is not approved in the United States as an anticancer compound.[17]

Dr. Szent-Györgyi discussed that methylglyoxal stops the growth of cancer cells without poisoning normal cells. He also found two substances: one called retine, which inhibited cancer growth; and the other, protamine, which enhanced cancer growth. Retine is produced by the body and prevents the growth of existing cancer cells. However, the body can lose the ability to produce this substance.[18]

Dr. Stanislaw Burzynski, in the 1970s, developed antineoplastons for the treatment of cancer. He also had, like Dr. Szent-Györgyi, the idea that our body produces natural anticancer compounds. He found that patients who do not have cancer do have certain molecules in the body, that he named antineoplastons, that appear to have a protective effect. Antineoplaston AS2-1 inhibits the incorporation of L-glutamine into tumor cell proteins, leading to the cell cycle arrest in the G1 phase and inhibition of cell division. This agent may also inhibit the RAS oncogene expression (a family of retrovirus-associated DNA sequences that have been shown to cause human cancers) and activate tumor suppressor gene p53. This resulted in cell differentiation and cancer cell death.

Dr. Burzynski has been persecuted for forty years for his research. He isolated those molecules, gave them to cancer patients, and achieved remissions and cures in remarkably difficult-to-treat cancers, including childhood brain tumors. He published several hundred scientific journal articles regarding his findings.[19]

Dr. Harry M. Hoxsey was a former coal miner who in the 1920s was operating cancer clinics and curing tens of thousands of patients with an herbal formula that he had inherited from his father. By 1962, he had seventeen clinics, with one in every major city throughout the United States and was treating twelve thousand cases of cancer. By 1964, the controversy between the American Medical Association, Dr. Fishbein, and Dr. Hoxsey culminated in a landmark lawsuit resulting in Harry Hoxey's win by proving the herbal formulas were successful in treating many cancers. Immediately thereafter, the FDA padlocked all 17 clinics in operation, on account of using unapproved medicines. The clinic moved to Tijuana, Mexico, exemplifying another prominent case of the suppression of natural cancer treatments by the FDA and AMA.

In 1953, the Fitzgerald Report was commissioned by a United States Senate committee. It concluded that the organized medicine apparatus had "conspired" to suppress the Hoxsey therapy and many other promising cancer treatments, which included Mucorhicin, Coley's immunotherapy, and the Krebiozen formula. The proponents of these methods were respected doctors and scientists who had developed nutritional or immunological approaches. Panels of opposing surgeons and radiation therapists had dismissed the therapies as quackery. Consequently, these promising treatments were banned without a serious investigation.[20]

The Hoxsey formula contains natural substances with high antioxidant value, including red clover, licorice, burdock, prickly ash, and others.

The Canadian nurse, Rene Caisse, utilized essiac tea, that treated and cured cancer in the 1920s. She was shut down by the authorities. Her tea contained antioxidant herbs like burdock root, slippery elm bark, sheep sorrel leaves, and Indian rhubarb root.[21] Both the Hoxsey formula and essiac tea contain herbal compounds with great antioxidant and electron donor capacity, indicating high light value.

There are many more such cases of natural cancer treatments which were effective, and because of that, all were labeled as quackery. The suppression of the FDA, AMA, and Rockefeller puppet masters, who have perpetrated great suffering upon humanity by withholding natural cures, goes way beyond what is discussed here. This kind of suppression continues to this day in all areas of medicine, as has been so overtly visible with the suppression of the effective treatment hydroxychloroquine for COVID-19.

Combination Therapies

Many common, natural compounds have been shown to have anticancer properties. For example, berberine is a natural compound that has been shown to inhibit the proliferation and reproduction of certain microorganisms and viruses that can cause cancer, like helicobacter pylori and hepatitis B virus. Berberine was found to regulate certain oncogenes as well as cancer-related gene expression. Berberine is an enzyme inhibitor and it can also regulate reactive oxygen species, which are part of the causation of aging. Mitochondrial transmembrane potential is positively affected. Berberine exhibits suppression of tumor growth metastases.[22] Berberine has also been shown to reduce blood sugar levels in diabetics. Taking 500 mg two to three times daily for up to three months might control blood sugar as effectively as metformin or rosiglitazone.[23] As cancers have been shown to have high glucose utilization, lowering blood sugar is an important mechanism to treat cancer.

Curcumin, derived from turmeric, is well known for its anti-inflammatory and antioxidant activity. The two isomers of curcumin react by hydrogen atom transfer mechanism and by electron transfer.[24] Curcumin is a medicinal agent that exhibits anticancer properties and has a huge, therapeutic value. We propose in our Light Medicine model that the fact that curcumin is such a strong donor of hydrogen atoms as well as electrons, this is what regulates anticancer gene expression and molecular reactions.

Curcumin has been found to possess anticancer activities via its effect on a variety of biological pathways involved in mutagenesis, oncogene expression, cell cycle regulation, apoptosis, tumorigenesis, and metastasis. Curcumin has shown antiproliferative effect in multiple cancers and is an inhibitor of the transcription factor NF-κB (nuclear factor kappa-light-chain-enhancer of activated B cells) and downstream gene products, including c-Myc (family of regulator genes and proto-oncogenes that code for transcription factors), Bcl-2 (B-cell lymphoma 2), COX-2 (cyclooxygenase-2), NOS (nitric oxide synthases), Cyclin D1, TNF-α (tumor necrosis factor alpha), interleukins, and MMP-9 (Matrix metallopeptidase 9). In addition, curcumin affects a variety of growth factor receptors and cell adhesion molecules involved in tumor growth, angiogenesis, and metastasis.[25] As such, our theory proposes that we can evaluate numerous natural biological substances and predict their anticancer property based on their electrical properties, electron donor status, and antioxidant ability.

Vitamins in Cancer Therapy

Vitamin C in humans must be ingested for survival, as we have a genetic defect that does not allow us to synthesize it out of glucose. Vitamin C is an electron donor. This property accounts for all its known functions and thereby is a potent water-soluble antioxidant in humans. Human diseases, such as atherosclerosis and cancer, might occur in part from oxidant damage to tissues; therefore vitamin C has a role in prevention and treatment of cancer.[26]

Linus Pauling, Ph.D., and Ewan Cameron, M.D., published many papers and books regarding the effectiveness of vitamin C treatment in cancer.[27] Vitamin C has long been attacked by the medical establishment, despite significant scientific evidence of its usefulness in cancer therapy. Two mechanisms of anticancer activity with ascorbate have gained prominence: hydrogen peroxide induced oxidative stress and DNA demethylation. Only ascorbic acid at pharmacologic concentrations from intravenous dosing—and that would not occur from oral dosing—acted as a prodrug for hydrogen peroxide (H_2O_2) formation. Pharmacologic ascorbic acid was selectively toxic to cancer cells while having no toxicity in healthy cells. In animal models, ascorbate has anticancer activity similar to conventional chemotherapy and has also been shown to synergize with it. Findings in mice suggest oral ascorbate delays cancer development.[28]

A 2015 study published in the journal *Science* showed that in KRAS (an oncogene) and BRAF gene mutation driven cancer cells, which is prevalent in more than half of human colorectal cancers, high-dose vitamin C treatment induces cell death. The colorectal cancer cells metabolize vitamin C in a different way than other cells. Because a certain receptor is upregulated in the cancer cells, they take up the oxidized form of vitamin C (dehydroascorbate). This leads to oxidative stress, inactivation of a glycolytic enzyme required by the cells for growth, and finally cancer cell death.[29]

Antioxidants have antitumor activity. This is in line with our theory of the loss of light and the loss of cellular electricity as indicated by changes in transmembrane potential and changes in ionic flux across the cell membrane. When this is repaired and ATP production in the cell is increased and free radical production via antioxidant properties decreased, we can prevent development of cancer and reverse cellular existing damage.

Other vitamins, like vitamin E, cause antitumor and antimetastatic effects in several animal models of cancer. For example, it suppresses the transcription factor NFkB (nuclear factor kappa beta) in prostate cell lines. NFκB regulates pro-apoptotic and pro-metastatic proteins, which induce cell death and metastatic spread; thus suppression of this gene results in antitumor effects.[30]

Higher intake of dietary folate and vitamin B has been associated with lower incidence of colorectal cancer in women. Recent work suggests that hypoxia-inducible factor 1α (HIF), which plays a key role in tumorigenesis by facilitating adaptation to hypoxia (low cellular oxygen levels), is diminished by microtubule inhibitors. Some antioxidants may exert their antitumor effects through reducing HIF rather than by reducing genetic instability.[31]

The Use of Repurpose Drugs

Repurpose drugs in cancer treatment is the use of medications that have been approved for other indications and have also been shown to have anticancer properties. Many antifungal, antibacterial, and antimalarial agents have proven to be helpful in the fight against cancer. When combined with high-dose nutrients and herbal supplements with high antioxidant value, they can contribute in the natural fight against this disease. A few examples will be given.

Chloroquine and Hydroxychloroquine

Chloroquine (CQ) and hydroxychloroquine (HCQ) are antimalarial drugs. Hydroxychloroquine is a drug that inhibits autophagy and affects lysosomes in cancer cells. Autophagy is a process with which normal cells devour those components that are dysfunctional. Cancer cells protect themselves during chemotherapeutic treatment by eating themselves to stay alive. Once cancer has formed, autophagy may protect the cancer cells by providing extra nutrients to them or by keeping anticancer drugs or other substances from destroying them.

Studies show that hydroxychloroquine elevates the lysosomal pH of cancer cells. Lysosomes play a critical role in cellular processes, for example, the ability to secrete proteins, in energy metabolism, and cell signaling. The autophagy-lysosome pathway is associated with the hallmarks of cancer, such as escaping cell death pathways, evading immune surveillance, and deregulating metabolism. Lysosomes represent a weakness of cancer cells and, when targeted, have great therapeutic potential in cancer because they trigger apoptotic and lysosomal cell death pathways and inhibit cell protective autophagy. Lysosomes are involved in cancer drug resistance by capturing cancer drugs in their acidic environment, resulting in a reduction of the drug's effects.

In lung cancer, hydroxychloroquine exerts anticancer effects by reversing the drug sequestration in lysosomes and enhancing the CD8+ T-cell immune response. These findings suggest that HCQ could act as a promising chemosensitizer and immune regulator.[32] Autophagy appears to inhibit malignant transformation, reflecting its capability to limit the accumulation of cancer inducing entities like dysfunctional mitochondria, which overproduce genotoxic reactive oxygen species. Autophagy supports the progression and metastatic dissemination of established tumors by increasing the ability of malignant cells to cope with adverse microenvironmental conditions like nutrient deprivation and hypoxia. These are two common features of rapidly growing, solid tumors.[33]

As an autophagy inhibitor, hydroxychloroquine has been combined with multiple chemotherapeutic agents that have been and are currently being evaluated in various clinical trials. This includes studies in lymphoma,[34] brain metastases,[35] as well as other advanced solid tumors.[36] Hydroxychloroquine has also been evaluated in prostate cancer and shown to increase chemosensitivity as well as inhibiting proliferation.[37] There are ongoing trials evaluating the use of the antifungal medication itraconazole in combination with hydroxychloroquine for prostate cancer. Both have anticancer properties. Antifungal medications have been utilized as effective repurpose cancer drugs.[38] Hydroxychloroquine's anticancer effectiveness makes it a great chemosensitizer.[39]

Triple negative breast cancer is known to be associated with a high percentage of cancer stem cells, which in turn results in a poor prognosis, despite systemic chemotherapy. This has been associated not just with poor prognosis but also recurrent metastatic disease. In a study with this breast cancer type and hydroxychloroquine, the drug was able to reduce cancer stem cells.[40] It has been shown in studies that chemotherapy increases the amount of cancer stem cells and thereby increases the risk of metastatic relapse.[41] Treating and eliminating cancer stem cells is an important component of any effective cancer treatment, as we want to not only treat the cancer now but prevent later recurrence. Hydroxychloroquine additionally overcomes tamoxifen resistance in breast cancer.[42] Tamoxifen is a drug that blocks the effects of estrogen in the breast tissue and has been used as an adjuvant treatment after surgery and other chemotherapeutic treatments for breast cancer.

In summary, we extrapolate from this research that the addition of hydroxychloroquine to natural compounds with anticancer effects or repurpose drugs may increase their anticancer activity as well.

Fenbendazole, Artemisinin, and Salinomycin

Fenbendazole and its sister drug mebendazole are antiparasitic agents. They interfere with microtubulin and exert cytotoxicity to human cancer cells at micromolar concentrations. It joins the effective antimicrobial group of repurpose drugs in the fight against cancer. Fenbendazole caused mitochondrial translocation of p53, a tumor suppressor gene frequently mutated in cancers. It effectively inhibited glucose uptake, which is the primary energy source for cancer cells. Fenbendazole interferes with expression of GLUT (Glucose transporters) as well as hexokinase, which is a key glycolytic enzyme needed for energy utilization that most cancer cells thrive on.[43]

Fenbendazole has effects on multiple cellular pathways leading to effective elimination of cancer cells, and its activities are enhanced by using supplementary vitamins.[44]

Another antimalarial drug with significant anticancer properties is sweet wormwood or artemisinin. It has been shown to block prostate cancer growth.[45] Artemisinin disrupts the responsiveness of prostate cancer cells to androgens.[46] We know that estrogen is also a driving force in the growth of prostate cancer.[47] Artemisinin has been found to be a natural estrogen and progesterone receptor blocker and can be utilized in cancers that have these hormone receptors, like breast cancer and prostate cancer.[48]

There are other repurpose drugs with significant anticancer effects, like salinomycin, which has been studied in a novel combination therapy for triple negative breast cancer.[49] Salinomycin is an antibiotic that has both antimicrobial and antifungal properties. Salinomycin can be effective in killing cancer stem cells.

Daniel Stanciu, Ph.D., is founder of the blog, Cancer Treatments – From Research to Application, a scientific research resource of cancer treatments from all over the world. Dr. Stanciu describes salinomycin as one of the most effective compounds for a wide variety of cancers. He has had contact with patients who have successfully used it worldwide.[50]

Daniel Stanciu has been my friend and colleague in cancer research. He has been an invaluable resource in the development of the most effective combination therapies for my cancer patients. His work and collaboration with worldwide, renowned cancer researchers has led to a wealth of accessible information. His site is giving resources to cancer patients about the numerous, possible treatment options that are available.

Salinomycin, says Dr. Stanciu, acts via multiple pathways in inhibiting tumor growth. It can overcome multidrug resistance and targets cancer stem cells. However, the compound does have side effects and potential toxicity, due to possible tumor lysis syndrome from rapid cancer cell death and needs to be carefully administered. Salinomycin is not authorized in the United States, but in other parts of the world it has shown promising effects in cancer treatments.

Salinomycin is another excellent example of a compound with antimicrobial and antifungal properties acting as an effective agent in cancer therapy. This again raises the question regarding the etiology of cancer and its association with chronic infections. Salinomycin has been studied in a wide variety of cancers where effects have been substantial.[51]

Salinomycin induces cancer cell death and effectively eliminates cancer stem cells to induce partial clinical regression of heavily pretreated and therapy resistant cancers. The rare ability of salinomycin to kill both stem cells and therapy resistant cancer cells defines it as an effective anticancer drug.[52,53]

Due to its multiple abilities of action, salinomycin has been described in the scientific literature as a new paradigm in cancer therapy.[54]

Amygdalin

Amygdalin, also called laetrile, is found in many plants but most notably in the seeds or kernels of apricots, bitter almonds, apples, peaches, and plums. Amygdalin is classified as a cyanogenic glycoside because each amygdalin molecule includes a nitrile group, which can be released as the toxic cyanide anion by the action of a beta-glucosidase. Laetrile is another anticancer compound that has been attacked with false, corrupt science.

The history of laetrile was outlined by G. Edward Griffin in the book *World Without Cancer*. The original senior researcher at Sloan Kettering, Dr. Kanematsu Sugiura—who was silenced—clearly showed that laetrile was more effective in the control of cancer than any substance he had ever tested. The drug was discredited due to a false claim that it would cause cyanide poisoning. The FDA then made it illegal for United States physicians to use laetrile. These lies by the FDA have since been debunked, and the research needs to be reevaluated by competent physicians who do not have biased intentions.

Recent reviews show that amygdalin causes cancer cell death, called apoptosis, by upregulating expression of pro-apoptotic proteins and downregulating expression of anti-apoptotic proteins. It also promotes arrest of cell cycle in G0/G1 phase and decreases the number of cells entering S and G2/M phases, thereby preventing the cancer cells from multiplying.[55]

In an Iranian study from 2019, amygdalin has been shown to have anticancer effects due to various gene expressions that induced cancer cell death.[56]

Amygdalin has anticancer function by decomposing carcinogenic substances in the body, killing cancer cells, blocking nutrient source of tumor cells, inhibiting cancer cell growth, and could also reduce the incidence of prostate, lung, colon, and rectal cancers. It has been manufactured and used to treat cancer in America, Germany, Italy, Japan, the Philippines, and twenty other countries. It can also ameliorate the symptoms of patients in advanced stage of cancer and prolong their survival period.[57]

Peptides Used to Support Cancer Patients

We have discussed in a previous chapter the vast applications of peptides as novel agents for healing. Some peptides can be used to support cancer patients.

Thymosin alpha one (TA1) is a thymus peptide that modulates the immune system by augmenting T-cell function and has been used in cancer patients to combat tumors and prevent opportunistic infections. It inhibits cell proliferation and induces apoptosis in human leukemia, hepatocellular carcinoma, non-small cell lung cancer, melanoma, and other human cancers.[58] A double-blind, randomized trial involving 42 patients with localized, unresectable non-small cell lung cancer—who were given TA1 treatment for up to one year following radiation therapy—showed statistically significant improvement in relapse-free and overall survival correlated to T-cell levels previously depleted by radiation.[59]

GHK is a peptide that has been found to effectively downregulate expression of metastatic genes. GHK suppressed RNA production in 70% of 54 human genes overexpressed in patients with an aggressive metastatic form of colon cancer.[60]

GHK is capable of regulating various biochemical pathways on a gene level and resetting the gene activity of 30%

of the human genome back to health. In human neuroblastoma and breast cancer cells incubated in culture with GHK, the programmed cell death system (apoptosis) was reactivated and cell growth inhibited.[61]

Epitalon is a tripeptide that lengthens telomeres via increased telomerase activity and prolongs life span in multiple animal models and humans. It has been shown to restore melatonin secretion in the pineal gland and to have strong antioxidant properties via increase in antioxidant enzyme activity of superoxide dismutase, glutathione peroxidase, and glutathione S-transferase.[62]

Epitalon reduces the incidence of chromosomal aberrations, consistent with increases in telomere length.[63] It increases the proliferation of lymphocytes in the thymus and interferon gamma production by T-cells.[64] Epitalon has an inhibitory effect on Her2/neu gene expression in breast cancer and provided protection from development of leukemia in mice.[65,66] In M-1 sarcoma studied in rats, epitalon had cytostatic action on tumor cells, increased apoptosis, and hemorrhagic necrosis of tumor.[67] The effects on proliferation of colon tumors were evaluated and resulted in significant inhibition of mitotic activity of tumor cells, and a high level of apoptosis was seen.[68]

Met-enkephalin is an opioid growth factor that has been shown to selectively enhance the lymphoproliferative response to the T-cell mitogen concanavalin A.[69] Twenty subjects with advanced pancreatic cancer who had failed chemotherapy were treated weekly with Met5-enkephalin. Clinical benefit was experienced by 53% of the subjects surviving more than eight weeks, and 62% showed either a decrease or stabilization in tumor size by computed tomography.[70]

IRGD is a peptide that binds to integrins that are expressed on tumor endothelial cells. IRGD increased vascular and tissue permeability in a tumor-specific and neuropilin-1-dependent manner, allowing coadministered drugs to penetrate extra-vascular tumor tissue. Systemic injection with iRGD improved the therapeutic index of drugs of various compositions, including doxorubicin, with nearly complete growth inhibition. The monoclonal antibody trastuzumab, when given with iRGD, increased the concentration of the antibody in tumor cells by 40-fold.

The iRGD-mediated enhancement in drug penetration persisted even after more than three weeks of antibody treatment. IRGD has been shown to enhance drug delivery for ten different drugs, thereby enhancing efficacy of anticancer drugs while reducing side effects.[71]

PNC-27, an anticancer peptide, which contains an HDM-2-binding domain corresponding to residues 12-26 of p53 and a transmembrane-penetrating domain, has been found to kill cancer cells—but not normal cells—by inducing membranolysis.[72,73] It has been approved for treatment outside of the U.S. However, concerns in application include risk of tumor lysis syndrome and reports of gastrointestinal bleeding.

Delta-sleep-inducing peptide (DSIP) has been shown to have reduction of chemotherapy-induced impairment of bioelectrical brain activity, called "chemobrain." Ten children, aged three to sixteen years, were given a ten-day course of DSIP and their bioelectric activity was recorded. Nine out of the ten children showed improvement in brain activity with DSIP.[74] DSIP was found in mice to decrease spontaneous tumor incidence by 2.6-fold.[75]

Hyperbaric Oxygen in Cancer Treatment

Hyperbaric oxygen can be an important adjunct in cancer therapy. Low cellular oxygen levels are a significant component in cancer progression and a critical hallmark of solid tumors. Low oxygen levels involve enhanced cancer cell survival, angiogenesis, which is the growing of new blood vessels to provide nourishment to the cancer, glycolytic metabolism, and the development of metastasis. Hyperbaric oxygen (HBO) treatment has been used to improve disorders involving hypoxia and ischemia by enhancing the amount of dissolved oxygen in the plasma and thereby increasing oxygen delivery to the tissue.

Oxygen levels in the body are directly correlated to pH. Increasing pH from 4.0 pH to 5.0 pH increases oxygen to the cells by tenfold. Each whole number increases by tenfold again, so a 4.0 pH to a 6.0 pH increases oxygen by 100 times, and raising pH from 4.0 pH to 7.0 pH increases oxygen levels by 1,000 times.

Unless the body's pH level is slightly alkaline, the body cannot optimally heal itself. You cannot effectively improve cellular regeneration until pH levels are above 7. PH is directly correlated to the electrical conductivity of the biological system. The more acidic the body, the lower the electrical power in the cell.

Acid decreases the body's ability to repair damaged cells and to get rid of toxic and cancer-causing heavy metals. It makes the body more susceptible to fatigue, illness, and accelerated aging. Electromedicine and Light Medicine take into account a balanced pH. When body pH drops, enzymes are deactivated, digestion is interrupted, and vital nutrients are not effectively assimilated. While disease cannot survive in an alkaline state, in a low oxygen/low pH (acidic) state, viruses, bacteria, yeast, mold, fungus, candida, and cancer cells all thrive. As we discussed above, the reactivation and thriving of these pathogens could be the actual cause for cancer developing in the first place.

Cancers have a metabolism called glycolysis that doesn't use oxygen. Many integrative cancer clinics are combining their treatments with a hyperbaric oxygen chamber. Hyperbaric oxygen is very important and, unfortunately, a much-undervalued safe treatment for all chronic diseases and adjunct to cancer treatment.

The Effects of Light in Photodynamic Cancer Therapy

Blue light-emitting diodes are known to inhibit cancer proliferation and induce cancer cell death by increasing intracellular reactive oxygen species (ROS) and activating a family of protease enzymes playing essential roles in programmed cell death called caspase.

The Blu Room, which will be discussed in the following chapter, could be an important mechanism to be further evaluated when utilized as an adjunct therapy in cancer treatment. Blu Room technology contains both medical UV light lamps, producing ultraviolet light in the 310 nm range, as well as blue LED lights used as an ambient light source which generally emits light at 400-450 nm. Both light sources have shown through research to directly affect cancer cell death alone as well as in combination with natural photosensitizers like curcumin, C60, fisetin, and others.

In a study published in 2019, the naturally occurring, photosensitizer molecule curcumin was used in photodynamic therapy mediated by a blue light-emitting diode. Researchers show that a curcumin encapsulated nanoplatform activated with a blue light-emitting diode induces cell death in cancer and represents a new class of cancer therapy.[76]

Blue LED light irradiation, with wavelengths of 400-480 nm, transmits high levels of energy and induces apoptosis by stimulating a mitochondrial pathway and reduces the early growth rate of melanoma cells in mice. The induction of apoptotic cell death and formation of autophagosome in human B lymphoma cells, after irradiation with blue LED, has also been detected.[77] Blue light-emitting diodes irradiation causes cell death in colorectal cancer by inducing ROS (reactive oxygen species) production and DNA damage while having no harmful effect on healthy cells.[78]

Two cell lines of melanoma and bovine endothelial cells were irradiated with blue light. Exposure to blue light (wavelength 450 nm, 10 J/cm^2 from a Waldman lamp) induced a rapid and large reduction in viability followed by the death of virtually all the irradiated cancer cells within 24 hours. These results led to exposure of a patient with hemorrhagic cutaneous melanoma metastasis to blue light. Irradiation led to an immediate arrest of hemorrhage, an inhibition of tumor growth, and extensive tumor necrosis 24 hours after irradiation.[79]

Blue light was evaluated in another study to determine the pro-apoptotic effects in promyelocytic leukemia cells. Blue light reduced the viability and enhanced the mortality of cells in a time-dependent manner. Exposure to blue light for 24 hours caused depolarization of the mitochondrial membrane potential and the overproduction of reactive oxygen species in these leukemia cells. In a mouse model, 9-day exposure to blue light markedly suppressed the growth of tumors.[80]

These results indicate a preventative and adjunctive treatment role for blue light therapy against cancer.

To explore the possibility of using blue light for extracorporeal circulation therapy in patients with leukemia, the effects of blue light on cell growth in vitro and in the extracorporeally circulated blood of rats with leukemia were evaluated. When leukemia cells—circulated extracorporeally using a peristaltic pump—were exposed to blue light for 5 hours, the growth of the cells was found to be markedly suppressed. Then the blood of rats with erythroblastic leukemia was circulated extracorporeally and exposed to blue light for three hours. Lymphocytes were separated from the peripheral blood immediately after the end of blue-light exposure and incubated for seven days. The growth of leukemic cells was found to be significantly suppressed following exposure to blue light, whereas the growth of normal lymphocytes was unaffected. These findings suggest that cancer cells may be more sensitive to blue light than normal cells.[81]

The occurrence of lung metastases was effectively inhibited when melanoma cells from tumors in mice were exposed to blue light.[82]

A study evaluating the cytotoxic effects of blue light on melanoma cells, when combined with vitamins like riboflavin, showed that the vitamins had a significant contribution in the ability of the blue light to kill cancer cells. Cell necrosis was observed only in media containing riboflavin. The effects of other components of visible light on riboflavin were also studied. Riboflavin-containing media were exposed to light from each of the three primary colors—red, green, and blue—and the effects on the melanoma cells were evaluated. Cell necrosis was induced only in media exposed to blue light. The effects of riboflavin increased in a concentration-dependent manner in the range from 0.3 to 1.0 mg/l in blue-light exposed media. These findings suggest that cell necrosis is probably induced by active oxygen species, such as hydrogen peroxide formed by the reaction of riboflavin with blue light.[83]

This combination approach is important in evaluating the effectiveness of blue light in the treatment of cancer. When it is combined with certain vitamins, as well as other photosensitizers like curcumin, the effectiveness against cancer is significantly enhanced.[84]

There are many other natural compounds that have been shown to have anticancer activity, which correlates with their ability of electron donation and antioxidant properties. ECGC (epigallocatechin gallate) extract from green tea has effects in prevention and treatment of breast and prostate cancer. It has anticancer properties in multiple other cancer categories like leukemia and has been successfully used as a photosensitizer.[85,86]

The information in this chapter is by no means exhaustive but gives an overview and understanding of how to combine natural molecules and repurpose drugs with light therapy, hyperbaric oxygen therapy, and peptides to support and treat cancer patients who do not want to undergo chemotherapeutic or radiation treatment for their illness or want to augment their current treatment with more natural, supportive means. It also outlines strategies for preventions by optimizing vitamin intake, strengthening the immune system, and using certain natural, antioxidant compounds for cancer prevention.

Another interesting molecule in photodynamic cancer therapy worth mentioning, given its blue color, is methylene blue (MB). Methylene blue has been shown to have renewable auto-oxidizing properties, which acts as an electron cycler that allows MB to redirect electrons to the mitochondrial electron transport chain. This enhances adenosine triphosphate (ATP) energy production and promotes cell survival. This means MB directly gives electricity to the mitochondria, the powerhouse of the cell, and helps regenerate the cells. MB reduces reactive oxygen species production from the mitochondrial electron transport chain.

The antioxidant and electron donor property of MB is unique and can be utilized for photodynamic cancer treatment, neuro-regeneration, antiaging, and pain relief. It has anti-malarial, antiviral and antidepressant properties. Studies have established that MB enhances cytochrome c oxidase (complex IV) activity to produce more ATP (energy) in cells under normal oxygen conditions. MB replaces oxygen as the oxidant to sustain ATP generation under low oxygen conditions while simultaneously reducing oxidative stress. MB is one of the most effective compounds to delay senescence.[87]

MB photodynamic therapy (PDT) has been shown to induce massive cell death in breast cancer models, while having no effect on healthy cells. It therefore has been recommended as an adjunctive treatment to conventional treatments.[88] PDT has been effective in melanoma, basal cell carcinoma, prostate cancer, and Kaposi Sarcoma.[89]

There have been great advances in the field of integrative cancer treatments. Many more promising advances, like the antisense oligodeoxynucleotide mRNA therapy and CRISPR gene editing, open up this field for novel, less toxic therapies than what conventional chemotherapy and radiation treatment currently offers.

At AM Medical and other clinics around the county, we can offer repurpose drugs in combination with high-dose vitamin C infusions and other compounds with high light value. Integrating natural compounds that have been shown to have anticancer activity with the anticancer properties of blue and UV light is an interesting and promising new field of study.

CHAPTER 23
LIGHT MEDICINE AND
THE MERCY BLU ROOM PROGRAM

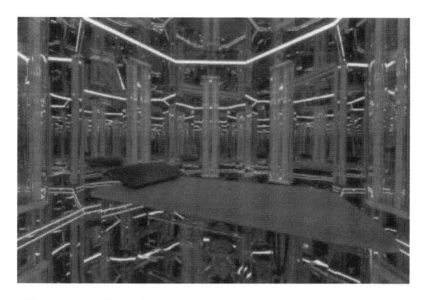

Figure 13: Healing With Light – The Blu Rooms. Photo Credit: Rory Sagner Photography, © 2018.[1]

The Blu Room is a patented technology (patent number: 9919162) that was invented by the great American channel JZ Knight.[2]

The Blu Room is based upon the metaphysical science of elsewhere—"on Earth as it is in heaven." The Blu Room creates an atmosphere that insulates the participant from the daily environment and provides them with a mind/body/Spirit consciousness-lifting experience that can augment one's state of creative focus. The Blu Room is an atmosphere created by the entire structure that reproduces a portion of the ultraviolet spectrum that JZ Knight, the inventor, experiences when she leaves her body and goes beyond the visible-light realm. According to Ramtha's teachings, visible light is where polarity began, the origins of positive and negative, and what became the concepts of good and bad, morality and karma. To move in consciousness beyond the visible-light level into ultraviolet blue provides a period of calm, peace, and even joy in the absence of polarized thought.[3]

Diseases in the body begin as inharmonious and polarized attitudes. When polarity is removed, space is created for a greater mind to be present that allows for restoration of harmony, and therefore healing in the body.

As Ramtha discussed in the beginning of our journey: "All things have a lightbody, and because it is from light, they descend to mass. You are a conglomerate of a neighborhood of diversified light whose harmony is you." This diversified light is represented by the visible-light spectrum. According to Ramtha, consciousness and energy are inextricably combined. Ramtha has taught about the healing power of the fourth level which he describes as bridge consciousness and ultraviolet-blue energy. He has told us, "The Blu Room can take you to the fourth level for a while." In his light medicine teaching included in Chapter 10, Ramtha refers to the Blu Room as "the God machine."

Currently there are thirty-six operational Blu Room locations, with 11 additional facilities under construction. Countries with Blu Room services include Argentina, Australia, Austria, Canada, Colombia, Germany, Italy, Japan, Mexico, Romania, Spain, Switzerland, Taiwan, and U.S.A. Three locations are for private use or employee-only programs and the remaining locations are open to the public in either clinical or spa/wellness settings.

Thirteen Blu Rooms are affiliated with healthcare providers in clinical settings. All providers have expressed great pleasure at having the Blu Room unit to support their clinical practices and augment their patient care with this technology.

Not long after her invention of the Blu Room, JZ Knight gave a phone interview with radio host, Rob Simone: "The Blu Room consists of panels of light that are comprised of the ultraviolet (UV) light spectrum. These are long-canister, medical lights set in a room that is all stainless steel and mirrored—top, bottom, all around—in an octagon according to the mathematics of Nikola Tesla. These frequencies reach exclusively to the center of the room, the mysterious number 9. So the room is an octagon and everything is precisely stationed. All points come to the center of the room, which I call the 'atmosphere,' and it is 9."[4]

The book, *Blu Room: Experience the Future, Building Bridges with Light, Frequency, and Sound*, by Irmgard Maria Graf, provides further, excellent information.[5]

Looking at the Blu Room through the eyes of new and ancient science, we see an octagonal, sacred geometry—mirrors that represent matter, antimatter, and ultraviolet-blue light—which is a specific healing frequency and its corresponding information in the light spectrum. Within this construction, there is a combination of the healing frequency of light and healing sound.

In the Science of Light Medicine chapter, I spoke of Stephen Phillips and the mathematical association between the geometrical shape, like the Platonic solids and the simplification of the octagon, and the mathematical reverse engineering of the body's matter, from bones to DNA to particle structure.[6] Everything is a mathematical code. Not only can the octagonal shape be reverse engineered according to this code, but Dr. Glen Rein has conducted experiments in the interaction of subtle energy with DNA. When certain geometries were applied to DNA, the DNA unwound and began absorbing more UV light.

As such, a geometric shape may have a direct effect on our DNA.[7]

The perfect body blueprint is, according to Ramtha, in the ultraviolet realm and there is a resonance that occurs with that frequency. Ramtha describes the Blue Body® consists of blue webs. These blue webs most closely resemble the cellular cytoskeleton microtubule network.[8] In all plant cells the cytoskeletal structures can be involved in intracellular UV-B signaling. Hence, tubulin in microtubules and/or actin in microfilaments, as well as proteins of intermediate filaments, may perceive and propagate the signal from UV-B playing a role of UV-B mediated downstream effects via light-sensitive proteins. Scientists have shown in humans that all cell cycle mechanisms, including gene transcription, can be manipulated via these light-sensitive proteins.[9]

Our skin absorbs photons and can store them as energy. In the research by Dr. Mae-Wan Ho, it was pointed out that DNA and other biomolecules have a highly nonlinear behavior and that all organisms act as a multimodal frequency system. This means that if a biophoton is absorbed into the body, the energy output occurs in many frequencies. Biophotons do not act like a typical thermodynamic system. Instead, there are many more biophotons at high frequencies in living organisms than one would expect to find in a nonliving system. At 300 nm of UV light, which is close to the 310 nm of the Blu Room, there has been shown to be 10^{40} more photons than would be expected.[10]

In the Blu Room, if skin is exposed to the light, biophotons can be absorbed by melanin, the skin pigment. This absorption increases the density of biophotons in the human biophoton field significantly, hence increasing the light in the body. It is known that chronic diseases are associated with an accelerated loss of biophotonic light from the body. Therefore, this mechanism of light absorption could be contributing to the beneficial health effects of the Blu Room by reversing the loss of light caused by the aging and disease process. The Blu Room is in effect using a natural, antiaging mechanism.

As we discussed in previous chapters, the body can transform any energy source into ATP, the energy unit used in the cells. Ultraviolet light waves and certain frequencies of sound are energy waves that can be utilized to generate enhanced energy in the body. The greater the ability of mitochondria in the cell to produce energy or ATP, the greater the ability to regenerate and age-reverse any cell and enhance its function.

Biophotons can excite electrons to higher states, which in turn makes them unstable and able to give off electrons to other molecules, effectively giving off electricity. The ability to give off electrons in the body is called antioxidant capacity. Antioxidants are able to reduce inflammation and reduce oxidative stress, some of the major mechanisms of aging. This in turn downregulates disease-promoting genes and upregulates health-promoting genes. Considering the scientific biophysical research, the Blu Room would be able to enhance this mechanism of cellular regeneration.

The inventor, JZ Knight, introduced the frequency of 111 Hz as a healing sound inside the Blu Room while the clients were experiencing a session. The sound frequency 111 Hz is known for cell rejuvenation and regeneration. The use of this frequency in wound healing has been explored in mice, where 111 Hz frequency made the wound healing process faster. This specific frequency is known to induce the release of beta-endorphins. Beta-endorphins are opioid neuropeptide and peptide hormones that are produced by certain neurons in the brain as well as the peripheral nervous system. They enhance mood and create feelings of relaxation in the body. Beta-endorphins activate the expression of the cytokeratin 16 gene. This gene produces the protein keratin 16 (KRT16) which speeds up the wound healing process.[11]

In a 1994 study from the California Institute of Technology, the frequency of 111 Hz was found to be the main firing frequency of the Purkinje cells in the cerebellum. The cerebellum has 80% of the neurons in the human brain. The cerebellum receives information from the sensory systems, the spinal cord, and other parts of the brain and then regulates motor movements. The cerebellum coordinates posture, balance, coordination, and speech, resulting in smooth and balanced muscular activity. The Purkinje cells function like a hub that receives information and transmits it to the nuclei neurons that send instructions to the brain.[12]

Interestingly, Ramtha has taught that the lower cerebellum is able to process the information frequency of Infinite Unknown consciousness, or the mind of God.[13]

That science is yet to be discovered.

Ultraviolet-light therapy has a rich history and utilization in medical science. The effects of ultraviolet light have been shown to include bacterial and viral toxin inactivation, including inhibition of bacterial growth. Steroids in the body are activated and synthesized into vitamin D in a process that occurs by ultraviolet light exposure of the precursor hormone 7-dehydrocholesterol within the microvessels of the skin. This results in the production of vitamin D3. Later in life this process can be impaired, leading to less endogenous production of vitamin D3 and increasing the necessity for nutritional supplementation.

Treatment of skin conditions with UV light started in the 1880s. The 1903 Nobel Prize in physiology or medicine was awarded to Niels Ryberg Finsen "in recognition of his contribution to the treatment of diseases, especially lupus vulgaris, with concentrated light radiation, whereby he has opened a new avenue for medical science."[14]

In the 1940s, thousands of patients were treated with photo bioluminescence—UV light blood irradiation—in hospitals in the United States with excellent success in even advanced cases of sepsis. Due to the emergence of pharmaceutical drug companies and antibiotics, these methods have been marginalized and all but forgotten. UV light blood irradiation increases the oxygen binding capacity of blood, thereby alkalinizing the blood and suppressing the growth of pathogens. Alkalization of the blood and the suppression of growth of pathogens are important contributors to treating chronic diseases.

In an earlier chapter I discussed that many scientific studies point to infectious diseases as the cause for chronic diseasement. UV light therapy has been shown to eradicate pathogens, which could also be a pathway in which the Blu Room contributes to healing. A further, excellent review of the history of UV light therapy is found in the book *Into the Light*, by William Campbell Douglass, M.D.

A more recent study to evaluate the addictive properties of ultraviolet radiation experienced by tanning bed users found that beta endorphins are formed in the skin of humans.[15] This endorphin release could be related to the profound relaxation and mood elevation effects that people experience in the Blu Room. Many Blu Room users report improved mental clarity and creativity enhancement. Another study validated these experiences by showing the benefits of blue light in patients with traumatic brain injury. Mild traumatic brain injury (mTBI) is associated with sleep problems. Results indicated that morning blue light may re-entrain the circadian rhythm and improve sleep problems. Blue light improved sleep timing, daytime sleepiness, and executive functioning. Blue light increased thalamic volume and functional and structural connectivity. The thalamus is a mass of gray matter that allows a hub-like exchange of information, including sensory input, motor signals, regulation of consciousness, sleep, and alertness.[16]

Recent studies showed that UVB light improves the gut microbiome. In a study of twenty-one subjects, three UVB light exposures within the same week increased the vitamin D levels by 7.3 nmol/l. The researchers sequenced fecal microbiota composition and found significant increase in diversity which is correlated with improved gut health. Improved gut microbiome has been shown to have beneficial effects on metabolism, the immune system, and mental health.[17]

In a study using mice, UVB exposure inhibited the development and progression of atherosclerosis by enhancing immune function of T-cells which are involved in the development of atherosclerotic plaque.[18] This research provides ample evidence of possible mechanisms for health benefits associated with Blu Room use.

The more molecular pathways that are to be investigated, the more effects of UVB light will be found. It is my hypothesis that the enhancement of biophotonic light in the body and its subsequent electrical effects is the underlying cause for these beneficial health effects.

Unfortunately, aging reduces vitamin D production in skin, as there is a decrease in the concentration of 7-dehydrocholesterol in the epidermis in older compared with younger individuals and a reduced response to UV light, resulting in a 50% decrease in the formation of previtamin D3.[19]

After testing many patients in different age groups who have used the Blu Room regularly, it has become evident to me that the mechanism of healing is not just related to vitamin D production, as most older patients continued to be deficient in their levels and still required oral supplementation.

The Mercy Blu Room Program

The Mercy Blu Room program is sponsored by JZ Knight and was started in 2015 at the beautiful Shiva Blu Room complex in Yelm, Washington. In this program, many people who suffered from devastating chronic diseases and were unable to financially afford Blu Room and other medical treatments were treated at greatly reduced cost or often without charge. Since I have been the overseeing physician at the Mercy Blu Room, many of the participants have been under my care. At my medical office, I had the opportunity to provide an intensive combination of medical management with Blu Room sessions two to three times a week, which allowed close monitoring for progress. The admission criteria for the Mercy Blu Room program included severe medical disease as well as financial need. Patients would come to my office once a month for follow-up to monitor progress.

Different treatment protocols—with novel natural supplements, peptides, neutraceuticals, and pharmaceutical medications—were developed according to the medical needs of the patients and implemented. The costs for many of the medications and supplements to the patients were covered by JZ Knight. All had training in the teachings of Ramtha's model of reality and were using techniques learned at Ramtha's School of Enlightenment to focus on their healing.

Mindful participation in healing was emphasized throughout the Mercy Blu Room program duration for all participants. This was to help their acceptance that healing can come their way, to understand mind causality, that changing their mind is what will allow the healing, and to remind them of self-inspiration and self-correction.

Ramtha teaches that "It is not what you say that you need to self-correct. It is what you think, and that your thoughts can be seen by all." He says, "It is what think you that is everything. If you want money, if you want genius, indeed if you want radiant health, you want everlasting beauty inward and outwards, you can't just say it. You have to think it. And every errant thought against such an idea, you must stop and self-correct and send it away and replace it with what you want. Now that is called conquering yourself."[20]

The Mercy Blu Room cancer program utilized a variety of natural compounds. Iscador, which is a mistletoe extract, was given either orally or in injectable form. Iscador is the most common chemotherapeutic agent used in Europe and has been shown to stimulate an anticancer immune response.

Photorepair in cancer has been studied by Dr. Alexander Popp, a biophysicist from Germany. According to Dr. Popp, if 99% of a cell is destroyed through UV light, including its DNA, and if more light is shined on it but at a lower intensity, the cell will regrow.

Cancer cells do not have a functioning photorepair mechanism. They scramble light and do not allow a light ray to pass through unaltered. Iscador allows the emission of light to go through and the mechanism of photorepair to happen.

Dr. Popp showed that cancers had a significant biophoton emission. The one natural substance that reversed this accelerated photon emission of tumor cells was mistletoe.[21]

All patients were also taking Carbon 60 because of its light value. Carbon 60, when activated with diode light, has been shown to kill 50% of leukemia cells in cell culture within 24 hours.[22] In addition, most cancer patients received a peptide, epitalon, that lengthens telomeres, and GHK copper, a peptide that resets 30% of the genome back to health. Other peptides were utilized as needed, depending on the case.

Vitamin supplementation was emphasized. While exposure to ultraviolet light can increase vitamin D synthesis in younger people, it has been shown that older individuals are not able to adequately produce vitamin D3 through the exposure of sunlight. The patients' vitamin D3 levels were measured and increased orally in order to reach serum blood levels greater than 75. Vitamin D has been clearly shown to have anticancer properties and it is also said that most of the boom of chronic diseases in our society have occurred because 80% of the population is deficient in vitamin D3.

Other natural compounds with anticancer effects were utilized based on their light value—the structure of the atoms that we discussed earlier in reference to their electrical conductivity properties. These included magnolia bark and curcumin. Melatonin in high doses is used in Europe for cancer treatment due to its extraordinary antioxidant value.

There is evidence that the administration of melatonin alone, or in combination with interleukin-2 in conjunction with chemoradiotherapy supportive care in cancer patients with advanced solid tumors, has been associated with improved outcomes of tumor regression and survival. Moreover, chemotherapy has been shown to be better tolerated in patients treated with melatonin.[23]

As discussed earlier, senolytics are a group of compounds that have been shown to aid the body in removing aged and senescent cells. Research has shown that cells that are aging "infect" surrounding cells with age via cellular messengers called cytokines. The most powerful compound in that group has been shown to be fisetin, which is found in strawberries. In mice fed this substance, there's a substantial improvement in longevity. In very old mice, fisetin extended the projected life span by 50%.[24]

Senolytics are also photosensitizers. Photosensitizers have been used in conjunction with laser light for the treatment of cancer. Cancer cells absorb photosensitizers more readily than normal cells, and when activated through a light source they can selectively kill cancer cells. In order to reach deeper regions of the body, usually lasers are applied.[25]

It has been shown that 4-strand DNA quadruplexes are a regulatory mechanism to our genetic code that provides a reading switch. Telomeres are regulated by this 4-strand DNA. Senolytics, such as fisetin, can stabilize that complex and allow the genetic code to be read.[26] Therefore, fisetin was added for its multiple beneficial actions in enhancing the well-being of my patients.

The interactions of UV light with different healing compounds used in the treatment of the Mercy Blu Room patients were considered a possible mechanism whereby the healing process might be supported.

Participants with a cancer diagnosis attended Blu Room sessions three times a week, with self-correction and mindfulness techniques they were learning at Ramtha's School of Enlightenment highly encouraged. These patients had either received previous surgery, chemotherapy or radiation, or were on hospice.

In a retrospective chart review of the patients, trends in outcomes emerged. We had a wide variety of cancer patients who were in advanced stages of their disease, many of them stage 4 cancer with large tumor burden, who were currently receiving palliative care treatment. Some had chosen not to undergo chemotherapy or radiation. They were at a point where they were seeking a different kind of help that could augment their regular medical care.

All participants were instructed that the Blu Room should never be used instead of regular medical care and conventional treatment. The retrospective review showed that combination therapy with the Blu Room improved quality of life in all cases, and many reported a decrease in anxiety and improved energy.

Dealing with the mental aspects of having cancer, and coping with the fear of death, was a big, recurrent experience for patients in this program. The Blu Room was integral to helping them deal with that fear and anxiety. One hundred percent of participants reported improvement in quality of life on their monthly follow-up questionnaires.

Recent studies have revealed that sympathetic nervous system stress response promotes metastatic spread and shapes the tumor microenvironment. Chronic stress from breast cancer accelerated breast cancer metastasis. According to my assessment, as witnessed in my patients, the stress reduction effects of the Blu Room can have significantly beneficial effects in reducing cancer promoting stress response.[27]

There was a wide variety of cancer patients in the Mercy Blu Room program. We had an end-stage colon cancer patient with a large mass in the abdomen and current colostomy. His quality of life while on hospice was increased with Blu Room visits prior to his passing, identified as decreased pain and overall improvement in energy and well-being. Another very ill patient on hospice with high tumor burden, metastatic prostate cancer, and recurrent anemia, experienced decreased pain and improved quality of life during treatment time but unfortunately succumbed to the disease. A patient with localized prostate cancer achieved biopsy proven remission with this combination treatment regimen. His personal healing journey is outlined later in this chapter.

One stage IV breast cancer patient with documented metastatic disease to the lung and femur achieved complete remission, as documented by serial PET scans, and her healing story is outlined later in this chapter. One 87-year-old patient with stage IV breast cancer—with previous mastectomy and chemotherapy—had metastases to the skull, skeleton, and liver. She achieved complete resolution of her bone pain due to natural combination therapy and Blu Room support that has lasted for two years. This patient has been part of the Mercy Blu Room program, after failing multiple chemotherapeutic regimens prior to entering the program, and has chosen a transition to palliative care. She is still enjoying her functionality and good quality of life.

A cervical cancer patient used the Blu Room to support her through active chemotherapy and radiation and reported great benefit in energy and stamina to be able to endure her treatment regimen better.

The trends I have observed suggest potential clinical benefit in supporting cancer patients at any stage of their disease with regular Blu Room visits to augment their treatment. In particular, there may be benefits to quality-of-life experience, improved mood, and decrease in anxiety and stress. There may also be potential benefits as an adjunct for palliative care patients to possibly ease their symptoms by improving relaxation at the end of life.

The Mercy Blu Room program also included complex patients with cardiovascular problems ranging from advanced congestive heart failure to heart transplant candidates, cardiac arrest survivors, stroke survivors, patients with recent severe heart attacks, chronic kidney disease, including end-stage renal disease on dialysis, chronic high blood pressure, and atrial fibrillation. Patients continued to receive care by their specialty providers.

With heart failure participants, we used a combination of peptides, nutraceuticals, and nutritional optimization in combination with standard medical treatment. Epitalon has been shown to lengthen telomeres and help prevent ischemic heart disease.[28] High-dose CoQ10 is an important natural supplement and has been shown to improve ejection fraction in heart failure patients.[29] Coenzyme Q10 is part of the mitochondrial Krebs cycle, the mechanism by which the cells make energy. As a cardiac cell has more than 5,000 mitochondria, compared to a biceps muscle cell having about 200 mitochondria, in order to make cardiac cells function well, we need to give them all of the nutrients necessary. Vitamin D levels were monitored via blood tests and optimized with supplementation to levels >75mg/dl. And we stopped statin drugs, as they have been shown to interfere with mitochondrial health and promote atherosclerosis and congestive heart failure.[30]

Heart patients used other natural treatments like curcumin to decrease inflammation. Participants came to the Blu Room twice a week and were given monthly follow-ups for medication management and tapering of the cardiac medication when indicated. Several patients had advanced congestive heart failure.

Congestive heart failure with an ejection fraction of 17%, when normal is considered between 50-70%, indicates very advanced heart disease with high risk of sudden cardiac death. We had patients with previous cardiac arrest. Three of them had a cardiac arrest and were successfully resuscitated. We had two patients with an implanted defibrillator, because of their risk of cardiac death. The combination therapy of Blu Room with medication management, nutritional optimization, and peptides improved their quality of life and mood. Symptom improvement in shortness of breath and fatigue was significant and heart pump function improved in six out of eight people who had a follow-up echocardiogram.

There has not yet been a randomized, controlled trial to independently assess the effects of the Blu Room related to mindful focus, nutraceuticals, peptides, and medications. The Blu Room is not a medical treatment device. However, if we are able to lift depression, mood, and improve levels of fatigue, there can very well be a significant effect on health based on prior research evaluating the negative effects of depression, stress, and anxiety on the state of health of patients.

According to the teachings of Ramtha, the ultraviolet realm is beyond polarity, beyond the positive and negative emotions that can cause afflictions in the body. The Blu Room creates stasis, a detachment from polarized emotions, which allows healing to occur. This is because, as we discussed in previous chapters, research studies have indicated the significant, possible health effects of UVB light, blue light, and sound frequencies like 111 Hz.

As a practicing internal medicine physician with twenty years' experience, it became apparent to me that there was a substantial benefit to patients in the Mercy Blu Room program. The combination of Blu Room treatments with medical treatments like peptides, neutraceuticals, and hormonal optimization produced favorable outcomes in many patients.

The greatest effect I observed was the subjective increase in the hope of my patients, who were fearful of certain conventional treatments. Instead of being antagonized for their desire to find natural ways of self-healing, they were supported in their belief. This created a harmony of intent that was empowered by like-minded people who were supportive of each other.

In the case reports included at the end of this chapter, of note is that the self-healing techniques taught at Ramtha's School of Enlightenment contributed to the subjective and objective improvement of individual patients. A randomized controlled, double-blind trial would elucidate these effects and is recommended in the future.

Every healing journey is unique with its own challenges, its own hurdles to overcome. The following case reports reveal the medical interventions and convey some of the spiritual and emotional breakthroughs in the minds of these patients—which is in the forefront of their focus—that have substantially contributed to their improvement in health.

Case Studies in the Application of Light Medicine

Many patients at my office have undergone treatment with patient specific, previously described alternative treatment modalities, according to the Light Medicine model introduced in this book. The treatment combinations administered continue to evolve. All patients, whose stories have been included below, gave written consent for treatment as well as case report documentation.

The following interviews describe a wide variety of disease states and very personal and unique journeys of healing. Further Mercy Blu Room case studies can be found in the book *The Radical Few: Ordinary People Manifesting the Extraordinary,* by Sophie Sykes.[31]

Case 1: Healing journey with atrial fibrillation (March 2018)

Donna is a 75-year-old woman with a longstanding history of heart problems. She had chronic mitral valve prolapse with degenerative changes, causing a leaky mitral valve. This led to a mitral valve replacement in 1998. She has had a complex history of recurrent atrial fibrillation treated with cardioversion and antiarrhythmic drugs over several years. She did have recurrent hospitalizations from flareups, and the paroxysmal atrial fibrillation caused acute congestive heart failure, with intermittent heart pump function as low as an ejection fraction (EF) of 20-25%. Those numbers improved to EF 55% after further electrophysiologic intervention. She had a biventricular pacemaker placed, now with an improved EF of 55%.

Over the years Donna has had significant symptoms from her heart condition and at times she was bedridden due to low energy. During times when she has had fast heart rates, she would become dehydrated and get short of breath with minimal activities and was unable to complete even the simplest tasks due to her low energy.

Since Donna started Blu Room therapy, she has had less symptoms of her atrial fibrillation impacting her abilities, even though her pacemaker readings show that the problem persists. She has greater stamina and no longer experiences shortness of breath. She has experienced a more serene ability to manage stress in her life due to her Blu Room visits, which is important for healing with any heart patient. Over several months of Blu Room use, her overall condition continued to improve. Most recently she had a work-related assignment and was able to work for twelve hours in perpetual motion, with all her coworkers amazed at her stamina and "go-getter" attitude.

Donna attributes these improvements in her condition to the Blu Room and feels they are nothing short of miraculous. She continues to feel great after having left the Mercy Blu Room program and remains symptom free.

Case 2: Healing journey with psoriasis (April 2018)

Bob is 74 years old with a history of atrial fibrillation, congestive heart failure, insulin dependent diabetes, and marginal cell lymphoma affecting lymph nodes in his abdomen. He has had psoriasis for many years. Bob had been going to the Blu Room twice a week for two months. Within two sessions he noted marked improvement of his psoriasis, which was severe and was covering his arms, legs, abdomen, and scalp with so much scarring that he had patches of permanent hair loss. Bob had complete sustained remission of his psoriasis in the last two months and states that his skin looks now like he never had the disease.

During the time of his Blu Room treatments his diabetes also improved, and he was able to lower his insulin doses from 45 units twice a day to 30 units twice a day and maintain the same diabetic control, with his last HgA1c of 6.8 indicating good diabetic control. He did not change his lifestyle during this time but attributes the improvement to how the Blu Room helped him heal himself.

Bob believes that his negative attitudes, emotions, and the induced stress by them, caused his health problems. He is constantly working on improving himself and feels the Blu Room helps to "mellow him out." He feels noticeably less depressed, can cope better with his stress, and now maintains a positive outlook on life, which helps his overall health status. He does not have significant heart-related symptoms.

Bob chose not to undergo chemotherapy or radiation for his lymphoma. He is feeling healthier and can cope with the stressor of having been diagnosed with cancer. He feels the Blu Room helped him to look deeper at his attitudes and he experiences a personal sense of forgiveness during Blu Room sessions. He says, "Everything is gone" when he is in the Blu Room. When he goes back to his life, reality sets in, but slowly he is seeing his life changing for the better. Bob notes that the changes he is experiencing from Blu Room visits are subtle but represent powerful and profound levels of personal transformation.

Case 3: Healing journey with chronic pain (May 2018)

Molly is an 81-year-old woman who had both knees replaced in 2003. She has had chronic knee pain ever since. In 2013, she was unable to walk and had to have both of her knee replacements revised. After she had the second surgery to replace her right knee, she was unable to feel her leg after the procedure and fell. This caused her to have a complex left bimalleolar ankle fracture and dislocation of her new right knee replacement which completely opened her surgical site. Molly was wheelchair-bound for three months, as her right knee continued to have severe pain, requiring opiate pain medications.

She started having night sweats and fevers over the course of a year and then developed an open, draining wound on her right knee that was treated with wound care. One year later, after several hospital visits, she was diagnosed with a failed and infected prosthesis and the infection had eaten through her bone. Her right knee was removed. She was treated with antibiotics, having a spacer only in her leg. The doctors were concerned they would have to amputate.

After three months of intensive antibiotics, she was clear of infection and was able to get a new knee. She was in chronic pain, had to use a walker, and needed ongoing opiate pain medications. She could not get up out of a chair without help. Pain in her leg was her constant companion. She tried everything from Tens units, topical pain relievers, and opiate medications to rid herself of the severe, chronic pain.

Molly started going to the Blu Room in February 2017. She noticed easing of her right knee pain after each session. One day while at home, after her seventeenth Mercy Blu Room session, she noticed that she could walk without discomfort. The pain had disappeared completely and it never came back. One year later, Molly remains pain free in her knee. She can get up out of a chair without help and she no longer uses a walker. Molly attributes this miraculous healing to the Blu Room. Now she is working on healing her back.

Case 4: Healing journey from PTSD and depression (May 2018)

David is a 71-year-old Vietnam veteran with a history of posttraumatic stress disorder (PTSD) who had a severe heart attack in April 2014 and subsequently a stroke in August of the same year.

His heart attack was so severe that on the way to the hospital he went into cardiac arrest. He was successfully resuscitated and required stents in two of his heart arteries. The sustained heart damage caused him to have congestive heart failure from severe ischemic cardiomyopathy with a heart pump fraction of 27%, normal being over 55%.

Only four months after this heart attack, he had a severe stroke, which left him with right-sided weakness and expressive aphasia, the inability to speak. He had a vocabulary of two words—"yes" and "no." After his stroke, he was in a rehabilitation center for a month. He has been doing speech therapy for the last four years.

David started using the Blu Room in February of 2017 and has been coming twice a week for more than fourteen months, sometimes more often. He still has speech difficulties and his memory is affected, but he is doing a lot better. He must pause and find his words but is now able to speak in full sentences. Sometimes he must try several times to say what he means before it comes out with the meaning he intended. His speech therapists are amazed at his remarkable progress. He gets teary-eyed when he talks about his journey with the Blu Room. He says it is not because of his PTSD, in that he only killed one person in the war and was able to cope with the horrible things he saw. After the war, it took him about eight years to come to terms with his life. There was something else that happened to bring about his improvement.

David explains that he experienced the Blu Room as both negative and positive for 150 sessions. Then something happened to him in January of this year, and since then all his sessions were positive. He says that it was not the Blu Room that was negative; it was that something in his being was out of sync. David did not realize that his body and mind were not in harmony. Then in January in the Blu Room, he felt as if his body, his age, and everything about him caught up with who he was. After that, everything was all right.

His neighbor notes that she was the one he came to when he had his heart attack in 2014 and she called 9-1-1. Having known him for many years, she describes David's transformation over the past year as nothing short of miraculous. She says David used to be a grouchy, grumpy man, easy to get angry, with a temper. In the last few months, she notes that he is so sweet, completely transformed, moved to tears in his emotions, and able to express them with the people around him. His neighbor notes that this is not the old David. He is completely new, completely transformed, and unrecognizable from his old self.

David explains that the Blu Room can help you heal at your own pace. If you add to it by intentionally working on healing yourself and your attitudes, it can help you speed up your healing. He says he added to his healing by looking at this "negative" in his life, his "shadow," this being out of sync with himself. He explains that if you are adding more to your healing, then it will take even less time in the Blu Room until there is a time where the negative "issue" is diminished to "nothing." The negative disappears; it is just gone one day. David says it depends on what you are doing and how you are in your own healing. That is what happened to David in January in the Blu Room. His negative disappeared to nothing, and what was left was love.

He cried, exhausted, after he explained this, and the look in his eyes spoke to a much greater understanding than he had words for.

David describes that after January the Blu Room helped him heal something that now is peaceful and calm, like a shadow that was lifted.

David cries because he has no words for what happened to him. How do you express with words something in the depth of your being that you felt throughout your life but could not give words to, something you could feel sitting there with every breath like a nagging shadow? That is what was healed in David through the Blu Room. He can best express it in his eyes with his tears, and this thing that happened is bigger than words. And yet because it happened, he is now able to speak better, and his brain is continuing to heal.

David continues to improve, and he surrenders to his journey. He had an implantable defibrillator put into his heart soon after his transformation, due to low pump function. A few months ago he had some chest pains but now, despite his poor heart function, he does not have any symptoms of heart failure. He is accepting and doing what he needs to do to support his improvement, including following up with his doctors and continuing the Blu Room treatments.

Case 5: Healing pain from a life-altering motor vehicle accident (June 2018)

Doris is a 78-year-old woman who sustained a life-threatening motor vehicle accident in November 2015. Doris remembers driving down the road, preparing to make a turn, and hearing a loud voice in her head say, "You are going to die!" Doris found herself yelling, "Nooo!!!" She was wondering why she was yelling out loud, being alone in the car.

The next thing she remembers is waking up in the hospital. She had been in a coma for more than six days.

Doris was hospitalized for one month. Her daughter reported that while she was in the hospital, Doris would mention that her deceased mother would come to visit her. The daughter asked Doris what Grandmother wanted and Doris said, "She wants me to go with her." Doris had replied to her mother, "I'm not ready to go."

Doris sustained traumatic, displaced fractures of three ribs, two cervical vertebral fractures, and fracture and dislocation of the left clavicle. She also sustained severe traumatic brain injury and intracranial bleeding from severe head trauma. After a hospitalization for one month, she was discharged to a nursing facility where she remained for three and a half months. She required assistance with all daily activities of living, such as bathing and dressing, help with transfers, and going to the restroom. Her injuries required the use of a wheelchair and, later, a walker.

Doris did not want to use narcotic pain medication. While convalescing in the nursing home, she weaned herself off all opiates. Seven years prior to the accident, she had a two-vessels coronary artery bypass graft with aortic valve replacement. She has not had any chest pain or shortness of breath since her bypass graft. Due to the multiple rib fractures, however, breathing had become quite painful, and the pain in her chest at times was almost unbearable.

After being discharged from the nursing facility, Doris started going to the Blu Room once a week. Her progress was gradual. She was unable to drive and still needed considerable assistance. All her movements were very slow, with her balance being impaired, and her memory was poor.

By early 2016, she was able to use the Blu Room every day for two weeks. When she began these two weeks of daily Blu Room visits, she needed help to lie down on the table, to transfer and move around, and could not get up by herself. After two weeks of daily treatment, she had improved so much that she had substantially decreased pain and was able to get up on her own. "I almost jumped off the table by myself!" she proudly says.

Since her rib fractures were displaced, they were unable to heal appropriately, and she was still experiencing substantial pain with movement, walking, lying down, and any position change. Doris was determined not to take any chronic pain medications at any time because she did not want the side effects of clouding her mind and her ability to think.

Doris experienced an enormous difference with decreased pain through regular Blu Room use, which was a relief beyond the descriptive power of words. Chronic pain can be a devastating experience for patients who live with it, often leading to severe depression, hopelessness, and substantially impaired functionality in life. Pain can become an all life-consuming experience of suffering. The gift of relief from this through the Blu Room, without the need for debilitating use of mind-altering, pain-relieving drugs, has been of unspeakable value for Doris.

After the motor vehicle accident, it had been recommended to Doris to undergo neurosurgical treatment for the two vertebral fractures in her neck. Doris declined and was able to progress with her healing without surgery. She was in a hard-collar neck brace for several months. Unfortunately, since her rib fractures were unable to completely heal—as the bones were dislocated and shattered so that the left clavicle fracture was causing pain when she was lying down—she felt compression to the soft tissue in her neck occasionally giving her even a choking sensation. Most recently in early 2018, during a reevaluation by a surgeon regarding the option to repair the dislocated, nonhealed left clavicle fracture, Doris opted against surgical intervention at her age. She prefers to heal herself. In fact, her right shoulder had substantially decreased mobility due to injury from the accident. Since starting the Mercy Blu Room program, she developed increased range of motion in her right shoulder and can now lift her arm and shoulders, reach for things, and comb her own hair.

Her overall mobility in her arms and upper torso improved so much since April 2018 that Doris can even drive again. She hadn't been physically able to do so since the accident. Doris also no longer uses a walker. She's careful not to fall and moves slowly. She is well enough to not have to utilize an assistive device. She fights for her independence of living alone and says, "I clean corners," meaning she cleans her house a little at a time and then sits down and rests, but she does it all herself. She can even use her own vacuum cleaner. Only someone with her experience understands what a miracle that is.

For many months Doris had difficulty sleeping due to ongoing pain. Her sleep significantly improved with her Blu Room use. She proudly says, "Now I sleep like a log!"

Doris feels that her mood is uplifted, and she is much improved. To maintain a willful, optimistic, and enthusiastic outlook when physical suffering is ongoing for so long is an extraordinary feat.

Throughout her journey, the Blu Room has been healing Doris significantly and on many levels of her being. Doris felt that the Blu Room was helping her to recover an enthusiasm about life and support her determination to master this challenge mindfully, emotionally, and physically. Doris has been using her focus to continually heal herself. Due to the severe brain injury, she had developed significant memory loss and problems with her balance. Gradually, with ongoing use of the Blu Room, her memory started improving. Doris has been going into the Blu Room with specific intents like healing her brain from memory loss. She would diligently work with her healing focus in the Blu Room and noticed that her ability to concentrate was improved and deepened.

Doris notes that she also underwent a profound personality transformation. She has been able to be more allowing of others and let go of control in her life. Doris feels that the extraordinary challenge of surviving from this motor vehicle accident and continually fighting to improve her physical and mental function has brought a wisdom and peace to her, and that the Blu Room has been supporting her to hold that tranquil, peaceful place in her daily life.

At 78 years old, Doris marvels at her own recovery, her determination to heal, and prides herself that she's living independently, taking care of herself. Throughout the years since the accident, her goal was to master her own suffering, and the mischievous twinkle in her eyes shows her knowing that she's doing it! Doris feels the Blu Room has been a tremendous gift in supporting her healing and rehabilitation to a functional life.

Case 6: Chronic open wound healed in two Blu Room sessions (June 2018)

Pat is a 77-year-old woman. In September 2017, she fell and tore the skin of her right lower leg, causing an approximately 5 cm open laceration. Pat was seen by her healthcare practitioner and was treated with standard wound care. She then developed a nonhealing, open wound that became infected and twice required oral antibiotic treatment. For months the wound would not heal with topical treatment and bandages. In March 2017, Pat started coming to the Mercy Blu Room program. Her wound was still open and had not changed much in appearance over the previous six months. She exposed the wound to UV light in the Blu Room. It took only two sessions for the laceration to completely close. She still had surrounding erythema but that also quickly resolved.

The effectiveness of UV light therapy use for chronic wound healing has long been established in clinical research studies. Prominent wound healing centers like the advanced wound care clinic at the University of Southern California utilizes UV light for advanced wound healing with remarkable success. UV activates genes that influence cell division and immune responses, acts as a bactericidal agent, and thereby promotes wound healing by diminishing the toxic effect of bacterial overgrowth on fibroblasts in the wound bed. Pat now has a well-healed scar without any pain.

Case 7: Healing heart failure and PTSD after cardiac arrest (November 2018)

Peter is 71 years old. In July 2018, he developed bilateral arm pain and sweats, then became unconscious. His wife started CPR and resuscitated him. At the hospital, three stents were placed into his left major artery which was completely occluded. The front and left parts of his heart muscle were not moving at all. He had congestive heart failure with an ejection fraction of 30% (normal is more than 55).

Even with the stents, Peter required multiple anti-arrhythmic medications. Peter experienced extreme side effects from medications that he described as a dark shadow and feeling like death itself was advancing toward him. It took all of his focus to ward off that feeling of absolute blackness.

In the ICU, his nurse asked if he was a student at Ramtha's School of Enlightenment, and he said, "Yes." This nurse urged him to find a Blu Room and to go to it as much as he could after his discharge from the hospital. When Peter was discharged after ten days, his heart's ejection fraction was 43%.

Within a couple of weeks, Peter was able to participate in the Mercy Blu Room program and visited three to four times a week. He also utilized the peptide epitalon and multiple other nutraceuticals and vitamins to support his healing journey. Peter improved significantly but the level of emotional trauma from the sudden death experience was still present. The shadow would come to him during the night and he had to fight to focus it away. It left a sense of uncertainty and fear in both him and his wife.

Peter describes going to the Blu Room several times a week as a peaceful, serene, powerful support that is difficult to describe. It was the Blu Room that eventually dissolved the awareness and fear of the shadow of death, along with all of the associated posttraumatic anxiety. Peter no longer has those attacks.

Peter says the Blu Room—through its profound atmosphere of healing—helped him reach a level of peace that has become a lasting companion in his life. He describes seeing his life now through clean glasses, when he never knew before that his lenses were dirty.

Peter was able to lower some of his blood pressure and antiarrhythmic medications, and his energy was returning. He was able to be more active in his cardiac rehabilitation program and can now undergo strenuous exercise without problems. His life has a new level of serene appreciation and gratitude that emanates from his being. When Peter had his repeat echocardiogram in September 2018, it showed that his left heart wall was moving normally and that his heart pump ejection fraction had normalized to 56%. He also has normal systolic and diastolic function of his heart, which was a fantastic improvement in only two months' time.

Peter attributes his fast recovery and profound life change to the help he received in the Mercy Blu Room program. His health continues to improve. Other areas like his knee and shoulder pain are also improving with physical therapy and Blu Room sessions. Peter is enjoying a new life with his lovely wife. He underwent chelation therapy for several months and subsequently had a repeat cardiac stress test at his one-year-follow-up. His results were normal.

Case 8: Healing congestive heart failure and depression (November 2018)

Rosa is 60 years old and has had congestive heart failure, chronic kidney disease, and high blood pressure since 2009.

When Rosa was first diagnosed with congestive heart failure, her ejection fraction was significantly reduced at 20% (normal is 55-70%). For a long time her heart failure presented an untreatable cough and it was hard for her to even complete a sentence without coughing and gasping for air. Rosa was seeing her cardiologists and receiving medical treatments. At times she was at odds with taking drugs, in part because she did not understand what was happening with her body medically and she wanted to do things more naturally.

For years Rosa would have intermittent improvement of heart function followed by exacerbations of heart failure, requiring hospitalization. At her worst, she was only able to walk minimal distances due to severe shortness of breath and fatigue. Rosa also had been battling depression on and off for several years. In June 2017, she had a heart attack and was again hospitalized. Her echocardiogram showed an ejection fraction of 27%, diffuse lack of movement of the heart wall, moderate inability of the heart muscle to relax, and moderately severe leaking of her mitral valve. Her kidney function was significantly impaired due to progressive chronic kidney disease.

Rosa was discharged on multiple heart medications that she took faithfully. She still had a hard time with chronic shortness of breath and fatigue. From May through December of 2018, Rosa participated in the Mercy Blu Room twice a week consistently and was also treated with the peptide epitalon. Gradually her mood got better and her energy increased. She was able to do things without severe shortness of breath, and her emotional resilience to stress greatly improved. Rosa had a repeat echocardiogram in November 2018, which showed that her ejection fraction had significantly increased to 47%, her ability to relax the heart muscle improved, and her mitral valve leakage improved as well.

Rosa is now exercising. Her stamina and physical energy are the best they have been in years. Her depression has lifted and her mood and outlook on life are much more optimistic. She attributes this remarkable healing to the Blu Room, which she continues to use twice per week. She is now working on healing her kidney function and has the confidence to know she can do it.

Case 9: Healing congestive heart failure and chronic depression (November 2018)

Diana is 72 years old. In February 2018, she developed severe shortness of breath and chest pain and thought she was going to die from fluid filling her lungs. She went to the emergency room and was found to be in acute respiratory failure and acute congestive heart failure, with a heart pump ejection fraction at 40-45% (normal is 55+). The left atrium of Diana's heart was severely dilated, and she had atrial fibrillation with a rapid heart rate in the 140's.

After she was stabilized and treated, Diana was discharged on higher doses of medications but continued to feel the irregular heart rate from her atrial fibrillation, shortness of breath with exertion, and severe fatigue that made it difficult to do anything. Diana had struggled with depression for much of her life. Prior to this episode, she was quite low in her mood and outlook on life. She started the Mercy Blu Room program in March 2018. Slowly but steadily her energy improved. Her mood got better, and Diana was able to mend relationships in her life that had caused her much pain before. She noticed that coming to the Blu Room lifted the cloud of depression and changed her outlook towards her life. She was able to do more things and feel less short of breath and fatigued.

Diana was treated with multiple nutritional supplements and the peptide epitalon and over time has been able to lower her blood pressure medications. She does not feel her atrial fibrillation anymore, when before there was an annoying presence of a highly irregular heartbeat. Diana had a repeat echocardiogram in September 2018, which showed that her ejection fraction had increased to normal function at 63%. She still has a dilated left atrium and atrial fibrillation, but her heart rate is under very good control with half the medication dose required that she needed in March.

Diana feels that the Blu Room helped her reconnect spiritually. Old patterns of emotional problems seem to no longer have a hold on her life and this has improved her well-being throughout. Her family has noticed marked improvement and she is once again able to enjoy her life with them.

Diana is not a woman of many words, but she said of the Blu Room, "I have a greatly heightened gratitude for the Mercy Blu Room program and for life itself." Where before she was contemplating death due to her illness and depression, she now is looking forward to life.

Case 10: Remission of stage 4 breast cancer (January 2019)

Chantal is a 72-year-old woman who was originally diagnosed with breast cancer in July 2012. She took alternative measures, including Blu Room treatments once or twice per month, but the mass did not resolve. In May of 2016, the tumor in the left breast showed lymphatic invasion and progression of the disease. Chantal proceeded with bilateral mastectomy in early June.

After the surgery she took a hormone receptor blocker and had radiation therapy, but no chemo. Nodules appeared and disappeared in her lung and she developed a lesion in her left femur that remained. These indications of metastases indicated her disease had progressed to stage 4.

Throughout 2017, Chantal did more alternative therapy during which all lung nodules disappeared. In July 2018, a chest CT scan showed four new nodules in the lungs. Chantal still had the ongoing lesion in the femur. She still only wanted to use alternative therapy.

In August 2018, Chantal began treatment in the Mercy Blu Room program with sessions three times a week. In addition, she was treated with other alternatives like bioregulatory peptides and natural anticancer compounds. She had a follow-up PET scan in January 2019, which showed no abnormal metabolic activity in her body, indicating resolution of all metastatic disease.

Chantal was able to achieve remission several times during the last seven years through the power of her mind and with the help of multiple alternative treatments. She knows none of the treatments would have helped if she had not addressed the attitudes she needed to conquer. Chantal is confident her journey with cancer is permanently finished. To others on the healing journey, Chantal says, "Dig deeper and don't give up!" At her one-year-follow-up PET scan, she remains cancer-free and continues to enjoy her life to the fullest.

Case 11: Healing prostate cancer with mind, Blu Room, and innovative treatments (March 2019)

Guenther is a 66-year-old gentleman who in 2015 was found to have a rising PSA value, the marker for prostate cancer. Guenther wanted to heal himself with his mind and natural interventions. His PSA continued to rise, and in February 2018, he finally had a prostate biopsy which did show prostate cancer.

In May of 2018, Guenther became part of the Mercy Blu Room program and started Blu Room treatments three times a week. Despite those interventions, his PSA continued to rise, increasing to 26.4 in October 2018. High-dose oral Iscador and an anticancer peptide was added to his regimen in addition to his ongoing Blu Room treatments.

In December 2018, Guenther underwent a transformation of mind. He became extremely passionate and excited about a new project. He knows that this passion and excitement about a new start was what changed everything for him. He had a total of 67 Mercy Blu Room sessions through February 2019. In March 2019, Guenther had a repeat prostate biopsy that showed only chronic inflammation but had no evidence of cancer. His repeat PSA had come down to 18. Guenther is grateful about his healing and excited to continue his newfound life.

Case 12: Healing blood clots (April 2019)

Sharon is 70 years old. During a trip in late December 2018, she fell on ice and by the next day developed extensive swelling and hardness in her left leg. She went to the emergency room and was diagnosed with blood clots in every vein of the lower and upper left leg. This was highly dangerous since such blood clots can dislodge and cause a life-threatening embolism in the lungs.

The doctors at the emergency room immediately started Sharon on blood thinners and warned her against doing any significant activity. Blood thinners don't dissolve clots but they can stop them from getting bigger and prevent new ones from forming. Two days later, Sharon returned to the ER due to severe discomfort caused by tightness of all the tissues in her leg. Upon returning from her trip, she started Blu Room sessions at Absolute Health Clinic and went to her primary care provider who ordered CT scans of her abdomen and pelvis. The scans showed that the blood clots had migrated into the veins in the pelvic area close to the inferior vena cava, the major vein in the body leading to the heart. She was immediately seen by a vascular surgeon who did not recommend surgery just yet.

Sharon increased her weekly Blu Room sessions to every other day by joining the Mercy Blu Room program where she was also started on nutraceuticals and peptides to stimulate blood clot dissolution while she stayed on the pharmaceutical blood thinner. With this treatment regime and her consistent healing focus, Sharon's leg swelling reduced substantially and her tissue softened in the following weeks.

Sharon continued her Blu Room sessions every other day through February and March. A follow-up ultrasound taken on April 5, 2019, showed the veins of her left leg were normal without any evidence of blood clots. The ultrasound showed some residual clots still present in the iliac veins in her pelvis.

Typically, a person stays on blood thinners for many months—even years—and scans will still show residual evidence of previous blood clots. To have a rapid resolution of so many blood clots, along with a return to normal of all leg veins in such a short period of time, is medically astounding. Sharon understood that it was critical to make a life change. It was a matter of life and death. Sharon addressed her changes with an intensity, acuity, and an absoluteness in applying all the techniques she had learned at Ramtha's School of Enlightenment. This was an opportunity to pause and reevaluate her mind, to have no regret about the trauma, and to intently focus on what she wanted her future to be.

Sharon continues to focus on complete resolution of clots in her iliac veins. She attributes her rapid healing to the combination of her focused mind, much-needed rest, frequent Blu Room sessions, and the use of natural compounds taken in conjunction with the blood thinners.

Case 13: Improving energy after a heart attack (September 2019)

Joseph is 83 years old. He enjoyed good health until September 2018, when he had a heart attack that required stents to his major heart arteries. Due to the heart attack, Joseph developed congestive heart failure. His heart pump function decreased from the normal of 65 down to 40%. At the same time, a blood clot was found in the left ventricle of his heart. He was started on blood thinners and heart medications.

Before the heart attack, Joseph never went to the doctor and did not take any type of medications. After the heart attack he experienced fatigue, along with shortness of breath, when he exerted himself. Adhering to his regimen was a challenge, but he supported himself diligently with nutritional supplements. He took his medications for many months, but some of them made him feel ill. So he gradually discontinued all of them except the blood thinner.

In January 2019, Joseph started the Mercy Blu Room program twice a week. His fatigue was lifted and his energy level continued to increase. He was able to walk up the hill on his property without being exhausted. Since then, Joseph has remained very active—chopping wood, taking care of his house and property. He no longer has leg swelling, shortness of breath, chest discomfort, or any other heart symptoms.

Through this journey with using the Blu Room, Joseph has become more aware of his thoughts and is able to correct his self-judgments easier. He is more detached. He experiences a deeper level of focus. This has been important to him. Before every Blu Room session, he pauses and says, "I accept all healing for my body." He is not sure if he falls asleep, but he loses time in the Blu Room. It seems to him that he is only in there for a minute, so deep is his ability to relax into his healing intention. Joseph is grateful that the Blu Room helped his healing journey and aided his improvement in quality of life.

Case 14: Healing from lung cancer and finding a new self (September 2019)

Cynthia is a 66-year-old woman. A longtime smoker, she suffered from significant anxiety, high blood pressure, and high cholesterol. Since the Blu Room first became available in 2015, she went two to three times per week to support herself in her healing. Cynthia had a journey of many experiences in the Blu Room.

In 2018, Cynthia had two major surgeries. First, she had a partial lung resection for localized lung cancer. Then only a few months later, she underwent a repair of an abdominal aneurysm of the aorta. After being diagnosed with such severe medical conditions, her anxiety and fear were severe. She started the Mercy Blu Room program in September 2018, after her lung cancer surgery.

The two major surgeries caused a profound level of fatigue. Cynthia found herself close to giving up, not seeing the sense in her suffering and poor quality of life. The Blu Room allowed her to surrender. Cynthia attributes a great deal of her healing to this process of surrender—letting go.

After many months of struggle, Cynthia suddenly realized that she had stopped dreaming of a brighter future. That realization caused an earthquake of change in her life. Now she was on a mission. She could not afford to be sloppy in her mind if she wanted her life and health back!

In October 2019, on her one-year follow-up lung CT scan, a new 4-millimeter nodule was found. While the doctors were not excluding that this was inflammation, they wanted to watch her closely for recurrence of her cancer. Cynthia was adamant that she would not have to undergo any more suffering or further surgery but that she would beat this challenge in her mind!

Cynthia completely changed her lifestyle, found new passions and hobbies in her life, exercised, used the Blu Room faithfully twice a week, and got busy enjoying life to the fullest and growing younger and healthier. Anxiety and fear were a relic of the past! She found a new best friend: herself!

The gleeful confirmation of her mindful change arrived on her chest CT scan in August 2020. The 4-millimeter nodule had resolved and her lungs were clear.

Cynthia gratefully credits the frequency of the Blu Room for her profound healing and transformation. She is convinced she will continue her Blu Room sessions as part of her youthful, healthy future and ever unfolding dreams.

Case 15: Healing a broken heart and atrial fibrillation (November 2019)

Mary is a 61-year-old woman who was diagnosed with atrial fibrillation several years ago. She also has hypertrophic cardiomyopathy, a condition causing muscle thickening of the septum of the heart. Mary has led a life of significant, emotional stress due to her relationship with her son, who suffered from drug addiction.

Over the years, during times of exacerbated stress, Mary would develop episodes of uncontrolled atrial fibrillation with extremely high heart rates, necessitating multiple hospital visits and medication treatments. Mary always knew that her emotional anguish would eventually cause significant heart problems.

Tragically, Mary's son committed suicide. One day after her son's memorial, in January 2020, Mary's heart went into the worst episode of atrial fibrillation. She had severe chest pain and sustained heart rates of over 200 beats per minute. She prayed to God to let her die, unable to endure the pain in her chest.

Mary underwent cardioversion procedure with electro-shocks. After hospital discharge, she was admitted to the Mercy Blu Room program where she had two sessions per week for five months.

Mary underwent a heart ablation to eliminate the electrical pathways in the heart that were causing the problem and continued to take the heart medications that were regulating her rhythm.

Mary describes that the Blu Room helped her with healing after the ablation. Even after the procedure, she had an episode of chest discomfort possibly indicating recurrence of her atrial fibrillation. She knew that the same emotions and attitudes would re-create her heart condition. She weaned herself off her antiarrhythmic and has been maintained on only one medication without recurrence.

The Blu Room lifted Mary's stress and severe depression. She also regained her strength and energy, feeling like her aging reversed 20 years. She stated adamantly, "The Blu Room gave me my life back. I feel great!"

It is well known that severe chronic stress can make heart rhythm abnormalities extremely difficult to control, and even with surgical intervention, symptoms can return. The rapid, emotional recovery from her devastating loss is the most miraculous, transformative aspect of Mary's journey. As the broken heart could mend in the light of the Blu Room, the heart condition also improved and a new life emerged.

Case 16: New hope in life – improving Parkinson's symptoms (November 2019)

Neil O. is an 85-year-old gentleman who had experienced a significant decline in his functional life when he developed Parkinson's symptoms over the last several years. Gradually his world slowed down and his ability to walk, care for himself, and interact with his surroundings were severely impaired, and it took a long time for him to speak and articulate words.

At the beginning of his treatment at Mercy Blu Room in May 2019, his gait was so impaired that with his walker, he would take a long time just to complete a few steps, and even lifting his foot was an enormous challenge. It took him thirty minutes to traverse thirty yards from the entrance of the Blu Room complex to the Blu Room. Neil was also experiencing significant anxiety. When observed, he often just had a blank stare on his face. He was no longer able to stand up from a chair without significant help, and his condition became so critical that he was close to having to transfer to a nursing facility. He was unable to even write his name.

Neil was started on levodopa/carbidopa, a medication for Parkinson's, and a neurotropic peptide named selank that blocks anxiety pathways in the brain while enhancing new neuronal growth. He was also started on nutritional supplementation in addition to his twice-a-week Blu Room sessions.

Gradually his symptoms improved and his anxiety subsided. He was able to walk faster. While previously he was unable to maneuver his walker to turn in a new direction and would stay frozen in one place, he was now able to pick up his walker, turn around briskly, and walk down the hallway by himself. Neil's cognition improved and he was able to speak better. At this point Neil started writing his own progress notes at his Blu Room sessions, was having conversations, and had a present twinkle in his eyes.

From the beginning of his Blu Room sessions, and even more so when the 111 Hz sound of divine healing was added, Neil noted more exhilaration after visits. His mental and even visual acuity became clearer. He started eating more, was physically getting stronger, and felt he was more present in the moment. In the Blu Room he had experiences of seeing fields of brilliant flowers and having a lightness of being, which were very meaningful to him. He was getting more enthusiastic, and on his daily progress sheets would note how wonderful he felt. When asked if there was anything else he would like to share, he noted, "Endless love."

Neil's confidence in his own possibilities of healing increased tremendously, and he feels empowered. Sometimes things get more challenging but Neil does not give up. He began taking Dihexa for several months, a peptide that is an Alzheimer's drug ten million times stronger than brain-derived, nerve growth factor for new synapse formation. He has made significant improvements and recently even walked around his house without a walker. He is happy that he is continually improving.

Case 17: Healing journey after colon cancer (November 2019)

Priscilla is 74 years old. She enjoyed excellent health all her life until she was diagnosed with severe anemia in 2018. A colonoscopy showed colon cancer. Priscilla underwent surgery and had the cancer removed. It was stage 3. This was a huge, life-altering shock for her. She started going to the Blu Room two to three times a week immediately after the diagnosis and then joined the Mercy Blu Room program in February 2019.

Priscilla recovered well after her surgery. When further tests in July 2019 indicated atherosclerosis, she became very proactive in learning about the different causes of illness and addressing them. She underwent intravenous chelation, nutritional therapy, and daily nutritional optimization while altering her diet, lifestyle, and using supplements as she continued to focus on healing. She learned about the dental connection to illness and is now having her root canals removed.

Keeping her anxiety and stress level down has been one of the greatest challenges for Priscilla. The Blu Room has helped her tremendously with that. She reports that going to the Blu Room, as well as engaging all these different modalities to heal herself, has given her a solid sense of self. It is a feeling of reliance and trust in her abilities that she has the capacity to meet challenges full-on and can overcome anything.

In mid-2019, while in the Blu Room, Priscilla had what she described as a physical experience of profound gratitude—an overwhelming feeling of realizing the blessing of her life and all the purposeful help she had received on her journey. She recognized how the teachings in Ramtha's School of Enlightenment, its events and disciplines, the support of family and friends, and the innovative treatments at AM Medical have been hugely instrumental in her journey. Priscilla said, "In this past year, one healing experience has led to another and then led to yet another. I was exactly in the right place at the right time during the whole of 2019. This continues to this day. I have felt, and continue to feel, an overwhelming sense of gratitude for my life."

Case 18: Reversing the need for dialysis (August 2020)

Judy is a 61-year-old woman who developed nausea and vomiting in early 2019. She was diagnosed with acute kidney injury and admitted to the hospital. Unfortunately, she had end-stage kidney failure requiring hemodialysis. Her glomerular filtration rate (GFR) was 8 with normal being over 100. Her creatinine was 5-6 with normal being around 1.

After her discharge, Judy entered the Mercy Blu Room program. She used the Blu Room twice a week before dialysis. This helped her very much to deal with the stress of dialysis and the significant challenges she faced, including the lack of medical insurance.

Judy used her mindful focus to reverse her condition and create healing in her body and her life. She used peptides like epitalon, which lengthen telomeres, and thymosin alpha-1, which downregulates inflammation in the body. She also used multiple nutraceuticals and vitamins to support her healing. Rapamycin was used every two weeks to inhibit the mTOR gene and reverse aging and chronic disease.

Judy reports that the Blu Room allowed her to have the peace of mind to create resolution to all her problems. Her accumulated debt from dialysis at $60,000 per month was forgiven. She was able to get medical insurance to cover her subsequent treatment costs. Doors would open to her and the help would come.

After six months of receiving hemodialysis, she was switched to peritoneal dialysis at home. After sixteen total months of being on dialysis, her kidneys improved enough to function on their own. This is a medical miracle. After two weeks off dialysis, Judy's GFR was at 21 and the creatinine 3.3.

Judy reports that the Blu Room put her in a state of acceptance that her miracle could happen. She is so excited and thankful that it indeed has arrived.

Case 19: Overcoming depression (August 2020)

Bruna is a 72-year-old woman who went through an exceedingly difficult personal time when caring for a family member with debilitating illness. Over many months of chronic stress, she became progressively more fatigued and unable to focus. She had difficulty performing her duties at work, due to the profound mental, physical, and emotional exhaustion that she was experiencing. She did not realize that she was depressed for quite some time. However, when speaking with others, she was often crying.

Bruna felt that she was in a situation where she could not see a way out. She was referred to the Mercy Blu Room program. She was also started on the peptide selank, which lifts depression, anxiety, and stress while enhancing memory and neurogenesis in the brain.

Bruna underwent a remarkable transformation very rapidly. She felt that the Blu Room helped her detach from this internal program of hopelessness and depression that had taken over her life.

Suddenly Bruna was able to express herself freely, and her body recovered its stamina and well-being. She was mentally able to perform her work with ease. Bruna described that she not only could detach from her suffering about her family member but also start to relate to her friends and environment in a more detached and peaceful way. Bruna rediscovered her joy.

As Bruna's physician, I witnessed a profound transformation and a very rapid alleviation of severe clinical depression with the help of the Blu Room. From observing desperation, I can now see a glowing person filled with passion for life. This dramatic change occurred in a period of less than two months without the use of pharmaceutical antidepressants, which is medically remarkable.

Case 20: Healing congestive heart failure (August 2020)

Neil K. is a 72-year-old gentleman with a history of chronic lymphocytic leukemia and a right tonsillar mass suspicious for malignancy. He developed severe progressive shortness of breath in May 2020. He was admitted to the hospital and found to be in acute congestive heart failure, acute kidney failure, and have severe anemia due to the chronic leukemia. His echocardiogram showed an ejection fraction of 38% with normal being above 55%.

Neil received three blood transfusions and was aggressively treated for his fluid overload. He had previously had an abnormal stress test a couple years earlier, possibly indicating a blocked artery to the heart. At that time he chose not to have medical follow-up and had been visiting the Blu Room.

After discharge from the hospital, Neil resumed his Blu Room sessions twice a week. These significantly helped his anxiety and improved his energy. He also used the peptide epitalon for 50 days, as this peptide has been shown to improve left ventricular heart pump function, and continued other nutraceuticals and supplements.

Neil's energy improved. He had a follow-up nuclear stress test in August that showed normal heart perfusion with a normal ejection fraction of 67%. Not only was there normalization of his heart pump function but also the previous finding of the potentially blocked artery was resolved.

Neil has faced many severe health challenges during this journey. The Blu Room has been like a ray of hope in his life. He feels that the Blu Room helps his other medical interventions, like the peptides, to work better.

Neil continues to focus on healing his remaining health challenges. His dream is to be well enough to start riding motorcycles again.

Case 21: Reclaiming a functional life (November 2020)

Barbara is a 68-year-old woman who was diagnosed with rheumatoid arthritis in 2013. The disease manifested as swelling, pain, and inflammation in multiple joints in her body and subsequent severe impairment of her mobility due to progressive joint destruction. She refused to use a cane when her knees were so swollen and painful that she could barely put weight on them, because she never wanted to admit that she was decrepit. Instead, she used ski poles, having been a professional skier in her youth. However, there were days when getting out of bed seemed like an impossible feat due to her pain. Rheumatologists prescribed multiple immune modulating drugs, which caused her to experience extreme side effects. Her worsening condition and constant pain caused significant anxiety and depression.

Barbara decided to pursue a different route of treatment, prescribed by me, which included a broad approach comprised of nutritional optimization, peptides, anti-inflammatory nutraceuticals, low dose steroids, chiropractics, and massage. As a result, she experienced substantial improvement in symptoms without side effects. Barbara was referred to the Mercy Blu Room program to help address contributing stressors, where she participated twice a week for ten weeks.

The Blu Room provided Barbara with the ability to deeply relax. Her sense of well-being increased, allowing her to experience peace and expanded mental clarity. She was able to face her greatest fear, which was not the fear of death but her fear of enduring future years of increased pain, immobility, drugs, side effects, doctor visits, and not being able to live her life fully.

Over the summer of 2020, while engaging in this combination program, Barbara was able to go on prolonged hikes without pain, and work long hours in her garden without stopping, a previously impossible feat. Her energy levels improved from extremely low to excellent. She reports an ongoing, overall feeling of well-being that has persisted. Her hopelessness and depression regarding her condition lifted. She communicates her willful conviction, "I can't stop. I must keep moving. There are so many things I still want to do in my life."

The mental determination required to overcome chronic pain, the courage to choose an alternate route of treatment, and the ability to trust as her path unfolds, is most remarkable in Barbara's journey. The will to overcome severe physical limitations was greatly enhanced by her Blu Room visits, which have contributed to her phenomenal recovery. Barbara's remarkable fight for well-being and a functional life continues every day.

Case 22: Miraculous recovery from brain bleed (November 2020)

Diana B. is a 77-year-old woman with a history of previous strokes who suffered a brain hemorrhage in July 2020. Her brain CT showed additional severe narrowing in the frontal and posterior areas of the brain's arterial circulation. The brain bleed led to severe lethargy, the inability to swallow, requiring placement of a feeding tube, severe confusion, loss of vision, and the inability to communicate. Diana's condition perpetually declined, and it was decided to discontinue medical treatment and send her home on hospice to die. The hospital discharge summary noted that her expected death would be within 12 to 48 hours.

Diana did not pass, but she was severely impaired, lethargic, unable to walk or transfer herself, unable to express herself, as she could not find the words, had severe memory impairment, and was dependent in all activities on help from her loving family. Even when she had her eyes open, Diana's daughter described that it seemed as if there was no one home.

One month after hospital discharge, Diana's children brought her to my office. At the time, Diana was severely impaired, sitting in a wheelchair and lethargic. She was seeing double or triple and unable to read or write. She was so weak that she was unable to transfer from the wheelchair by herself. Diana told me that she wanted to live. I asked her if she was willing to fight for it, and she responded with a fatigued but determined, "Yes!"

I recommended a regimen of chelation therapy IVs, alternating with methylene blue intravenously, peptides, and other nutrients. This was in addition to daily high doses of nutritional supplements. She complied with every recommendation, despite having severe anxiety about doctors and medical treatment due to her traumatic hospital experience. She brought a friend to her infusions, a stuffed animal named Kajiri, to help her overcome her anxieties. I also recommended the Mercy Blu Room program. And within a very short time, Diana had a remarkable recovery.

Her children noted that following her first visit to the Blu Room, her responses changed dramatically. Diana showed significant functional improvement and started speaking from her soul, telling them how much she loved them. This was unusual for her character and has persisted ever since. After four chelation IVs, Diana started walking with a walker. Initially she was unable to tolerate the Blu Room, as it increased her confusion. Due to the traumatic experience at the hospital, she had PTSD symptoms of severe terrors and crying spells at night. However, after a two-week pause from the Blu Room, she bravely went back, and her experience improved. Her daughter noted that the night terrors went away after restarting Blu Room treatments.

After six chelations and two methylene Blu IVs, Diana's vision normalized. Being able to see normally again had been a significant focus during her Blu Room sessions. Diana has now recovered to where she can read and sign her name. Her memory has much improved and she can once again have a conversation and express herself very well.

Diana is delighted with the results of her efforts and the combination therapy she received. Her children are overjoyed by their mother's miraculous improvement and are grateful for the ability to enjoy quality family time together.

In Summary

These cases, and many more not included, are examples of natural treatment modalities, as explained in this book, that were utilized in the treatment of these patients according to our Light Medicine model and with remarkable healing results. Regardless of what treatment modalities anyone chooses, the Blu Room has shown great value as an adjunct to any treatment method, given its stress-relieving effects.

As their overseeing physician, I am ever hopeful that these inspiring case stories might invite independent researchers to investigate the health outcomes of combination therapies as tested and presented in this book.

CHAPTER 24
FUTURE FRONTIERS AND CREATING
SUPERHUMANS

Where does such a new model of Light Medicine and science lead us? To the realization of infinite possibilities as divine human beings.

In our genome we have infinite possibilities of regeneration and unfoldment of new transcribed information. Now we understand that the command center of DNA is the mind, and that by training the mind we unlock previously unchartered territory.

If we now combine the new gene-editing technology, the neurotropics for brain enhancement, the ability to control epigenetic expression through use of exosomes and peptides, mindfulness techniques, and advanced light and sound technologies, we have an infinite array of tools that allow exploration and progress to new frontiers of possible achievements.

In every human who has the will to change, we have the ability to create and cultivate any potential talent. Anyone can be trained in sciences, arts, and outstanding athletic, physical capacity. Our brains are neuroplastic and we can enhance and accelerate this neuroplasticity with neuropeptides and focused intent. Just like we train muscles in the gym, we can train our brain. And these training programs for any human being can be physiologically supported by optimizing nutrition, oxygen utilization, and overall health in an individual manner.

We can even unlock the abilities of the animal kingdom that lie dormant in our genome. Dr. Gariaev, with his linguistic-wave genome theory, described junk DNA as the language context for encoded, holographic genetic information. The expression of these gene possibilities is governed by mind.

In other words, if we can imagine it, we can become it.

We can regenerate limbs like the salamander. We can have sonar abilities like the bat and the dolphin. We can live without oxygen like the turtle. Does that sound outrageous?

The salamander regeneration gene is transforming growth factor beta 1 (TGF-β1). It is activated when a limb is amputated, and the process of regeneration starts. This gene, TGF-beta 1, controls the regeneration and movement of new cells and allows the salamander to regrow complex structures like limbs, tail, jaw, spinal cord, and even parts of its brain.[1]

Humans also have this gene. The difference is that in humans, instead of telling a limb to regenerate, the gene tells the wounded area to heal and form a scar. If scientists can find a way to manipulate TGF-beta 1 in humans, it could lead to the ability to regrow organs and limbs, as well as treatments for spinal cord injury and severe burns. This has already been done by using electrical currents to keep the scarring process at bay. The spatiotemporal expression pattern of TGF-β1 in regenerating limbs shows that this gene is upregulated during the preparation phase of regeneration. TGF-β is a multifunctional set of peptides that controls proliferation, differentiation, and other functions in many cell types. TGF-β1 was first identified in human platelets as a protein with a molecular mass of 25 kilodaltons with a potential role in wound healing. As we have discussed, TGF-β1 is also present in exosomes.

The early growth response (Egr) gene is another gene target for regeneration. Studies have been done on the three-banded panther worm, given their remarkable ability to regenerate any part of the body within a few days of amputation. Scientists at Harvard University now believe that Egr is thought to be the "master control gene" responsible for this regeneration. The results of the study have shown that Egr binding was strongly associated with accessibility of chromatin during regeneration and that in wounded cells, Egr was the most significant upregulated gene. Specifically, the answer lies in an area of noncoding DNA that controls the gene.

Initially, noncoding, or junk DNA, was believed to have no role. In recent years, researchers and scientists have realized that this DNA actually has a major impact. Andrew R. Gehrke and his team performed several experiments to show that Egr is a master regulator of a gene network of at least 61 genes that are responsible for "whole-body" regeneration. It works as a "DNA switch" that can "turn on and off" the network.[2,3]

Egr regulates the transcription of numerous target genes and thereby plays an important role in regulating the response to growth factors, DNA damage, and ischemia. It plays a role in the regulation of cell survival, proliferation, and cell death. Egr activates expression of TGF-β1, which we discussed above. The Egr gene mediates responses to lack of oxygen, regulates the expression of proteins that are involved in inflammatory processes, and aids in the development of tissue damage after ischemia. Egr also regulates the biosynthesis of luteinizing hormones in the pituitary and other processes.[4]

Scientists are now understanding the importance of what the noncoding or regulatory DNA's role is with regard to the Egr gene. Two percent of the human genome codes are for actual proteins while the other 98% are regulatory. Researchers have discovered that it is not the directly expressed aspects of our DNA that account for the greatest differences among species. It is the regulatory mechanisms that govern how those proteins are expressed that make this grand distinction.[5]

The implications for activation of such genes in humans is enormous.

Many animals have the gene to produce their own vitamin C. In humans, three exons are missing out of the gene encoding vitamin C production. It is quite easy to manufacture ascorbic acid from glucose. The gene that encodes for the enzyme of vitamin C synthesis, called gulonolactone oxidase, is inactive due to accumulation of several mutations that turned it into a nonfunctional pseudogene. Gorillas, chimps, orangutans, and some monkeys have this genetic flaw, meaning the loss of vitamin C biosynthesis has occurred first in one of our primate ancestors.[6,7]

A goat makes up to 13,000 mg of vitamin C per day.[8] If we were able to make our own vitamin C supply and were able to synthesize it in high doses, certain degenerative diseases would be prevented from developing. For example, the oxidation of LDL cholesterol that leads to deposition of cholesterol in the arterial wall can be inhibited by vitamin C. Vitamin C has been shown to be protective to the blood vessel walls. We also utilize vitamin C in the immune system, in particular the white blood cells, to create hydrogen peroxide. High-dose vitamin C can kill cancer cells. High doses of vitamin C have been shown to inactivate toxins. If we were able to produce our own supply, we would have the potential to be much more immune to the invasion of pathogens and possibly the development of cancer.

Scientists found that elephants have extra copies of a tumor-suppressing gene p53. Elephants have twenty p53 genes and they do not develop cancer. Humans have one copy; elephants have twenty. In humans it is the single most mutated gene.

Tumor suppressor protein p53 has a key role in suppressing malignant transformation in advanced species. Recent analyses reveal that corruption of p53 function occurs through mutation in approximately 50% of all human cancers.[9]

The gene p53 regulates the death of our cells. When the cell is aging and becoming dysfunctional, that gene is supposed to activate and lead to cell death so that cell can then be removed. Cancer inactivates or mutates the p53 gene and makes the cell immortal. Now there are dysfunctional cancerous cells that are reproducing themselves and are invading the organism. We understand that elephants do not get cancer due to having these multiple copies of the p53 gene. Whales also have multiple copies of p53 and are protected against cancer as well. Parts of the whale genome contain genes that control the cell cycle, cell proliferation, and DNA repair, which are essential for normal cell function. In human cancers, many of these genes are mutated. The whale genome also evolved many duplications in tumor suppressor genes. With the discovery of CRISPR gene-editing technology, potential future application in the prevention of cancer by adding p53 gene copies to our genome could be a preventative target.[10]

A study in turtles showed hearts can be programmed to survive without oxygen for up to six months. Exposure to low levels of oxygen during embryonic development programmed the animals' hearts to be more resilient to what is known as hypoxia for the rest of their lives.[11] Exposure to hypoxia during development causes epigenetic changes to the genome that can turn genes on or off, which is key to the remarkable ability of the turtle heart cells to tolerate zero oxygen. If these epigenetic switches can be accessed in humans, we would be able to prevent heart attacks and other diseases due to ischemia. This would also be a great development for the advancement of biological space travel.

Prestin genes encode the sonar ability of bats and dolphins and are also found in the human genome. Prestin has also independently evolved to play a critical role in the ultrasonic hearing range of animal sonar, or echolocation, to help dolphins navigate through murky waters or bats to find food in the dark.[12] Just like these animals, humans can also use echolocation, and we can activate these genes by training for these abilities.[13]

Our next frontier is space travel. If we are able to biologically enhance human beings to be able to withstand and adapt to environments in space as well as on other planets, we can expand our exploration. The idea of extreme muscular strength by deactivating the inhibition of myostatin, the protein that limits the amount of muscle growth that we can have, can be facilitated either by CRISPR gene editing or epigenetic transcription changes. We can accelerate neurogenesis via gene manipulation and the use of peptides, which would allow any human to accelerate the development of any talent.

What is required for this next frontier? The understanding that mind and DNA are inextricably combined. We can manipulate our genes with our thoughts. Thoughts are expressions of light. The technological equivalent will be the manipulation of genetic material via light and sound, as discussed in our introductory chapters explaining the fundamental science of this new Light Medicine model.

Regardless of what biological or genetic engineering solution is found, if the human being is not trained in the use of mind, uncontrolled thoughts will sabotage and destroy our progress. On the other hand, if we can train our mind to access the vast reservoir of what is now called junk DNA, what willful evolutionary journey are we not able to take in an accelerated fashion? The potentials are boundless. Our future choices will determine the answer to this question.

My personal journey has brought me to the conviction that Light Medicine is a science, both new and ancient, that ties all formerly known disciplines of scientific understanding to one origin: Light, which is God. The cases presented — from studies by renowned and barely known scientists, to JZ Knight's healing and Ramtha's physiology, to culminating in the miraculous healing journeys of so many people — indicate a yet unaccessed possibility within all of us. It is our divine nature that allows true healing, life-extension, and personal evolution to happen. Exploration of this unchartered Light Medicine model could provide a future basis in prevention and treatment methods to support divine human beings in their quest for extraordinary health and longevity.

About The Author

Ana Mihalcea, M.D., Ph.D., is a board-certified Internal Medicine Physician with over 20 years of clinical experience. She received her medical school training at the Rheinian Westfalian Technical University in Aachen, Germany, where she also completed her Ph.D in pathology involving her cancer research. Dr. Mihalcea pursued her internal medicine residency training at the University of Virginia in Charlottesville where she worked for a decade in the field of internal medicine and geriatrics. In May 2019, Dr. Mihalcea founded AM Medical LLC, an integrative health clinic located in Yelm, Washington. AM Medical is dedicated to the principles of Light Medicine: the reversal of all diseases and aging, the achievement of health and longevity, and bringing light back into our bodies and the world.

REFERENCES

PROLOGUE: IN SEARCH OF THE LIGHT
1. Ramtha. *A Beginner's Guide to Creating Reality*, Third Edition. Yelm, WA: JZK Publishing; 2004: Pages 190-198.
2. Ramtha's School of Enlightenment (RSE). *Class 101 – Remarkable Mind*. Yelm, WA. www.ramtha.com.
3. Graf Irmgard. *Blu Room – Experience The Future Building Bridges With Light, Frequency, and Sound*. Lacey, WA: Blu Room Enterprises, LLC; 2017.

CHAPTER 1: THE BEGINNING OF THE JOURNEY
1. Hoff Benjamin. *The Tao of Pooh*, Second Edition. New York: Penguin Books USA Inc., 1982.
2. Brennan Barbara. *Hands of Light: A Guide to Healing Through the Human Energy Field*. London: Transworld Publishers; 1993.

CHAPTER 2: A VERY DIFFERENT EDUCATION
1. Mihalcea Ana M., Smith DL, Monini P, Sgadari C, Ensoli B, and Gill PS. Treatment update for AIDS-related Kaposi's sarcoma. *AIDS* 1999: 13 Suppl A: S215-S225.
2. Arntz William, Vicente Mark, and Chasse Betsy. *What the Bleep Do We Know?* Captured Light, Lord of the Wind; 2005. DVD.
3. Ramtha. *The White Book*. Fourth Printing. Yelm, WA: JZK Publishing, 2007.
4. Melton Gordon J. *Encyclopedia of American Religions* 2002/2003, 9th Edition. Farmington Hills: Gale, 2009.
5. Ramtha's School of Enlightenment (RSE). *Class 101 – Remarkable Mind*. Yelm, WA. www.ramtha.com.
6. Ramtha. *A Beginner's Guide to Creating Reality*, Third Edition. Yelm, WA: JZK Publishing; 2004: pages 187, 296.

CHAPTER 4: MY JOURNEY OF HEALING CANCER
1. Ramtha. *A Beginner's Guide to Creating Reality*, Third Edition. Yelm, WA: JZK Publishing; 2004: pg. 295.
2. Ramtha's School of Enlightenment (RSE). *Class 101 – Remarkable Mind*. Yelm, WA. www.ramtha.com.

CHAPTER 5: HEALING MIND ACROSS TIME
1. Ramtha. *A Beginner's Guide to Creating Reality*, Third Edition. Yelm, WA: JZK Publishing; 2004: pg. 290.
2. Spencer Lawrence R. *Alien Interview*. 2008.
3. Ramtha, WA. *A Beginner's Guide to Creating Reality*, Third Edition. Yelm: JZK Publishing; 2004: pg. 298.

CHAPTER 9: HEALTHCARE POLITICS AND SUPPRESSION OF NATURAL TREATMENTS
1. Cooke M, Irby DM, Sullivan W, and Ludmerer KM. American medical education 100 years after the Flexner report. *N Engl J Med.* 2006 Sep 28; 355(13):1339-44.
2. JAMA Network Editors. Quackery Abroad. *JAMA.* 2012; 307(21):2236.
3. Starfield B. Is US health really the best in the world? *JAMA.* 2000 Jul 26; 284(4):483-5.
4. National Institute on Drug Abuse, Overdose Death Rates, https://www.drugabuse.gov/drug-topics/trends-statistics/overdose-death-rates Published March 10, 2020. Accessed April 20, 2020.
5. Makary MA, and Daniel M. Medical error – the third leading cause of death in the US. *BMJ.* 2016 May 3; 353: i2139.
6. TVR staff. Over $4 Billion Paid for Vaccine Injuries and Deaths. *Vaccination, Risk & Failure Reports.* https://thevaccinereaction.org/2019/01/over-4-billion-paid-for-vaccine-injuries-and-deaths/ Published Jan. 9 2019. Accessed March 13, 2020.
7. Wolfe, E. Federal Vaccine Court Quietly Pays Out Billions. *Fair Warning.* https://www.fairwarning.org/2018/12/vaccine-court-pays-billions/ Published Dec. 12, 2018. Accessed March 14, 2020.
8. HRSA. Vaccine Injury Compensation Data. Health Resources and Services Administration. https://www.hrsa.gov/vaccine-compensation/data/index.html. Published December 2018. Updated January 2021. Accessed May 15, 2020.
9. Morgan G, Ward R, and Barton M. The contribution of cytotoxic chemotherapy to 5-year survival in adult malignancies. *Clin Oncol (R Coll Radiol).* Dec. 2004; 16(8):549-60.
10. Raphael C, Ahrens J, and Fowler N. Financing end-of-life care in the USA. *Journal of the Royal Society of Medicine.* 2001; 94(9):458-467.
11. Powles TJ, Coombes RC, Smith IE, Jones JM, Ford HT, and Gazet JC. Failure of chemotherapy to prolong survival in a group of patients with metastatic breast cancer. *Lancet* 1980 Mar. 15; 1(8168 Pt 1):580-2.

REFERENCES

12. Fox MS. On the Diagnosis and Treatment of Breast Cancer. *JAMA* 1979; 241(5):489–494.
13. Wallington M, Bomb M, Smittenaar R, Wickenden M, McPhail S, Rashbass J, Chao D, Dewar J, Talbot D, Peake M, Perren T, Wilson C, and Dodwell D. 30-day mortality after systemic anticancer treatment for breast and lung cancer in England: a population-based, observational study. *Lancet Oncology* 2016 Sept. 1; Volume 17: Issue 9, P1203-1216.
14. Herman Zelek S. On Understanding the Hardin Jones-Pauling Biostatistical Theory of Survival Analysis for Cancer Patients. *The Journal of Orthomolecular Medicine* 1998 3rd Quarter; Vol. 13.
15. Rifkin Eric and Bouwer Edward. *The Illusion of Certainty (Health Benefits and Risks).* Springer Science and Business Media LLC; 2007.
16. Mehra MR, Ruschitzka F, and Patel AN. Hydroxychloroquine or chloroquine with or without a macrolide for treatment of COVID-19: a multinational registry analysis. *Lancet.* 2020 Jun 13; 395(10240):1820.
17. Mehra MR, et al. (2020 Jun. 13).
18. Lamas GA, Goertz C, Boineau R, Mark DB, Rozema T, Nahin RL, Lindblad L, Lewis EF, Drisko J, and Lee KL. TACT Investigators. Effect of disodium EDTA chelation regimen on cardiovascular events in patients with previous myocardial infarction: the TACT randomized trial. *JAMA.* 2013 Mar 27; 309(12):1241-50.
19. Lamas GA, Anstrom K, and Mark D. TACT2. Trial To Assess Chelation Therapy. Mount Sinai Medical Center https://tact2.org/ Accessed January 14, 2020.
20. Elizabeth Erin. The 101st Holistic Doctor Found Dead. https://thedailycoin.org/2020/04/07/the-101st-holistic-doctor-found-dead. Published April 7, 2020. Accessed May 5, 2020.
21. Nwo Report. Robert Kennedy Jr: CDC is a privately owned vaccine company. https://nworeport.me/2018/07/02/robert-kennedy-jr-cdc-is-a-privately-owned-vaccine-company/ Published July 2, 2018. Accessed January 2020.
22. Thomas John P. Health Impact News. https://www.globalresearch.ca/cancer-and-autism-mysterious-deaths-of-alternative-health-doctors-who-have-real-cures-not-approved-by-the-fda/5465809 Published February 21, 2018. Accessed April 5, 2020.
23. Griffin Edward. *World Without Cancer: The Story of Vitamin B17.* Westlake Village: American Media; 1974.
24. Merola Eric. *Second Opinion: Laetrile At Sloan-Kettering.* Merola Production LLC; 2014. DVD.

25. Gupta Chris. 1953 Fitzgerald Report – Suppressed Cancer Treatments. http://www.newmediaexplorer.org/chris/2007/04/03/1953_fitzgerald _report_suppressed_cancer_treatments.htm Published April 3, 2007. Updated April 4, 2007. Accessed April 2, 2020.

26. Merola Eric. *Burzynski The Movie, Cancer is Serious Business*. 2011; DVD.

27. Morgan G, Ward R, and Barton M. The contribution of cytotoxic chemotherapy to 5-year survival in adult malignancies. *Clin Oncol (R Coll Radiol)* 2004 Dec.; 16(8):549-60.

28. Gupta Chris. (2007).

29. Angell Marcia. What Ails the FDA? Payola. https://ahrp.org/what-ails-the-fda-payola-marcia-angell-boston-globe/ Published March 10, 2005. Accessed April 3, 2020.

30. Dorsey ER, de Roulet J, and Thompson JP. Funding of US Biomedical Research, 2003-2008. *JAMA* 2010; 303(2):137–143.

31. Liu Jessica L., Bell Chaim, Matelski John, Detsky Allan, and Cram Peter. Payments by US pharmaceutical and medical device manufacturers to US medical journal editors: retrospective observational study. *BMJ* 2017; 359: j4619.

32. Demicheli V, Jefferson T, Ferroni E, Rivetti A, and Di Pietrantonj C. Vaccines for preventing influenza in healthy adults. *Cochrane Database of Systematic Reviews* 2018; Issue 2.

33. Yan J, Grantham M, Pantelic J, Bueno de Mesquita PJ, Albert B, Liu F, Ehrman S, and Milton DK; EMIT Consortium. Infectious virus in exhaled breath of symptomatic seasonal influenza cases from a college community. *Proc Natl Acad Sci* U. S. A. 2018: Jan 30; 115(5):1081-1086.

34. Simonsen L, Reichert TA, Viboud C, Blackwelder WC, Taylor RJ, and Miller MA. Impact of Influenza Vaccination on Seasonal Mortality in the US Elderly Population. *Arch Intern Med.* 2005; 165(3):265–272.

35. Gates Bill. *"Innovating to zero!"* Ted Talk, 2010; Web.

36. Vaccine Adverse Event Reporting System. https://vaers.hhs.gov/ Accessed April 5, 2020.

CHAPTER 10: THE SCIENCE OF LIGHT MEDICINE

1. López-Otín C, Blasco MA, Partridge L, Serrano M, and Kroemer G. The Hallmarks of Aging. *Cell* 2013; 153(6):1194–1217.

2. Bohm David. *Wholeness and the Implicate Order*. New York: Routledge & Kegan Paul; 1980.

3. Ramtha. *A Beginner's Guide to Creating Reality*, Third Edition. Yelm, WA: JZK Publishing; 2004: pages 155-169.

4. Szent-Gorgyi Albert. *Introduction to a Submolecular Biology*. New York: Academic Press Inc.; 1960.
5. Ho Mae-Wan. *The Rainbow and The Worm, The Physics of Organisms*. Third edition. Singapore: World Scientific Publishing; 2008.
6. Ho Mae-Wan. (2008).
7. Mitov M. Cholesteric liquid crystals in living matter. *Soft Matter.* 2017; 13(23):4176–4209.
8. Mitov M. (2017).
9. Cosic I. Macromolecular bioactivity: is it resonant interaction between macromolecules? – Theory and applications. *IEEE Trans Biomed Eng.* 1994 Dec; 41(12):1101-14.
10. Ho Mae-Wan. *Living Rainbow H_2O*. Singapore: World Scientific Publishing; 2012.
11. Ho Mae-Wan. (2012).
12. Cosic I. (1994).
13. Mitov M. (2017).
14. Swanson Claude. *Life Force - The Scientific Basis: Breakthrough Physics Of Energy Medicine, Healing, Chi and Quantum Consciousness*. Volume 2 of The Synchronized Universe Series. Tucson: Poseida Press; 2010.
15. Swanson Claude. (2010).
16. Ho Mae-Wan. (2008).
17. Hameroff S.R., Kaszniak A.W., and A Scott. *Orchestrated Objective Reduction of Quantum Coherence in Brain Microtubules: The "Orch OR" Model for Consciousness Stuart Hameroff & Roger Penrose*. Toward a Science of Consciousness – The First Tucson Discussions and Debates. Cambridge, MA: MIT Press, 1996; pp. 507-540.
18. Cosic I. (1994).
19. Ramtha. *A Beginner's Guide to Creating Reality*, Third Edition. Yelm, WA: JZK Publishing; 2004: pages 45-47, 299.
20. Ho Mae-Wan. (2012).
21. Emoto Masaru. *The Hidden Messages in Water*. New York: Atria Books; 2005.
22. Russell Walter. *The Secret of Light*. Third Edition. Waynesboro: The University of Science and Philosophy; 1947.
23. Russell Walter. (1947).
24. Russell Walter. (1947).
25. Takeda M, Kobayashi M, Takayama M, Suzuki S, Ishida T, Ohnuki K, Moriya T, and Ohuchi N. Biophoton detection as a novel technique for cancer imaging. *Cancer science*. 2004 Sept.; 95(8):656-61.

26. Madl P, Verwanger T, Geppert M, and Scholkmann F. Oscillations of ultra-weak photon emission from cancer and non-cancer cells stressed by culture medium change and TNF-α. *Sci Rep 7*. 2017; 11249.
27. Dotta BT. Ultra-weak Photon Emissions Differentiate Malignant Cells from Non-Malignant Cells. *In Vitro*. Arch Can Res. 2016; 4: 2.
28. Wu Yao-Wen and Klewer Laura. Light-Induced Dimerization Approaches to Control Cellular Processes. *Chemistry*. 2019 Sep 25; 25(54): 12452–12463.
29. Repina NA, Rosenbloom A, Mukherjee A, Schaffer DV, and Kane RS. At Light Speed: Advances in Optogenetic Systems for Regulating Cell Signaling and Behavior. *Annu Rev Chem Biomol Eng*. 2017 Jun 7; 8:13-39.
30. Tesla Nikola. *My inventions – The Autobiography of Nikola Tesla*. 2018 Reprint of 1919 Edition.
31. Rodin Marko. *The Rodin Number Map and Rodin Coil*. Proceedings of the NPA 2010.
32. Phillips Stephen. *The Mathematical Connection Between Religion and Science*. Eastbourne: Anthony Rowe Publishing; 2009.
33. Phillips Stephen. Polygons enfolded in 10 trees of life. Figure 1. http://smphillips.mysite.com/ 2009.
34. Phillips Stephen. (2009).
35. Kepler Johannes. *Harmonies of the World*. New York: Prometheus Books; 2014.
36. Phillips Stephen. *Extra-Sensory perception of Quarks*. Madras/London: The Theosophical Publishing House; 1980.
37. Pond Dale. Keelys Contributions to Science. https://svpwiki.com/Keelys-Contributions-to-Science Published August 20, 2019. Accessed May 5, 2020.
38. Bloomfield Moore Clara Sophia Jessup. *Keely and His Discoveries*. Independently published, 2001.
39. Ramtha. *A Beginner's Guide to Creating Reality*, Third Edition. Yelm, WA: JZK Publishing; 2004: pages 190-192.
40. Vucevic D, Dordevic D, and Radosavljevic T. Nikola Tesla and Medicine: 160th Anniversary of the Birth of the Genius Who Gave Light to the World – PART II. *Med Pregl*. 2016; 69(11-12):391–401.
41. Vucevic D. (2016).
42. Strong Frederick Finch. *Electricity and Life*. 1917 Lecture on Electrotherapeutics, Tufts Medical School. *Boston Electrical Experimenter*. March 1917.
43. Tsong TY and Gross C. The language of cells - Molecular processing of electric signals by cell membranes, chapter 5. *Bio electrodynamics and Bio communication*. World Scientific; 1994.

44. Becker Robert. The significance of bioelectric potentials. *Bioelectrochemistry and Bioenergetics.* 1974; 1. 187-199.

45. Cosic I. Macromolecular bioactivity: is it resonant interaction between macromolecules? – theory and applications. *IEEE Transactions on Biomedical Engineering.* 1994 Dec.; Volume 41, no. 12: pp. 1101-1114.

46. Brown W. Unified Physics and the Entanglement Nexus of Awareness. *NeuroQuantology.* May 2019; Volume 17, Issue no. 07: pp 40-52.

47. Hameroff Stuart. Consciousness, Microtubules and 'Orch-OR': A 'Space-time' Odyssey. *Journal of Consciousness Studies*, 201. 2014; Volume 21, Numbers 3-4: pp 126-153

48. Blackburn Elisabeth and Epel Elissa. *The Telomere Effect – A Revolutionary Approach to Living Younger, Healthier, Longer.* New York: Grand Central Publishing; 2017.

49. Okereke OI., Prescott J, Wong JYY, Han J, and Rexrode KM. High Phobic Anxiety Is Related to Lower Leukocyte Telomere Length in Women. *PLoS One.* 2012; 7(7): e40516.

50. Epel E, Daubenmier J, Moskowitz JT, Folkman S, and Blackburn E. Can meditation slow rate of cellular aging? Cognitive stress, mindfulness, and telomeres. *Ann N Y Acad Sci.* 2009 Aug.; 1172: 34–53.

CHAPTER 11: LIGHT SPECTROSCOPY AND ELECTRON TRANSFER

1. Kazakevich Yuri. Analytical Chemistry. HPLC Textbook. Comprehensive textbook on Liquid Chromatography. http://hplc.chem.shu.edu/NEW/Undergrad/Molec_Spectr/molec.spect r.general.html Published copyright 1996-2010. Accessed May 4, 2020.

2. Ramtha. *A Beginner's Guide to Creating Reality*, Third Edition. Yelm, WA: JZK Publishing; 2004: page 289.

3. Khan Academy. Spectroscopy: Interaction of light and matter. https://www.khanacademy.org/science/chemistry/electronic-structure-of-atoms/bohr-model-hydrogen/a/spectroscopy-interaction-of-light-and-matter. Accessed May 4, 2020.

4. Bruno Thomas J and Svoronos Paris D.N. *CRC Handbook of Fundamental Spectroscopic Correlation Charts.* Boca Raton: CRC Press, Taylor & Francis; 2005.

5. Khan Academy. (2020).

6. Mariani C, Braca A, Vitalini S, De Tommasi N, Visioli F, and Fico G. Flavonoid characterization and in vitro antioxidant activity of Aconitum anthora L. (Ranunculaceae). *Phytochemistry.* 2008 Mar; 69(5):1220-6.

7. Bentz Alexandra B. A Review of Quercetin: Chemistry, Antioxidant Properties, and Bioavailability. *Journal of Young Investigators.* April 2009.

8. Saad R, Asmani F, Saad M, Hussain M, Khan J, Kaleemullah M, Bin Othman N, Tofigh A, and Yusuf E. New Approach for Predicting Antioxidant Property of Herbal Extracts. *Pharmacognosy and Phytochemical Research.* 2015; 7(1):166-174 A.

9. Barraza-Garza G, Castillo-Michel H, de la Rosa LA, Martinez-Martinez A, Pérez-León JA, Cotte M, and Alvarez-Parrilla E. Infrared Spectroscopy as a Tool to Study the Antioxidant Activity of Polyphenolic Compounds in Isolated Rat Enterocytes. *Oxidative Medicine and Cellular Longevity.* 2016; vol. 2016, Article ID 9245150: 10 pages.

10. Shen CY, Jiang JG, Yang L, Wang DW, and Zhu W. Anti-ageing active ingredients from herbs and nutraceuticals used in traditional Chinese medicine: pharmacological mechanisms and implications for drug discovery. *Br J Pharmacol.* 2017; 174(11):1395–1425.

11. Tóth M, Kukor Z, and Valent S. Chemical stabilization of tetrahydrobiopterin by L-ascorbic acid: contribution to placental endothelial nitric oxide synthase activity. *Molecular human reproduction.* 2002; 8. 271-80.

12. Getoff Nikola. Vitamin C: Electron Emission, Free Radicals and Biological Versatility. *In vivo.* Athens, Greece: 2013; 27. 565-70.

13. Getoff Nikola, Hartmann J, Huber JC, and Quint RM. Photo-induced electron emission from 17β-estradiol and progesterone and possible biological consequences. *J Photochem Photobiol.* 2008; B 92: 38-41.

14. Getoff Nikola. Hormones: Electron Emission, Communication, Mutual Interaction, Regeneration, Metabolites, Carcinogenesis and Receptor Action. A Review. *Horm Molec Biol Clin Invest.* 2012; 12: 363-375.

15. Getoff Nikola. Fundamental biological importance of solvated electrons in humans. Hormone molecular biology and clinical investigation. 2013; 16. 125-8.

16. Getoff Nikola. UV-radiation induced electron emission by hormones. Hypothesis for specific communication mechanisms. *Radiat Phys Chem.* 2009; 78: 945-950.

17. Getoff Nikola, Hartmann J, Schittl H, Gerschpacher M, and Quint RM. Photo-induced regeneration of hormones by electron transfer processes: Potential biological and medical consequences. *Radiat Phys Chem Oxf Engl.* 1993. 2011; 80(8):890–894.

18. Getoff Nikola. Vitamin-induced intracellular electrons are the mechanism for their well-known beneficial effects: a review. *Nutrition.* 2013 Apr; 29(4):597-604.

19. Giese Bernd. Long-Distance Electron Transfer Through DNA. *Annual Review of Biochemistry.* 2002; 71:1, 51-70.
20. Davydov A.S. Energy and Electron transport in biological systems, chapter 17, *Bio electrodynamics and Biocommunication.* Singapore: World Scientific; 1994
21. Clavin Whitney. Electrons Use DNA Like a Wire for Signaling DNA Replication. https://www.caltech.edu/about/news/electrons-use-dna-wire-signaling-dna-replication-54208. Published February 23, 2017. Accessed April 5, 2020.
22. Gariaev Peter. *Quantum Consciousness of the Linguistic-Wave Genome Theory and Practice.* Moscow: Institute of Quantum Genetics, First English edition. April 2016.
23. Gariaev Peter and Vasiliev Anatoly. Holographic associative memory and information transmission by solitary waves in biological systems. *Proceedings of SPIE - The International Society for Optical Engineering.* September 1993.
24. Gariaev Peter. (2016).
25. Gariaev Peter. (2016).
26. Gariaev Peter. (2016).
27. Swanson Claude. *Life Force, The Scientific Basis, Breakthrough Physics of Energy Medicine, Healing, Chi and Quantum Consciousness.* Volume 2 of The Synchronized Universe Series. Poseida Press; 2010.
28. Fen Yap Wing and Yunus W. Mahmood Mat. Characterization of the Optical Properties of Heavy Metal Ions Using Surface Plasmon Resonance Technique. *Optics and Photonics Journal.* 2011; 1, 116-123.
29. Menon VP and Sudheer AR. Antioxidant and anti-inflammatory properties of curcumin. *Adv Exp Med Biol.* 2007; 595:105-25.
30. Cataldo F, Iglesias-Groth S, and Hafez Y. On the molar extinction coefficients of the electronic absorption spectra of C60 and C70 fullerene radical cation. *European chemical bulletin.* 2013; 2. 1013.
31. Franskevych D, Palyvoda K, Petukhov D, Prylutska S, Grynyuk I, Schuetze C, Drobot L, Matyshevska O, and Ritter U. Fullerene C60 Penetration into Leukemic Cells and Its Photoinduced Cytotoxic Effects. *Nanoscale Research Letters.* 2017.
32. Dugan LL, Gabrielsen JK, Yu SP, Lin TS, and Choi DW. Buckminsterfullerenol free radical scavengers reduce excitotoxic and apoptotic death of cultured cortical neurons. *Neurobiol Dis.* 1996 Apr; 3(2):129-35.

33. Tsumoto H, Kawahara S, Fujisawa Y, Suzuki T, Nakagawa H, Kohda K, and Miyata N. Syntheses of water-soluble [60]fullerene derivatives and their enhancing effect on neurite outgrowth in NGF-treated PC12 cells. *Bioorganic & medicinal chemistry letters*. 2010; 20. 1948-52.

34. Baati T, Bourasset F, Gharbi N, Njim L, Abderrabba M, Kerkeni A, Szwarc H, and Moussa F. The prolongation of the lifespan of rats by repeated oral administration of [60]fullerene. Biomaterials. 2012 Jun; 33(19):4936-46.

35. Ryan JJ, Bateman HR, Stover A, Gomez G, Norton SK, Zhao W, Schwartz LB, Lenk R, and Kepley CL. Fullerene Nanomaterials Inhibit the Allergic Response. *Immunol.* 2007 Jul. 1; 179 (1) 665-672.

36. Liu Y, Jiao F, Qiu Y, Li W, Qu Y, Tian C, Li Y, Bai R, Lao F, Zhao Y, Chai Z, and Chen C. Immunostimulatory properties and enhanced TNF- alpha mediated cellular immunity for tumor therapy by C60(OH)20 nanoparticles. *Nanotechnology*. 2009 Oct 14; 20(41):415102.

37. Franskevych D, Palyvoda K, Petukhov Dmytro, Prylutska S., Grynyuk Iryna, Schuetze Christina, Drobot Liudmyla, Matyshevska Olga, and Ritter Uwe. Fullerene C60 Penetration into Leukemic Cells and Its Photoinduced Cytotoxic Effects. *Nanoscale Research Letters*. 2017.

38. Yudoh K, Shishido K, Murayama H, Yano M, Matsubayashi K, Takada H, Nakamura H, Masuko K, Kato T, and Nishioka K. Water-soluble C60 fullerene prevents degeneration of articular cartilage in osteoarthritis via down-regulation of chondrocyte catabolic activity and inhibition of cartilage degeneration during disease development. *Arthritis Rheum*. 2007 Oct; 56(10):3307-18.

39. Ma H. and Liang, X. Fullerenes as unique nanopharmaceuticals for disease treatment. *Sci. China Chem.* 2010; 53, 2233–2240.

40. Bakry R, Vallant RM, Najam-ul-Haq M, Rainer M, Szabo Z, Huck CW, and Bonn GK. Medicinal applications of fullerenes. *Int J Nanomedicine*. 2007; 2(4):639-649.

41. Aoshima H, Kokubo K, Shirakawa S, Ito M, Yamana S, and Oshima T. Antimicrobial Activity of Fullerenes and Their Hydroxylated Derivatives. *Biocontrol science*. 2009; 14. 69-72.

42. Kato S, Aoshima H, Saitoh Y, and Miwa N. Fullerene-C60/liposome complex: Defensive effects against UVA-induced damages in skin structure, nucleus and collagen type I/IV fibrils, and the permeability into human skin tissue. *J Photochem Photobiol B*. 2010 Jan 21; 98(1):99-105.

43. Sengupta B, Pahari B, Blackmon L, and Sengupta PK. Prospect of bioflavonoid fisetin as a quadruplex DNA ligand: a biophysical approach. *PLoS One*. 2013; 8(6): e65383.

CHAPTER 12: TORSION PHYSICS, THE DENSITY OF TIME, AND MIND

1. Swanson Claude. *Life Force, The Scientific Basis, Breakthrough Physics of Energy Medicine, Healing, Chi and Quantum Consciousness*. Volume 2 of The Synchronized Universe Series. Poseida Press; 2010.
2. Wikipedia. Elementary Particle. https://en.wikipedia.org/wiki/Elementary_particle Updated December 26, 2020. Accessed April 4, 2020.
3. Swanson Claude. (2010).
4. Swanson Claude. (2010).
5. Swanson Claude. (2010).
6. Swanson Claude. (2010).
7. Swanson Claude. (2010).
8. Swanson Claude. (2010).
9. Ramtha's School of Enlightenment (RSE). *Class 101 – Remarkable Mind*. Yelm, WA. www.ramtha.com.
10. Swanson Claude. (2010).
11. Ramtha's School of Enlightenment (RSE). *RSE students becoming invisible*. Figure 2. Blue College Follow-Up 2004. Yelm, WA.
12. Graham Danielle. Experimental Data Demonstrating Augmentation of Ambient Gravitational and Geomagnetic Fields, CP813. *Space Technologies and Applications International Forum*—STAIF 2006, edited by M. S. El-Genk. American Institute of Physics; February 2006.
13. Krippner Stanley, Ph.D, et al. Daylong Geomagnetic Baseline. Figure 3. *American Institute of Physics*. 2005.
14. Krippner Stanley, Ph.D, et al. Daylong Geomagnetic Experimental File. Figure 4. *American Institute of Physics*. 2005.
15. Krippner Stanley, Ph.D, et al. Controlled Laboratory Gravitational Force Dead Weight Baseline Data – Raw Data. Figure 5. *American Institute of Physics*. 2005.
16. Krippner Stanley, et al. Controlled Laboratory Gravitational Force Experimental Data – Raw Data. Figure 6. *American Institute of Physics* 2005.
17. Hageman Joan H, Krippner Stanley, and Wickramasekera Ian II. Sympathetic Reactivity During Meditation. *Subtle Energies & Energy Medicine*. 2008; Volume 19, Number 2: Pg 23.

18. Hageman Joan H, et al. (2008).
19. Krippner Stanley, Wickramasekera Ian, Wickramasekera Judy, and Winstead Charles. The Ramtha Phenomena: Psychological, Phenomenological, and Geomagnetic Data. Table 2. *Journal of the American Society for Psychical Research*. 1998; Volume 92.
20. Melton Gordon J. *Finding Enlightenment, Ramtha's School of Ancient Wisdom*. Hillboro: Beyond Words Publishing; 1998.
21. Robles Jair and Graham Danielle. Walker Between Two Worlds. *SuperConsciousness Magazine*. Fall 2010.
22. Graham Danielle. How to Become a Master of Time. Interview with JZ Knight. *Superconsciousness Magazine*. January 2008.
23. Peizer Melissa. Ramtha explaining torsion phenomenon. Figure 7. Copyright © JZ Knight. February 2, 2012.
24. Peizer Melissa. Torsion Effect. Figure 8. Copyright © JZ Knight. April 24, 2011.
25. Swanson Claude. (2010).
26. Tiller William A. Towards a Predictive Model of Subtle Domain Connections to the Physical Domain Aspect of Reality: The Origins of Wave-Particle Duality, Electric-Magnetic Monopoles and the Mirror Principle. *Journal of Scientific Exploration*. 1999; Vol. 13, No. 1: P. 41.
27. Swanson Claude. (2010).
28. Swanson Claude. (2010).
29. Ramtha. *To Life! A Masters Book of Toasts*. Revised Edition. Yelm, WA: JZK Publishing; 2020.
30. Ramtha. *A Beginner's Guide to Creating Reality*. Third Edition. Yelm, WA: JZK Publishing; 2004: pages 38-43.
31. Ramtha. *A Beginner's Guide to Creating Reality*, Third Edition. Yelm, WA: JZK Publishing; 2004: page 272.
32. Ramtha. *A Beginner's Guide to Creating Reality*, Third Edition. Yelm, WA: JZK Publishing; 2004: page 276.
33. Ramtha. *A Beginner's Guide to Creating Reality*, Third Edition. Yelm, WA: JZK Publishing; 2004: page 289.
34. Swanson, Claude. (2010).

CHAPTER 13: JZ KNIGHT AND RAMTHA – PROOF OF THE EXTRAORDINARY

1. Robles Jair and Graham Danielle. Walker Between Two Worlds. *SuperConsciousness Magazine*. Fall 2010.

REFERENCES

2. Krippner Stanley, Wickramasekera Ian, Wickramasekera Judy, and Winstead Charles. The Ramtha Phenomenon: Psychological, Phenomenological, and Geomagnetic Data. *Journal of the American Society for Psychical Research.* 1998 January; Volume 92.
3. Ramtha's School of Enlightenment (RSE). JZ Knight and Ramtha Testing. Figure 11. Copyright @ JZ Knight 1996. Yelm, WA.
4. Hageman Joan H., Krippner Stanley, and Wickramasekera Ian II. Sympathetic Reactivity During Meditation. *Subtle Energies & Energy Medicine.* 2008; Volume 19, Number 2: Page 23.
5. Krippner Stanley, et al. In Search of Self: The Role of Consciousness in the Construction of Reality Conference. Yelm, WA; February 1997.
6. Hageman Joan H., et al. (2008).
7. Robles Jair. (2010).
8. Robles Jair. (2010).
9. Wright Michael. DNA Test Report Samples 1 – JZ Knight and Ramtha. Table 3. Yelm, WA: Ramtha's School of Enlightenment; January 15, 2015.
10. Wright Michael. DNA Test Report Samples 2 – JZ Knight and Ramtha. Table 4. Yelm, WA: Ramtha's School of Enlightenment; January 15, 2015.
11. Wright, Michael. DNA Test Report Samples 3 – JZ Knight and Ramtha. Table 5. Yelm, WA: Ramtha's School of Enlightenment; January 15, 2015.
12. Wright, Michael. DNA Test Report Samples 4 – JZ Knight and Ramtha. Table 6. Yelm, WA: Ramtha's School of Enlightenment; January 15, 2015.
13. Mihalcea A. *Echocardiogram - Judith Knight.* Yelm, WA: AM Medical LLC; November 30, 2010.
14. Mihalcea, A. *Echocardiogram - Judith Knight.* Yelm, WA: AM Medical LLC; June 6, 2018.
15. Mihalcea, A. *Chronological Renal Function Test Results – Judith Knight.* Table 7. Yelm, WA: AM Medical LLC; 2014-2018.
16. Mihalcea, A. *CT Coronary Artery Calcium Score – Judith Knight.* Yelm, WA: AM Medical LLC; February 12, 2018.
17. Mihalcea, A. *MR Angiogram 2010 – Judith Knight.* Yelm, WA: AM Medical LLC; November 30, 2010.
18. Mihalcea, A. *MR Angiogram head and MRI brain 2020 – Judith Knight.* Yelm, WA: AM Medical LLC; November 13, 2020.
19. Krippner Stanley. (1997).
20. Stevenson Ian. *Children Who Remember Previous Lives: A Question of Reincarnation.* Jefferson: McFarland & Company Inc Publishers; 2001.

21. Mihalcea A. *MRI of Right Knee – Judith Knight.* Yelm, WA: AM Medical LLC. December 28, 2015.
22. Krippner Stanley. (1997).

CHAPTER 14: CHRONIC INFECTIONS AND DISEASE
1. Finlay B. Are noncommunicable diseases communicable? *Science.* 2020 Jan. 17; Vol. 367, Issue 6475: pp. 250-251.
2. Aykut B, Pushalkar S, Chen R, Li Q, Abengozar R, Kim JI, Shadaloey SA, Wu D, Preiss P, Verma N, Guo Y, Saxena A, Vardhan M, Diskin B, Wang W, Leinwand J, Kurz E, Kochen Rossi JA, Hundeyin M, Zambrinis C, Li X, Saxena D, and Miller G. The fungal mycobiome promotes pancreatic oncogenesis via activation of MBL. *Nature.* 2019; 574, 264–267.
3. De Martel C, Ferlay J, Franceschi S, Vignat J, Bray F, Forman D, and Plummer M. Global burden of cancers attributable to infections in 2008: a review and synthetic analysis. *Lancet Oncol.* 2012 Jun; 13(6):607-15.
4. Alibek K, Bekmurzayeva A, Mussabekova A, and Sultankulov B. Using antimicrobial adjuvant therapy in cancer treatment: a review. *Infect Agent Cancer.* 2012 Nov 20; 7(1):33.
5. Simoncini Tullio. Cancer is a Fungus. http://www.cancerisafungus.com/cancer-therapy-prologue.php. Accessed April 3, 2020.
6. Pothineni N, Venkata K, Subramany S, Kuriakose K, Shirazi LF, Romeo F, Shah PK, and Mehta JL. Infections, atherosclerosis, and coronary heart disease. *European Heart Journal.* 2017 November 14; Volume 38, Issue 43: Pages 3195–3201.
7. Naess H, Sundal E, Myhr KM, and Nyland HI. Postinfectious and chronic fatigue syndromes: clinical experience from a tertiary-referral centre in Norway. *In Vivo.* 2010 Mar-Apr; 24(2):185-8.
8. Rasa S, Nora-Krukle Z, Henning N, Eliassen E, Shikova E, Harrer T, Scheibenbogen C, Murovska M, and Prusty BK. European Network on ME/CFS (EUROMENE). Chronic viral infections in myalgic encephalomyelitis/chronic fatigue syndrome (ME/CFS). *J Transl Med.* 2018 Oct 1; 16(1):268.
9. Mikovits JA, Lombardi VC, Pfost MA, Hagen KS, and Ruscetti FW. Detection of an infectious retrovirus, XMRV, in blood cells of patients with chronic fatigue syndrome. *Virulence.* 2010; 1(5):386–390.

10. The Crazz Files. Vaccines and Retroviruses: A Whistleblower Reveals What the Government is Hiding. https://crazzfiles.com/vaccines-and-retroviruses-a-whistleblower-reveals-what-the-government-is-hiding/ Published December 30, 2015. Accessed May 5, 2020.

11. Heckenlively Kent and Mikovits Judy A. *Plague: One Scientist's Intrepid Search for the Truth about Human Retroviruses and Chronic Fatigue Syndrome (ME/CFS), Autism, and Other Diseases.* Skyhorse Publishing; 2014.

12. Latham Robinson Harriet. Retroviruses and Cancer. *Reviews of Infectious Diseases.* 1982 September; Volume 4, Issue 5: Pages 1015–1025.

13. Britannica, The Editors of Encyclopaedia. *Retrovirus.* Encyclopedia Britannic. March 1, 2019. https://www.britannica.com/science/retrovirus. Accessed April 5, 2020.

14. Traylen CM, Patel HR, Fondaw W, Mahatme S, Williams JF, Walker LR, Dyson OF, Arce S, and Akula SM. Virus reactivation: a panoramic view in human infections. *Future Virol.* 2011 Apr.; 6(4):451-463.

15. Ho Mae-Wan. DNA Sequence Reconstituted from Water Memory? *Science in Society 51.* July 2011.

16. Ho, Mae-Wan. Electromagnetic signals from HIV. *Science in Society.* 2010; 48, 40-43.

17. Montagnier L, Aïssa J, Lavallée C, Mbamy M, Varon J, and Chenal H. Electromagnetic detection of HIV DNA in the blood of patients treated by antiretroviral therapy. *Interdiscip Sci Compu Life Sci.* 2009; 1, 245-53.

18. Ho Mae-Wan. 'Homeopathic' signals from DNA. *Science in Society.* 2010; 48.

19. Montagnier L, Aïssa J, Lavallee C, Mbamy M, Varon J, Chenal H. DNA waves and water. *Interdiscip. Sci.* 2009.

20. Gariaev P, Vasiliev A, and Berezin, A. Holographic associative memory and information transmission by solitary waves in biological systems. *Proceedings of SPIE - The International Society for Optical Engineering.* 1993.

21. Uchinuma S, Shimada Y, Matin K, Hosaka K, Yoshiyama M, Sumi Y, and Tagami J. Effects of UVB and UVC irradiation on cariogenic bacteria in vitro. *Lasers Med Sci.* 2019 Jul; 34(5):981-989.

22. Takada A, Matsushita K, Horioka S, Furuichi Y, and Sumi Y. Bactericidal effects of 310 nm ultraviolet light-emitting diode irradiation on oral bacteria. *BMC Oral Health.* 2017; 17(1):96.

23. Nishisaka-Nonaka R, Mawatari K, Yamamoto T, Kojima M, Shimohata T, Uebanso T, Nakahashi M, Emoto T, Akutagawa M, Kinouchi Y, Wada T, Okamoto M, Ito H, Yoshida KI, Daidoji T, Nakaya T, and Takahashi A. Irradiation by ultraviolet light-emitting diodes inactivates influenza a viruses by inhibiting replication and transcription of viral RNA in host cells. *J Photochem Photobiol B.* 2018 Dec; 189:193-200.

24. Verbaanderd C, Maes H, Schaaf MB, Sukhatme VP, Pantziarka P, Sukhatme V, Agostinis P, and Bouche G. Repurposing Drugs in Oncology (ReDO)—chloroquine and hydroxychloroquine as anti-cancer agents. *Ecancer.* 2017; 11, 781.

25. Singh A, Roopkishora SP, Gupta R, Mondal N, Kumar S, and Kumar M. Development and validation of UV-spectrophotometric method for the estimation of hydroxychloroquine sulphate. *Indian Journal of Chemical Technology.* 2016; 23. 237-239.

26. Gao P, Dang CV, and Watson J. Unexpected antitumorigenic effect of fenbendazole when combined with supplementary vitamins. *J Am Assoc Lab Anim Sci.* 2008; 47(6):37–40.

27 National Center for Biotechnology Information. PubChem Compound Summary for CID 3334, Fenbendazole.https://pubchem.ncbi.nlm.nih.gov/compound/Fenbendazole. Accessed May 5, 2020.

28. Skoda AM, Simovic D, Karin V, Kardum V, Vranic S, and Serman L. The role of the Hedgehog signaling pathway in cancer: A comprehensive review. *Bosn J Basic Med Sci.* 2018 Feb 20; 18(1):8-20.

29. Pantziarka P, Sukhatme V, Bouche G, Meheus L, and Sukhatme VP. Repurposing Drugs in Oncology (ReDO)-itraconazole as an anti-cancer agent. *Ecancermedicalscience.* 2015 Apr 15; 9:521.

30. Kucuk I, Ahmad Z, Edirisinghe M, and Orlu-Gul M. Utilization of microfluidic V-junction device to prepare surface itraconazole adsorbed nanospheres. *Int J Pharm.* 2014 Sep 10; 472(1-2):339-46.

31. Lainey Flatow-Trujillo, Khine Win, Amy Jencks, Leslie Andritsos, and Cecilia Arana Yi. Spontaneous resolution of untreated diffuse large B-cell lymphoma of maxillary bone after incisional biopsy. *Clinical Case reports.* 2019 November; Volume 7, Issue 11: Pages 2082-2086.

REFERENCES

CHAPTER 15: DISEASES RELATED TO ELECTROPOLLUTION
1. Presman AS. *Electromagnetic fields and life*, New York: Plenum Press; 1970.
2. Haltiwanger Steve. The Electrical Properties of Cancer Cells. https://www.academia.edu/4553798/The_Electrical_Properties_of_C ancer_Cells Accessed April 16, 2020.
3. Pall, Martin L. Wi-Fi is an important threat to human health, *Environmental Research*. 2018 July; Volume 164: Pages 405-416.
4. Leitgeb N. Electromagnetic hypersensitivity. Lin JC, editor. *Advances in electromagnetic fields in living systems, health effects of cell phone radiation*. New York, NY: Springer; 2009.
5. Kaszuba-Zwoińska J, Gremba J, Gałdzińska-Calik B, Wójcik-Piotrowicz K, and Thor PJ. Electromagnetic field induced biological effects in humans. *Przegl Lek..* 2015; 72(11):636-41.

CHAPTER 16: ENVIRONMENTAL HEALTH AND CHELATION THERAPY
1. Fornell Dave. Magnetic Resonance Imaging (MRI), The Debate Over Gadolinium MRI Contrast Toxicity Imaging. *Technology news.* Published February 16, 2018. Accessed April 20, 2020.
2. Bridge Sarah. Toxic jewelry: Cadmium found in Ardene. Aldo products / Marketplace. *CBC News*. Published: Jan 15, 2016. Accessed March 6, 2020.
3. Goldberg Eleanor. High levels of arsenic have been found in baby cereal made with rice, and it could cause a drop in children's IQs. *Business Insider*. Published Oct 30, 2019. Accessed March 6, 2020.
4. Thompson Julie. Yes, There Is Arsenic In Your Rice. Here's What You Need To Know. *Huffpost.* Published February 14, 2017. Accessed March 6, 2020.
5. US Food and Drug Administration. Lead in Food, Foodwares, and Dietary Supplements. www.fda.gov/food/metals/lead-food-foodwares-and-dietary-supplements Published February 27, 2020. Accessed March 9, 2020.
6. Willmsen C, Kamb L, and Mayo J. Loaded with Lead: Lead poisoning is a major threat at America's shooting ranges, perpetuated by owners who have repeatedly violated laws even after workers have fallen painfully ill. *Seattle Times*. Published Oct. 17, 2014. Accessed March 11, 2020.
7. Campaign for Safe Cosmetics. Lead in Lipstick. http://www.safecosmetics.org/get-the-facts/regulations/us-laws/lead-in-lipstick/ Accessed March 13, 2020.

8. Liu S, Hammond SK, and Rojas-Cheatham A. Concentrations, and potential health risks of metals in lip products. *Environ Health Perspect.* 2013 Jun; 121(6):705-10.

9. Center for Environmental Health: Lead in Purses, Belts, and Shoes. https://ceh.org/product-testing/fashion/ Accessed March 19, 2020.

10. Pell MB and Schneyer J. A Quest for Clean Water: The corrosive dangers lurking in private wells. https://www.reuters.com/investigates/special-report/usa-water-lead/ Published March 9, 2016. Accessed March 15, 2020.

11. Peltier Elian, Glanz J, Weiyi C, and White J. Notre-Dames's Toxic Fallout. *New York Times.* Published September 14, 2019. Accessed March 23, 2020.

12. Pell MB and Schneyer J. The thousands of U.S. locales where lead poisoning is worse than in Flint. https://www.reuters.com/investigates/special-report/usa-lead-testing/ Published December 16, 2019. Accessed March 24, 2020.

13. Neltner Tom. Latest available national data shows increase in blood lead levels for at least 2 million kids. *Environmental Defense Fund.* Published April 15, 2019. Accessed March 23, 2020.

14. Patra RC, Rautray AK, and Swarup D. Oxidative stress in lead and cadmium toxicity and its amelioration. *Vet Med Int.* 2011; 2011:457327.

15. Kumar S. Occupational and Environmental Exposure to Lead and Reproductive Health Impairment: An Overview. *Indian J Occup Environ Med.* 2018; 22(3):128-137.

16. Orr SE and Bridges CC. Chronic Kidney Disease and Exposure to Nephrotoxic Metals. *Int J Mol Sci.* 2017 May 12; 18(5).

17. National Research Council (US) Committee on Measuring Lead in Critical Populations. Measuring Lead Exposure in Infants, Children, and Other Sensitive Populations. Washington (DC): *National Academies Press* (US); 1993. 2, Adverse Health Effects of Exposure to Lead. Available from: https://www.ncbi.nlm.nih.gov/books/NBK236465/

18. Reyes Jessica Wolpaw. Lead exposure and Behavior: Effects on Antisocial and Risky Behavior Among Children and Adolescents. *Economic Inquiry.* 2015 July; Volume 53, Issue 3: Pages 1580-1605

19. International Academy of Oral Medicine & Toxicology. https://iaomt.org/ Accessed April 10, 2020.

20. New Scientist. Tobacco's natural radiation dose higher than after Chernobyl. https://www.newscientist.com/article/dn11974-tobaccos-natural-radiation-dose-higher-than-after-chernobyl/ Published June 2, 2007. Accessed April 4, 2020.

21. Physicians for social responsibility. Prenatal exposure to chemicals. https://www.psr.org/wp-content/uploads/2018/05/prenatal-exposure-to-chemicals.pdf. Accessed March 2, 2020.

22. Ruden Douglas. National Institute for Environmental Health Sciences. Lead Exposure can cause Multigenerational Epigenetic Changes. Wayne State University. https://www.niehs.nih.gov/research/supported/sep/2015/lead_exposu re/index.cfm Published September 2015. Accessed March 9, 2020.

23. Sen A, Heredia N, Senut MC, Land S, Hollocher K, Lu X, Dereski MO, and Ruden DM. Multigenerational epigenetic inheritance in humans: DNA methylation changes associated with maternal exposure to lead can be transmitted to the grandchildren. *Sci Rep.* 2015; 5:14466.

24. Baccarelli A and Bollati V. Epigenetics and environmental chemicals. *Curr Opin Pediatr.* 2009 Apr.; 21(2):243-51.

25. Nash D, Magder L, Lustberg M, Sherwin RW, Rubin RJ, Kaufmann RB, and Silbergeld EK. Blood lead, blood pressure, and hypertension in perimenopausal and postmenopausal women. *JAMA.* 2003 Mar 26; 289(12):1523-32.

26. Lin JL, Lin-Tan DT, Li YJ, Chen KH, and Huang YL. Low-level environmental exposure to lead and progressive chronic kidney diseases. *Am J Med.* 2006 Aug; 119(8): 707.e1-9.

27. Barbosa F Jr, Sertorio JT, Gerlach RF, and Tanus-Santos JE. Clinical evidence for lead-induced inhibition of nitric oxide formation. *Arch Toxicol.* 2006 Dec; 80(12):811-6.

28. Lanphear BP, Rauch S, Auinger P, Allen RW, and Hornung RW. Low-level lead exposure and mortality in US adults: a population-based cohort study. *Lancet Public Health.* 2018 Apr; 3(4): e177-e184.

29. Lamas GA, Goertz C, Boineau R, Mark DB, Rozema T, Nahin RL, Lindblad L, Lewis EF, Drisko J, and Lee KL. TACT Investigators. Effect of disodium EDTA chelation regimen on cardiovascular events in patients with previous myocardial infarction: the TACT randomized trial. *JAMA.* 2013 Mar 27; 309(12):1241-50.

30. Hemdan NY, Emmrich F, Faber S, Lehmann J, and Sack U. Alterations of TH1/TH2 reactivity by heavy metals: possible consequences include induction of autoimmune diseases. *Ann N Y Acad Sci.* 2007 Aug; 1109:129-37.

31. Irfan S, Rani A, Riaz N, Arshad M, and Kashif Nawaz S. Comparative Evaluation of Heavy Metals in Patients with Rheumatoid Arthritis and Healthy Control in Pakistani Population. *Iran J Public Health.* 2017 May; 46(5):626-633.

32. Park SJ, Lee JH, Woo SJ, Kang SW, and Park KH. Epidemiologic Survey Committee of Korean Ophthalmologic Society. Five heavy metallic elements and age-related macular degeneration: Korean National Health and Nutrition Examination Survey, 2008-2011. *Ophthalmology.* 2015 Jan; 122(1):129-37.

33. Pollard KM, Cauvi DM, Toomey CB, Hultman P, and Kono DH. Mercury-induced inflammation and autoimmunity. *Biochim Biophys Acta Gen Subj.* 2019 Dec; 1863(12):129299.

34. Li X, Brejnrod AD, Ernst M, Rykær M, Herschend J, Olsen NMC, Dorrestein PC, Rensing C, and Sørensen SJ. Heavy metal exposure causes changes in the metabolic health-associated gut microbiome and metabolites. *Environ Int.* 2019 May; 126:454-467.

35. Shin SR and Han AL. Improved chronic fatigue symptoms after removal of mercury in patient with increased mercury concentration in hair toxic mineral assay: a case. *Korean J Fam Med.* 2012 Sep; 33(5):320-5.

36. Wang M, Xu Y, Pan S, Zhang J, Zhong A, Song H, and Ling W. Long-term heavy metal pollution and mortality in a Chinese population: an ecologic study. *Biol Trace Elem Res.* 2011 Sep; 142(3):362-79.

37. Kim Hyun, Kim Yeo, and Seo Young. An Overview of Carcinogenic Heavy Metal: Molecular Toxicity Mechanism and Prevention. *Journal of Cancer Prevention.* 2015; 20. 232-240.

38. Huat TJ, Camats-Perna J, Newcombe EA, Valmas N, Kitazawa M, and Medeiros R. Metal Toxicity Links to Alzheimer's Disease and Neuroinflammation. *J Mol Biol.* 2019 Apr 19; 431(9):1843-1868.

39. Belyaeva EA, Sokolova TV, Emelyanova LV, and Zakharova IO. Mitochondrial electron transport chain in heavy metal-induced neurotoxicity: effects of cadmium, mercury, and copper. *Scientific World Journal.* 2012; 2012:136063.

CHAPTER 17: REVERSING ATHEROSCLEROSIS

1. Levy Thomas E. *Stop America's #1 Killer! Proof that he Origin of all Coronary Heart Disease is a Clearly Reversible Arterial Scurvy.* Henderson: Med Fox Publishing; 2006.

2. Okuyama H, Langsjoen PH, Hamazaki T, Ogushi Y, Hama R, Kobayashi T, and Uchino H. Statins stimulate atherosclerosis and heart failure: pharmacological mechanisms. *Expert Rev Clin Pharmacol.* 2015 Mar; 8(2):189-99.

3. Mazzanti G, Moro PA, Raschi E, Da Cas R, and Menniti-Ippolito F. Adverse reactions to dietary supplements containing red yeast rice: assessment of cases from the Italian surveillance system. *Br J Clin Pharmacol.* 2017; 83(4):894–908.

4. Levy Thomas E. (2006).
5. Levy Thomas E. (2006).
6. Juraschek SP, Guallar E, Appel LJ, and Miller ER 3rd. Effects of vitamin C supplementation on blood pressure: a meta-analysis of randomized controlled trials. *Am J Clin Nutr.* 2012; 95:1079–1088.
7. Ness AR, Khaw K-T, Bingham S, and Day NE. Vitamin C status and blood pressure. *J Hypertens.* 1996; 14:503–508.
8. Drouin G, Godin JR, and Pagé B. The genetics of vitamin C loss in vertebrates. *Curr Genomics.* 2011; 12(5):371–378.
9. Michels AJ, Hagen TM, and Frei B. Human genetic variation influences vitamin C homeostasis by altering vitamin C transport and antioxidant enzyme function. *Annu Rev Nutr.* 2013; 33:45–70.
10. Levy Thomas E. (2006).
11. McRae MP. Vitamin C supplementation lowers serum low-density lipoprotein cholesterol and triglycerides: a meta-analysis of 13 randomized controlled trials. *J Chiropr Med.* 2008; 7(2):48-58.
12. Levy Thomas E. (2006).
13. Langlois M, Duprez D, Delanghe J, De Buyzere M, and Clement DL. Serum vitamin C concentration is low in peripheral arterial disease and is associated with inflammation and severity of atherosclerosis. *Circulation.* 2001 Apr 10; 103(14):1863-8.
14. Nosratola D. Vaziri, Yaoxian Ding, and Zhenmin Ni. Nitric Oxide Synthase Expression in the Course of Lead-Induced Hypertension. *Hypertension.* 1999 Oct.; Volume 34, Issue 41.
15. Lanphear BP, Rauch S, Auinger P, Allen RW, and Hornung RW. Low-level lead exposure and mortality in US adults: a population-based cohort study. *Lancet Public Health.* 2018 Apr; 3(4): e177-e184.
16. Hancke Claus and Flytlie K. Benefits of EDTA Chelation Therapy in Arteriosclerosis: A Restrospective Study of 470 Patients. *J. Adv. Med.* 1993; Vol. 6.
17. Chappell Terry and Stahl John. Meta-Analysis on EDTA Chelation. *Journal of Advancement in Medicine.* 1993; Volume 7, Number 3. Fall 1994.
18. Chappell Terry, Stahl John, and Evans Ronald. EDTA Chelation Treatment for Vascular Disease. *Journal of Advancement in Medicine.* 1994 Fall; Volume 7, Number 3.
19. Lamas GA, Goertz C, Boineau R, Mark DB, Rozema T, Nahin RL, Lindblad L, Lewis EF, Drisko J, and Lee KL. TACT Investigators. Effect of disodium EDTA chelation regimen on cardiovascular events in patients with previous myocardial infarction: the TACT randomized trial. *JAMA.* 2013 Mar 27; 309(12):1241-50.

20. Vissers LET, Dalmeijer GW, Boer JMA, Verschuren WMM, van der Schouw YT and Beulens JWJ. The relationship between vitamin K and peripheral arterial disease. *Atherosclerosis.* 2016 Sep; 252:15-20.
21. Prasad A, Andrews NP, Padder FA, Husain M, and Quyyumi AA. Glutathione reverses endothelial dysfunction and improves nitric oxide bioavailability. *J Am Coll Cardiol.* 1999 Aug; 34(2):507-14.
22. Lapenna D, de Gioia S, Ciofani G, Mezzetti A, Ucchino S, Calafiore AM, Napolitano AM, Di Ilio C, and Cuccurullo F. Glutathione-related antioxidant defenses in human atherosclerotic plaques. *Circulation.* 1998 May 19; 97(19):1930-4.
23. Barnes Broda. *Solved: The Riddle of Heart Attacks.* Broda Barnes Research Foundation; 1976.

CHAPTER 18: HYPERBARIC OXYGEN THERAPY
1. Brazier Yvette. What is Hyperbaric Oxygen good for? https://www.medicalnewstoday.com/articles/313155 Published August 20, 2019. Accessed March 15, 2020.
2. Mu J, Krafft PR, and Zhang JH. Hyperbaric oxygen therapy promotes neurogenesis: where do we stand? *Med Gas Res.* 2011 Jun 27; 1(1):14.
3. Harch PG and Fogarty EF. Hyperbaric oxygen therapy for Alzheimer's dementia with positron emission tomography imaging: a case report. *Med Gas Res.* 2019 Jan 9; 8(4):181-184.
4. Tennant Jerry. MD, MD (H), PSc.D. Healing is Voltage, Third Edition. 2013. www.tennantinstitute.com
5. Godman CA, Joshi R, Giardina C, Perdrizet G, and Hightower LE. Hyperbaric oxygen treatment induces antioxidant gene expression. *Ann N Y Acad Sci.* 2010 Jun; 1197:178-83.
6. Thom SR, Bhopale VM, Velazquez OC, Goldstein LJ, Thom LH, and Buerk DG. Stem cell mobilization by hyperbaric oxygen. *Am J Physiol Heart Circ Physiol.* 2006 Apr; 290(4):H1378-86.
7. Akarsu S, Tekin L, Ay H, Carli AB, Tok F, Simşek K, and Kiralp MZ. The efficacy of hyperbaric oxygen therapy in the management of chronic fatigue syndrome. *Undersea Hyperb Med.* 2013 Mar-Apr; 40(2):197-200. Erratum in: *Undersea Hyperb Med.* 2013 May-Jun; 40(3):312.
8. Chen SY, Chen YC, Wang JK, Hsu HP, Ho PS, Chen YC, and Sytwu HK. Early hyperbaric oxygen therapy attenuates disease severity in lupus-prone autoimmune (NZB x NZW) F1 mice. *Clin Immunol.* 2003 Aug; 108(2):103-10.

9. Slade JB, Potts MV, Flower AM, Sky KM, Sit MT, and Schmidt TW. Pain improvement in rheumatoid arthritis with hyperbaric oxygen: report of three cases. *Undersea Hyperb Med.* 2016 Jul-Aug;43(4):467-472. Erratum in: *Undersea Hyperb Med.* 2017 May-Jun; 44(3):298.

CHAPTER 19: PEPTIDES

1. Khavinson VKh, Bondarev IE, and Butyugov AA. Epithalon peptide induces telomerase activity and telomere elongation in human somatic cells. *Bull Exp Biol Med.* 2003; 135 (6): 590–592
2. Kozina LS, Arutjunyan AV, and Khavinson VKh. Antioxidant properties of geroprotective peptides of the pineal gland. *Arch Gerontol Geriatr.* 2007; 44 Suppl 1:213-216.
3. Goncharova ND, Vengerin AA, Khavinson VKh, and Lapin BA. Peptide correction of age-related hormonal dysfunction of the pancreas in monkeys. *Bull Exp Biol Med.* 2004; 138(1):80-83.
4. Khavinson VK and Myl'nikov SV. Effect of epithalone on the age-specific changes in the time course of lipid peroxidation in Drosophila melanogaster. *Bull. Exp. Biol. Med.* 2000; 130(11): 1116-1119.
5. Anisimov VN, Mylnikov SV, and Khavinson VK. Pineal peptide preparation epithalamin increases the lifespan of fruit flies, mice and rats. *Mech Ageing Dev.* 1998; 103(2):123-132.
6. Khavinson VKh and Morozov VG. Peptides of pineal gland and thymus prolong human life. *Neuro Endocrinol Lett.* 2003; 24 (3): 233–240.
7. Khavinson VKh and Morozov VG. Geroprotective effect of thymalin and epithalamin. *Adv Gerontol.* 2002; 10: 74–84.
8. Korkushko O, Khavinson VKh, Shatilo VB, and Antonyk-Sheglova IA. Geroprotective effect of thymalin and epithalamin. *Adv Gerontol.* 2011; 10: 74–84.
9. Korkushko OV, Khavinson VKh, Shatilo VB, and Antonyuk-Shcheglova IA. Geroprotective effect of epithalamine (pineal gland peptide preparation) in elderly subjects with accelerated aging. *Bull Exp Biol Med.* 2006 Sep; 142(3):356-9.
10. Khavinson V, Razumovsky M, Trofimova S, Grigorian R, and Razumovskaya A. Pineal-regulating tetrapeptide epitalon improves eye retina condition in retinitis pigmentosa. *Neuro Endocrinol Lett.* 2002 Aug; 23(4):365-8.
11. Pickart L, Vasquez-Soltero JM, and Margolina A. The Effect of the Human Peptide GHK on Gene Expression Relevant to Nervous System Function and Cognitive Decline. *Brain Sci.* 2017 Feb 15; 7(2):20.

12. Pickart L, Vasquez-Soltero JM, and Margolina A. GHK Peptide as a Natural Modulator of Multiple Cellular Pathways in Skin Regeneration. *Biomed Res Int.* 2015; 2015:648108.
13. Fuku N, Pareja-Galeano H, Zempo H, Alis R, Arai Y, Lucia A, and Hirose N. The mitochondrial-derived peptide MOTS-c: a player in exceptional longevity? *Aging Cell.* 2015 Dec; 14(6):921-3.
14. Allegri RF and Guekht A. Cerebrolysin improves symptoms and delays progression in patients with Alzheimer's disease and vascular dementia. *Drugs Today* (Barc). 2012 Apr; 48 Suppl A:25-41.
15. Benoist CC, Kawas LH, Zhu M, Tyson KA, Stillmaker L, Appleyard SM, Wright JW, Wayman GA, and Harding JW. The procognitive and synaptogenic effects of angiotensin IV-derived peptides are dependent on activation of the hepatocyte growth factor/c-met system. *J Pharmacol Exp Ther.* 2014 Nov; 351(2):390-402.
16. Zozulia AA, Neznamov GG, Siuniakov TS, Kost NV, Gabaeva MV, Sokolov OIu, Serebriakova EV, Siranchieva OA, Andriushenko AV, Telesheva ES, Siuniakov SA, Smulevich AB, Miasoedov NF, and Seredenin SB. [Efficacy and possible mechanisms of action of a new peptide anxiolytic selank in the therapy of generalized anxiety disorders and neurasthenia]. *Zh Nevrol Psikhiatr Im S S Korsakova.* 2008; 108(4):38-48.
17. Bhasin M, Wu M, and Tsirka SE. Modulation of microglial/macrophage activation by macrophage inhibitory factor (TKP) or tuftsin (TKPR) attenuates the disease course of experimental autoimmune encephalomyelitis. *BMC Immunol.* 2007 Jul 16; 8:10.
18. Polunin GS, Nurieva SM, Baiandin DL, Sheremet NL, and Andreeva LA. Opredelenie terapevticheskoĭ éffektivnosti novogo otechestvennogo preparata "Semaks" pri zabolevaniiakh zritel'nogo nerva [Evaluation of therapeutic effect of new Russian drug semax in optic nerve disease]. *Vestn Oftalmol.* 2000; 116(1):15-18.
19. Alexeev M, Grosenbaugh DK, Mott DD, and Fisher JL. The natural products magnolol and honokiol are positive allosteric modulators of both synaptic and extra-synaptic GABA(A) receptors. *Neuropharmacology.* 2012; 62(8):2507-2514.
20. Florea V, Majid S, Kanashiro TR, Block N, Schally A, Hare J, and Rodrigues C. Cytoprotective Effect of Growth Hormone Releasing Hormone Agonist in Cardiac Stem Cells. *Am Coll Cardiol.* 2013 Mar; 61 (10 Supplement) E1820.

21. Florea V, Majid SS, Kanashiro-Takeuchi RM, Cai RZ, Block NL, Schally AV, Hare JM, and Rodrigues CO. Agonists of growth hormone-releasing hormone stimulate self-renewal of cardiac stem cells and promote their survival. *Proc Natl Acad Sci U S A.* 2014; 111(48):17260-17265.

22. Schally AV, Zhang X, Cai R, Hare JM, Granata R, and Bartoli M. Actions and Potential Therapeutic Applications of Growth Hormone-Releasing Hormone Agonists. *Endocrinology.* 2019 Jul 1; 160(7):1600-1612.

23. Kim SB, Kwon DR, Kwak H, Shin YB, Han HJ, Lee JH, and Choi SH. Additive effects of intra-articular injection of growth hormone and hyaluronic acid in rabbit model of collagenase-induced osteoarthritis. *J Korean Med Sci.* 2010 May; 25(5):776-80.

24. Chang CH, Tsai WC, Lin MS, Hsu YH, and Pang JH. The promoting effect of pentadecapeptide BPC 157 on tendon healing involves tendon outgrowth, cell survival, and cell migration. *J Appl Physiol* (1985). 2011 Mar; 110(3):774-80.

25. Duzel A, Vlainic J, Antunovic M, Malekinusic D, Vrdoljak B, Samara M, Gojkovic S, Krezic I, Vidovic T, Bilic Z, Knezevic M, Sever M, Lojo N, Kokot A, Kolovrat M, Drmic D, Vukojevic J, Kralj T, Kasnik K, Siroglavic M, Seiwerth S, and Sikiric P. Stable gastric pentadecapeptide BPC 157 in the treatment of colitis and ischemia and reperfusion in rats: New insights. *World J Gastroenterol.* 2017 Dec 28; 23(48):8465-8488.

26. Strinic D, Belosic Halle Z, Luetic K, Nedic A, Petrovic I, Sucic M, Zivanovic Posilovic G, Balenovic D, Strbe S, Udovicic M, Drmic D, Stupnisek M, Lovric Bencic M, Seiwerth S, and Sikiric P. BPC 157 counteracts QTc prolongation induced by haloperidol, fluphenazine, clozapine, olanzapine, quetiapine, sulpiride, and metoclopramide in rats. *Life Sci.* 2017 Oct 1; 186:66-79.

27. Drmic D, Kolenc D, Ilic S, Bauk L, Sever M, Zenko Sever A, Luetic K, Suran J, Seiwerth S, and Sikiric P. Celecoxib-induced gastrointestinal, liver and brain lesions in rats, counteraction by BPC 157 or L-arginine, aggravation by L-NAME. *World J Gastroenterol.* 2017 Aug 7; 23(29):5304-5312.

28. Malinda KM, Sidhu GS, Mani H, Banaudha K, Maheshwari RK, Goldstein AL, and Kleinman HK. Thymosin beta4 accelerates wound healing. *J Invest Dermatol.* 1999 Sep; 113(3):364-8.

29. Bjelakovic G, Stojanovic I, Jevtovic-Stoimenov T, and Bjelakovic B. *Glucocorticoids, thymus function and sex hormone in human body growing.* Adverse effect of Steroid (pp.187-210) Chapter 6. New York: Nova Science Publishers; 2008.

30. Bodey B, Bodey B Jr, Siegel SE, and Kaiser HE. Involution of the mammalian thymus, one of the leading regulators of aging. *In Vivo*. 1997 Sep-Oct; 11(5):421-40.

31. Palmer DB. The effect of age on thymic function. *Front Immunol*. 2013 Oct 7; 4:316.

32. Aspinall R. Longevity and the immune response. *Biogerontology*. 2000; 1(3):273-278.

33. Napolitano LA, Schmidt D, Gotway MB, Ameli N, Filbert EL, Ng MM, Clor JL, Epling L, Sinclair E, Baum PD, Li K, Killian ML, Bacchetti P, and McCune JM. Growth hormone enhances thymic function in HIV-1-infected adults. *J Clin Invest*. 2008 Mar; 118(3):1085-98.

34. Fahy GM, Brooke RT, Watson JP, Good Z, Vasanawala SS, Maecker H, Leipold MD, Lin DTS, Kobor MS, and Horvath S. Reversal of epigenetic aging and immunosenescent trends in humans. *Aging Cell*. 2019 Dec; 18(6): e13028.

CHAPTER 20: EXOSOMES

1. Vono R, Jover Garcia E, Spinetti G, and Madeddu P. Oxidative Stress in Mesenchymal Stem Cell Senescence: Regulation by Coding and Noncoding RNAs. *Antioxid Redox Signal*. 2018; 29(9):864-879.

2. Li SP, Lin ZX, Jiang XY, and Yu XY. Exosomal cargo-loading and synthetic exosome-mimics as potential therapeutic tools. *Acta Pharmacol Sin*. 2018 Apr; 39(4):542-551.

3. Noren Hooten N, Fitzpatrick M, Wood WH 3rd, De S, Ejiogu N, Zhang Y, Mattison JA, Becker KG, Zonderman AB, and Evans MK. Age-related changes in microRNA levels in serum. *Aging* (Albany NY). 2013 Oct; 5(10):725-40.

4. Singh R, Kølvraa S, Bross P, Christensen K, Bathum L, Gregersen N, Tan Q, and Rattan SI. Anti-inflammatory heat shock protein 70 genes are positively associated with human survival. *Curr Pharm Des*. 2010; 16(7):796-801.

5. Noren Hooten N. (2013).

6. Zhang ZG, Buller B, and Chopp M. Exosomes - beyond stem cells for restorative therapy in stroke and neurological injury. *Nat Rev Neurol*. 2019 Apr; 15(4):193-203.

7. Geng W, Tang H, Luo S, Lv Y, Liang D, Kang X, and Hong W. Exosomes from miRNA-126-modified ADSCs promotes functional recovery after stroke in rats by improving neurogenesis and suppressing microglia activation. *Am J Transl Res*. 2019 Feb 15; 11(2):780-792.

8. Zhang J, Li S, Li L, Li M, Guo C, Yao J, and Mi S. Exosome and exosomal microRNA: trafficking, sorting, and function. *Genomics Proteomics Bioinformatics.* 2015 Feb; 13(1):17-24.

9. Simons M and Raposo G. Exosomes--vesicular carriers for intercellular communication. *Curr Opin Cell Biol.* 2009 Aug; 21(4):575-81.

10. Xu H, Jia S, and Xu H. Potential therapeutic applications of exosomes in different autoimmune diseases. *Clin Immunol.* 2019 Aug; 205:116-124.

11. Vicencio JM, Yellon DM, Sivaraman V, Das D, Boi-Doku C, Arjun S, Zheng Y, Riquelme JA, Kearney J, Sharma V, Multhoff G, Hall AR, and Davidson SM. Plasma exosomes protect the myocardium from ischemia-reperfusion injury. *J Am Coll Cardiol.* 2015 Apr 21; 65(15):1525-36.

12. Ye M, Ni Q, Qi H, Qian X, Chen J, Guo X, Li M, Zhao Y, Xue G, Deng H, and Zhang L. Exosomes Derived from Human Induced Pluripotent Stem Cells-Endothelia Cells Promotes Postnatal Angiogenesis in Mice Bearing Ischemic Limbs. *Int J Biol Sci* 2019; 15(1):158-168.

13. Lee BR, Kim JH, Choi ES, Cho JH, and Kim E. Effect of young exosomes injected in aged mice. *Int J Nanomedicine.* 2018; 13:5335-5345.

14. Yoshida M, Satoh A, Lin JB, Mills KF, Sasaki Y, Rensing N, Wong M, Apte RS, and Imai SI. Extracellular Vesicle-Contained eNAMPT Delays Aging and Extends Lifespan in Mice. *Cell Metab.* 2019 Aug 6; 30(2):329-342.e5.

15. Panagiotou N, Neytchev O, Selman C, and Shiels PG. Extracellular Vesicles, Ageing, and Therapeutic Interventions. *Cells.* 2018; 7(8):110.

16. Wu P, Zhang B, Shi H, Qian H, and Xu W. MSC-exosome: A novel cell-free therapy for cutaneous regeneration. *Cytotherapy.* 2018 Mar; 20(3):291-301.

17. Zhang ZG and Chopp M. Exosomes in stroke pathogenesis and therapy. *J Clin Invest.* 2016; 126(4):1190-1197.

18. Cai ZY, Xiao M, Quazi SH, and Ke ZY. Exosomes: a novel therapeutic target for Alzheimer's disease? *Neural Regen Res.* 2018; 13(5):930-935.

19. Dong R, Liu Y, Yang Y, Wang H, Xu Y, and Zhang Z. MSC-Derived Exosomes-Based Therapy for Peripheral Nerve Injury: A Novel Therapeutic Strategy. *Biomed Res Int.* 2019 Aug 18; 2019:6458237.

20. Ruppert KA, Nguyen TT, Prabhakara KS, Toledano Furman NE, Srivastava AK, Harting MT, Cox CS Jr, and Olson SD. Human Mesenchymal Stromal Cell-Derived Extracellular Vesicles Modify Microglial Response and Improve Clinical Outcomes in Experimental Spinal Cord Injury. *Sci Rep.* 2018 Jan 11; 8(1):480.

21. Otani K, Yokoya M, Kodama T, Hori K, Matsumoto K, Okada M, and Yamawaki H. Plasma exosomes regulate systemic blood pressure in rats. *Biochem Biophys Res Commun.* 2018 Sep 5; 503(2):776-783.

22. Sun Y, Shi H, Yin S, Ji C, Zhang X, Zhang B, Wu P, Shi Y, Mao F, Yan Y, Xu W, and Qian H. Human Mesenchymal Stem Cell Derived Exosomes Alleviate Type 2 Diabetes Mellitus by Reversing Peripheral Insulin Resistance and Relieving β-Cell Destruction. *ACS Nano.* 2018 Aug 28; 12(8):7613-7628.

23. Barile L, Milano G, and Vassalli G. Beneficial effects of exosomes secreted by cardiac-derived progenitor cells and other cell types in myocardial ischemia. *Stem Cell Investig.* 2017 Nov 18; 4:93.

24. Cavallari C, Ranghino A, Tapparo M, Cedrino M, Figliolini F, Grange C, Giannachi V, Garneri P, Deregibus MC, Collino F, Rispoli P, Camussi G, and Brizzi MF. Serum-derived extracellular vesicles (EVs) impact on vascular remodeling and prevent muscle damage in acute hind limb ischemia. *Sci Rep.* 2017 Aug 15; 7(1):8180.

25. Ezquer F, Morales P, Quintanilla ME, Santapau D, Lespay-Rebolledo C, Ezquer M, Herrera-Marschitz M, and Israel Y. Intravenous administration of anti-inflammatory mesenchymal stem cell spheroids reduces chronic alcohol intake and abolishes binge-drinking. *Sci Rep.* 2018 Mar 22; 8(1):4325.

26. Li JJ, Hosseini-Beheshti E, Grau GE, Zreiqat H, and Little CB. Stem Cell-Derived Extracellular Vesicles for Treating Joint Injury and Osteoarthritis. *Nanomaterials* (Basel). 2019 Feb 14; 9(2):261.

27. Lai P, Weng J, Guo L, Chen X, and Du X. Novel insights into MSC-EVs therapy for immune diseases. *Biomark Res.* 2019 Mar 18; 7:6.

28. Zhu T, Wang Y, and Jin H, Li L. The role of exosome in autoimmune connective tissue disease. *Ann Med.* 2019 Mar; 51(2):101-108.

CHAPTER 21: AGE REVERSAL, LONGEVITY, AND IMMORTALITY MEDICINE

1. Tchkonia T, Zhu Y, van Deursen J, Campisi J, and Kirkland JL. Cellular senescence and the senescent secretory phenotype: therapeutic opportunities. *J Clin Invest*. 2013 Mar; 123(3):966-72.

2. Huang Y, Cai X, Mai W, Li M, and Hu Y. Association between prediabetes and risk of cardiovascular disease and all-cause mortality: systematic review and meta-analysis. *BMJ*. 2016 Nov 23; 355: i5953.

3. Unnikrishnan A, Freeman WM, Jackson J, Wren JD, Porter H, and Richardson A. The role of DNA methylation in epigenetics of aging. *Pharmacol Ther*. 2019 Mar; 195:172-185.

4. López-Otín C, Blasco MA, Partridge L, Serrano M, and Kroemer G. The hallmarks of aging. *Cell*. 2013; 153(6):1194-1217.

5. Johnson SC, Rabinovitch PS, and Kaeberlein M. mTOR is a key modulator of ageing and age-related disease. *Nature*. 2013; 493(7432):338-345.

6. Arriola Apelo SI and Lamming DW. Rapamycin: An InhibiTOR of Aging Emerges From the Soil of Easter Island. *J Gerontol A Biol Sci Med Sci*. 2016 Jul; 71(7):841-9.

7. Mannick JB, Del Giudice G, Lattanzi M, Valiante NM, Praestgaard J, Huang B, Lonetto MA, Maecker HT, Kovarik J, Carson S, Glass DJ, and Klickstein LB. mTOR inhibition improves immune function in the elderly. *Sci Transl Med*. 2014 Dec 24; 6(268):268ra179.

8. Urfer SR, Kaeberlein TL, Mailheau S, Bergman PJ, Creevy KE, Promislow DEL, and Kaeberlein M. A randomized controlled trial to establish effects of short-term rapamycin treatment in 24 middle-aged companion dogs. *Geroscience*. 2017 Apr; 39(2):117-127

9. Bitto A, Ito TK, Pineda VV, LeTexier NJ, Huang HZ, Sutlief E, Tung H, Vizzini N, Chen B, Smith K, Meza D, Yajima M, Beyer RP, Kerr KF, Davis DJ, Gillespie CH, Snyder JM, Treuting PM, and Kaeberlein M. Transient rapamycin treatment can increase lifespan and healthspan in middle-aged mice. *Elife*. 2016 Aug 23; 5: e16351.

10. Lin'kova NS, Poliakova VO, Trofimov AV, Sevost'ianova NN, and Kvetnoĭ IM. [Influence of peptides from pineal gland on thymus function at aging]. *Adv Gerontol*. 2010; 23(4):543-6.

11. Hickson LJ, Langhi Prata LGP, Bobart SA, Evans TK, Giorgadze N, Hashmi SK, Herrmann SM, Jensen MD, Jia Q, Jordan KL, Kellogg TA, Khosla S, Koerber DM, Lagnado AB, Lawson DK, LeBrasseur NK, Lerman LO, McDonald KM, McKenzie TJ, Passos JF, Pignolo RJ, Pirtskhalava T, Saadiq IM, Schaefer KK, Textor SC, Victorelli SG, Volkman TL, Xue A, Wentworth MA, Wissler Gerdes EO, Zhu Y, Tchkonia T, and Kirkland JL. Senolytics decrease senescent cells in humans: Preliminary report from a clinical trial of Dasatinib plus Quercetin in individuals with diabetic kidney disease. *EBioMedicine.* 2019 Sep; 47:446-456.

12. Kurosu H, Yamamoto M, Clark JD, Pastor JV, Nandi A, Gurnani P, McGuinness OP, Chikuda H, Yamaguchi M, Kawaguchi H, Shimomura I, Takayama Y, Herz J, Kahn CR, Rosenblatt KP, and Kuro-o M. Suppression of aging in mice by the hormone Klotho. *Science.* 2005 Sep 16; 309(5742):1829-33.

13. Castilho RM, Squarize CH, Chodosh LA, Williams BO, and Gutkind JS. mTOR mediates Wnt-induced epidermal stem cell exhaustion and aging. *Cell Stem Cell.* 2009 Sep 4; 5(3):279-89.

14. Takahashi K and Yamanaka S. Induction of pluripotent stem cells from mouse embryonic and adult fibroblast cultures by defined factors. *Cell.* 2006 Aug 25; 126(4):663-76.

15. Mikirova NA, Jackson JA, Hunninghake R, Kenyon J, Chan KW, Swindlehurst CA, Minev B, Patel AN, Murphy MP, Smith L, Ramos F, Ichim TE, and Riordan NH. Nutraceutical augmentation of circulating endothelial progenitor cells and hematopoietic stem cells in human subjects. *J Transl Med.* 2010 Apr 8; 8: 34.

16. Yousefzadeh MJ, Zhu Y, McGowan SJ, Angelini L, Fuhrmann-Stroissnigg H, Xu M, Ling YY, Melos KI, Pirtskhalava T, Inman CL, McGuckian C, Wade EA, Kato JI, Grassi D, Wentworth M, Burd CE, Arriaga EA, Ladiges WL, Tchkonia T, Kirkland JL, Robbins PD, and Niedernhofer LJ. Fisetin is a senotherapeutic that extends health and lifespan. *EBioMedicine.* 2018 Oct; 36:18-28.

CHAPTER 22: ALTERNATIVE CANCER TREATMENTS

1. Takeda M, Kobayashi M, Takayama M, Suzuki S, Ishida T, Ohnuki K, Moriya T, and Ohuchi N. Biophoton detection as a novel technique for cancer imaging. *Cancer Sci.* 2004 Aug; 95(8):656-61.

2. Gross AL, Gallo JJ, and Eaton WW. Depression and cancer risk: 24 years of follow-up of the Baltimore Epidemiologic Catchment Area sample. *Cancer Causes Control.* 2010 Feb; 21(2):191-9.

3. Warburg Otto. On the origin of cancer cells. *Science.* 1956 Feb 24; 123 (3191):309-14.

4. Gonzalez MJ, Miranda Massari JR, Duconge J, Riordan NH, Ichim T, Quintero-Del-Rio AI, and Ortiz N. The bio-energetic theory of carcinogenesis. *Med Hypotheses.* 2012 Oct; 79(4):433-9.

5. Rohani N, Hao L, Alexis MS, Joughin BA, Krismer K, Moufarrej MN, Soltis AR, Lauffenburger DA, Yaffe MB, Burge CB, Bhatia SN, and Gertler FB. Acidification of Tumor at Stromal Boundaries Drives Transcriptome Alterations Associated with Aggressive Phenotypes. *Cancer Res.* 2019 Apr 15; 79(8):1952-1966.

6. Cone CD. The role of surface electrical transmembrane potential in normal and malignant mitogenesis. *Ann NY Acad Sci.* 1975; 238:420-35.

7. Payne SL, Levin M, and Oudin MJ. Bioelectric Control of Metastasis in Solid Tumors. *Bioelectricity.* 2019 Sep 1; 1(3):114-130.

8. Becchetti A, Munaron L, and Arcangeli A. The role of ion channels and transporters in cell proliferation and cancer. *Front Physiol.* 2013 Oct 29; 4:312.

9. Griffin DT, Dodd NJ, Moore JV, Pullan BR, and Taylor TV. The effects of low-level direct current therapy on a preclinical mammary carcinoma: tumour regression and systemic biochemical sequelae. *Br J Cancer.* 1994; 69(5):875-878.

10. Turler A, Schaefer H, Schaefer N, Maintz D, Wagner M, Qiao JC, and Hoelscher AH. Local treatment of hepatic metastases with low-level direct electric current: experimental results. *Scand J Gastroenterol.* 2000 Mar; 35(3):322-8.

11. Lee Bok Y, Koonin Alfred J, Wendell Keith, and Hillard John. Antioxidant Effects of Ultra-Low Microcurrents, *Educational Forum with Clinical Studies.* December 14, 2010.

12. Gonzalez Nicholas. *Conquering Cancer (Volume One): 50 Pancreatic and Breast Cancer Patients on The Gonzalez Nutritional Protocol.* New York: New Spring Press; 2016.

13. Gonzalez, Nicholas. *Conquering Cancer (Volume Two): 62 Patients on The Gonzalez Protocol.* New York: New Spring Press; 2017.

14. Gerson Max. *A Cancer Therapy: Results of 50 Cases & The Cure of Advanced Cancer by Diet.* New York, NY: Whittier Books; 1958.

15. Együd LG and Szent-Györgyi A. Cancerostatic action of methylglyoxal. *Science.* 1968 Jun 7; 160(3832):1140.

16. Talukdar D, Ray S, Ray M, and Das S. A brief critical overview of the biological effects of methylglyoxal and further evaluation of a methylglyoxal-based anticancer formulation in treating cancer patients. *Drug Metabol Drug Interact.* 2008; 23(1-2):175-210.

17. Pal A, Roy A, and Ray M. Creatine supplementation with methylglyoxal: a potent therapy for cancer in experimental models. *Amino Acids.* 2016 Aug; 48(8):2003-13.

18. Szent-Gyorgyi A, Hegyeli A, and McLaughlin JA. Cancer therapy: a possible new approach. *Science.* 1963 Jun 28; 140(3574):1391-2.
19. Burzynski SR. The Burzynski Clinic. Scientific publications. https://www.burzynskiclinic.com/scientific-publications/ Accessed April 5, 2020.
20. Fitzgerald Benedict F. Fitzgerald Report written by Special Counsel for the Senate Interstate and Foreign Commerce Committee member. 1953. http://whale.to/a/report_cancer.html. Accessed April 3, 2020.
21. Sun Y, Xun K, Wang Y, and Chen X. A systematic review of the anticancer properties of berberine, a natural product from Chinese herbs. *Anticancer Drugs.* 2009 Oct; 20(9):757-69.
22. Yin J, Xing H, and Ye J. Efficacy of berberine in patients with type 2 diabetes mellitus. *Metabolism.* 2008 May; 57(5):712-7.
23. Barzegar A. The role of electron-transfer and H-atom donation on the superb antioxidant activity and free radical reaction of curcumin. *Food Chem.* 2012; 135(3):1369–1376.
24. Wilken R, Veena MS, Wang MB, and Srivatsan ES. Curcumin: A review of anti-cancer properties and therapeutic activity in head and neck squamous cell carcinoma. *Mol Cancer.* 2011; 10:12.
25. Padayatty SJ, Katz A, Wang Y, Eck P, Kwon O, Lee JH, Chen S, Corpe C, Dutta A, Dutta SK, and Levine M. Vitamin C as an antioxidant: evaluation of its role in disease prevention. *J Am Coll Nutr.* 2003; 22(1):18–35.
26. Linus Pauling and Ewan Cameron. *Cancer and Vitamin C*, Linus Pauling Institute of Science and Medicine. 1979.
27. Shenoy N, Creagan E, Witzig T, and Levine M. Ascorbic Acid in Cancer Treatment: Let the Phoenix Fly. *Cancer Cell.* 2018 Nov 12; 34(5):700-706.
28. Yun J, Mullarky E, Lu C, Bosch KN, Kavalier A, Rivera K, Roper J, Chio II, Giannopoulou EG, Rago C, Muley A, Asara JM, Paik J, Elemento O, Chen Z, Pappin DJ, Dow LE, Papadopoulos N, Gross SS, and Cantley LC. Vitamin C selectively kills KRAS and BRAF mutant colorectal cancer cells by targeting GAPDH. *Science.* 2015 Dec 11; 350(6266):1391-6.
29. Ni J and Yeh S. The roles of α-vitamin E and its analogues in prostate cancer. *Vitam Horm.* 2007; 76:493–518.
30. Zhang SM, Moore SC, Lin J, Cook NR, Manson JE, Lee IM, and Buring JE. Folate, vitamin B6, multivitamin supplements, and colorectal cancer risk in women. *Am J Epidemiol..* 2006; 163:108–115.

31. Li Y, Cao F, Li M, Li P, Yu Y, Xiang L, Xu T, Lei J, Tai YY, Zhu J, Yang B, Jiang Y, Zhang X, Duo L, Chen P, and Yu X. Hydroxychloroquine induced lung cancer suppression by enhancing chemo-sensitization and promoting the transition of M2-TAMs to M1-like macrophages. *J Exp Clin Cancer Res*. 2018 Oct 29; 37(1):259.

32. Manic G, Obrist F, Kroemer G, Vitale I and Galluzzi L. Chloroquine and hydroxychloroquine for cancer therapy. *Mol Cell Oncol*. 2014; 1(1): e29911.

33. Barnard RA, Wittenburg LA, Amaravadi RK, Gustafson DL, Thorburn A, and Thamm DH. Phase I clinical trial and pharmacodynamic evaluation of combination hydroxychloroquine and doxorubicin treatment in pet dogs treated for spontaneously occurring lymphoma. *Autophagy*. 2014; 10(8):1415-1425.

34. Rojas-Puentes LL, Gonzalez-Pinedo M, Crismatt A, Ortega-Gomez A, Gamboa-Vignolle C, Nuñez-Gomez R, Dorantes-Gallareta Y, Arce-Salinas C, and Arrieta O. Phase II randomized, double-blind, placebo-controlled study of whole-brain irradiation with concomitant chloroquine for brain metastases. *Radiat Oncol*. 2013; 8:209.

35. Mahalingam D, Mita M, Sarantopoulos J, Wood L, Amaravadi RK, Davis LE, Mita AC, Curiel TJ, Espitia CM, Nawrocki ST, Giles FJ, and Carew JS. Combined autophagy and HDAC inhibition: a phase I safety, tolerability, pharmacokinetic, and pharmacodynamic analysis of hydroxychloroquine in combination with the HDAC inhibitor vorinostat in patients with advanced solid tumors. *Autophagy*. 2014; 10(8):1403-1414.

36. Zhang Y, Luo P, and Leng P. [Effect of Autophagy Inhibitor Hydroxychloroquine on Chemosensitivity of Castration-resistant Prostate Cancer]. *Sichuan Da Xue Xue Bao Yi Xue Ban*. 2019 May; 50(3):323-327.

37. Anthony, Joshua. St Vincent's Hospital, Sydney. Phase I/II Study of Hydroxychloroquine With Itraconazole With Biochemically Recurrent Prostate Cancer (HITMAN-PC). https://clinicaltrials.gov/ct2/show/NCT03513211 Accessed September 4, 2020.

38. Manic G, Obrist F, Kroemer G, Vitale I, and Galluzzi L. Chloroquine and hydroxychloroquine for cancer therapy. *Mol Cell Oncol*. 2014; 1(1): e29911.

39. Choi DS, Blanco E, Kim YS, Rodriguez AA, Zhao H, Huang TH, Chen CL, Jin G, Landis MD, Burey LA, Qian W, Granados SM, Dave B, Wong HH, Ferrari M, Wong ST and Chang JC. Chloroquine eliminates cancer stem cells through deregulation of Jak2 and DNMT1. *Stem Cells*. 2014 Sep; 32(9):2309-23.

40. Lu H, Chen I, Shimoda LA, Park Y, Zhang C, Tran L, Zhang H, and Semenza GL. Chemotherapy-Induced Ca^{2+} Release Stimulates Breast Cancer Stem Cell Enrichment. *Cell Rep.* 2017 Feb 21; 18(8):1946-1957.

41. Cook KL, Wärri A, Soto-Pantoja DR, Clarke PA, Cruz MI, Zwart A, and Clarke R. Hydroxychloroquine inhibits autophagy to potentiate antiestrogen responsiveness in ER+ breast cancer. *Clin Cancer Res.* 2014 Jun 15; 20(12):3222-32. Erratum in: *Clin Cancer Res.* 2016 Jun 1; 22(11):2825.

42. Dogra N, Kumar A, and Mukhopadhyay T. Fenbendazole acts as a moderate microtubule destabilizing agent and causes cancer cell death by modulating multiple cellular pathways. *Sci Rep.* 2018; 8, 11926.

43. Gao P, Dang CV, and Watson J. Unexpected antitumorigenic effect of fenbendazole when combined with supplementary vitamins. *J Am Assoc Lab Anim Sci.* 2008; 47(6):37–40.

44. Willoughby JA Sr, Sundar SN, Cheung M, Tin AS, Modiano J, and Firestone GL. Artemisinin blocks prostate cancer growth and cell cycle progression by disrupting Sp1 interactions with the cyclin-dependent kinase-4 (CDK4) promoter and inhibiting CDK4 gene expression. *J Biol Chem.* 2009 Jan 23; 284(4):2203-13.

45. Steely AM, Willoughby JA Sr, Sundar SN, Aivaliotis VI, and Firestone GL. Artemisinin disrupts androgen responsiveness of human prostate cancer cells by stimulating the 26S proteasome-mediated degradation of the androgen receptor protein. *Anticancer Drugs.* 2017 Oct; 28(9):1018-1031.

46. Nelles JL, Hu WY, and Prins GS. Estrogen action and prostate cancer. *Expert Rev Endocrinol Metab.* 2011; 6(3):437-451.

47. Sundar SN, Marconett CN, Doan VB, Willoughby JA Sr, and Firestone GL. Artemisinin selectively decreases functional levels of estrogen receptor-alpha and ablates estrogen-induced proliferation in human breast cancer cells. *Carcinogenesis.* 2008; 29(12):2252-2258.

48. Kai M, Kanaya N, Wu SV, Mendez C, Nguyen D, Luu T, and Chen S. Targeting breast cancer stem cells in triple-negative breast cancer using a combination of LBH589 and salinomycin. *Breast Cancer Res Treat.* 2015 Jun; 151(2):281-94

49. Jangamreddy JR, Ghavami S, Grabarek J, Kratz G, Wiechec E, Fredriksson BA, Rao Pariti RK, Cieślar-Pobuda A, Panigrahi S, and Łos MJ. Salinomycin induces activation of autophagy, mitophagy and affects mitochondrial polarity: differences between primary and cancer cells. *Biochim Biophys Acta.* 2013 Sep; 1833(9):2057-69.

50. Stanciu Daniel. Cancer Treatments – From Research to Application. MCS Foundations for Life. www.cancertreatmentsresearch.com. Accessed October 5, 2020.

51. Zhou S, Wang F, Wong ET, Fonkem E, Hsieh TC, Wu JM, and Wu E. Salinomycin: a novel anti-cancer agent with known anti-coccidial activities. *Curr Med Chem*. 2013; 20(33):4095-101.

52. Naujokat C and Steinhart R. Salinomycin as a Drug for Targeting Human Cancer Stem Cells. *Journal of Biomedicine and Biotechnology*. 2012; 2012:950658.

53. Gupta PB, Onder TT, Jiang G, Tao K, Kuperwasser C, Weinberg RA, and Lander ES. Identification of selective inhibitors of cancer stem cells by high-throughput screening. *Cell*. 2009 Aug 21; 138(4):645-659.

54. Dewangan J, Srivastava S, and Rath SK. Salinomycin: A new paradigm in cancer therapy. *Tumour Biol*. 2017 Mar; 39(3):1010428317695035.

55. Saleem M, Asif J, Asif M, and Saleem U. Amygdalin from Apricot Kernels Induces Apoptosis and Causes Cell Cycle Arrest in Cancer Cells: An Updated Review. *Anticancer Agents Med Chem*. 2018; 18(12):1650-1655.

56. Arshi A, Hosseini SM, Hosseini FSK, Amiri ZY, Hosseini FS, Sheikholia Lavasani M, Kerdarian H, and Dehkordi MS. The anti-cancer effect of amygdalin on human cancer cell lines. *Mol Biol Rep*. 2019 Apr; 46(2):2059-2066.

57. Song Z and Xu X. Advanced research on anti-tumor effects of amygdalin. *J Cancer Res Ther*. 2014 Aug; 10 Suppl 1:3-7.

58. Costantini C, Bellet MM, Pariano M, Renga G, Stincardini C, Goldstein AL, Garaci E, and Romani L. A Reappraisal of Thymosin Alpha1 in Cancer Therapy. *Front Oncol*. 2019 Sep 6; 9:873.

59. Schulof RS, Lloyd MJ, Cleary PA, Palaszynski SR, Mai DA, Cox JW Jr, Alabaster O, and Goldstein AL. A randomized trial to evaluate the immunorestorative properties of synthetic thymosin-alpha 1 in patients with lung cancer. *J Biol Response Mod*. 1985 Apr; 4(2):147-58.

60. Hong Y, Downey T, Eu KW, Koh PK, and Cheah PY. A 'metastasis-prone' signature for early-stage mismatch-repair proficient sporadic colorectal cancer patients and its implications for possible therapeutics. *Clin Exp Metastasis*. 2010; 27(2):83–90.

61. Matalka Luay. The Tripeptide, GHK, Induces Programmed Cell Death in SH-SY5Y Neuroblastoma Cells, *J Biotechnol Biomater*. 2012; 2:5

62. Kozina LS, Arutjunyan AV, and Khavinson VKh. Antioxidant properties of geroprotective peptides of the pineal gland. *Arch Gerontol Geriatr.* 2007; 44: 213–216

63. Rosenfeld SV, Togo EF, Mikheev VS, Popovich IG, Khavinson,VKh, and Anisimov VN. Effect of epithalon on the incidence of chromosome aberrations in senescence-accelerated mice. *Bull Exp Biol Med.* 2002; 133 (3): 274–276.

64. Lin'kova NS, Kuznik BI, and Khavinson VKh. Peptide Ala-Glu-Asp-Gly and interferon gamma: their role in immune response during aging. *Adv Gerontol.* 2012; 25 (3): 478–482.

65. Anisimov VN, Khavinson VK, Provinciali M, Alimova IN, Baturin DA, Popovich IG, Zabezhinski MA, Imyanitov EN, Mancini R, and Franceschi C.Inhibitory effect of the peptide epitalon on the development of spontaneous mammary tumors in HER-2/neu transgenic mice. *Int J Cancer.* 2002; 101(1):7–10.

66. Anisimov VN, Khavinson VK, Popovich IG, Zabezhinski MA, Alimova IN, Rosenfeld SV, Zavarzina NY, Semenchenko AV, and Yashin AI. Effect of Epitalon on biomarkers of aging, life span and spontaneous tumor incidence in female Swiss-derived SHR mice. *Biogerontology.*. 2003; 4, 193–202.

67. Khavinson VKh, Iuzhakov VV, Kvetnoĭ IM, and Malinin VV. Vliianie épitalona na kinetiku rosta i funktsional'nuiu morfologiiu sarkomy M-1 [Effect of epithalone on growth kinetics and functional morphology of M-1 sarcoma]. *Vopr Onkol.* 2001; 47(4):461–466.

68. Kossoy G, Zandbank J, Tendler E, Anisimov V, Khavinson V, Popovich I, Zabezhinski M, Zusman I, and Ben-Hur H. Epitalon and colon carcinogenesis in rats: proliferative activity and apoptosis in colon tumors and mucosa. *Int J Mol Med.* 2003 Oct; 12(4):473-7.

69. Srisuchart B, Fuchs BA, Sikorski EE, Munson AE, and Loveless SE. Antitumor activity of enkephalin analogues in inhibiting PYB6 tumor growth in mice and immunological effects of methionine enkephalinamide. *Int J Immunopharmacol.* 1989; 11(5):487–500.

70. Smith JP, Bingaman SI, Mauger DT, Harvey HH, Demers LM, and Zagon IS. Opioid growth factor improves clinical benefit and survival in patients with advanced pancreatic cancer. *Open Access J Clin Trials.* 2010; 2010(2):37–48.

71. Sugahara KN, Teesalu T, Karmali PP, Kotamraju VR, Agemy L, Greenwald DR, and Ruoslahti E. Coadministration of a tumor-penetrating peptide enhances the efficacy of cancer drugs. *Science.* 2010 May 21; 328(5981):1031-5.

72. Davitt K, Babcock BD, Fenelus M, Poon CK, Sarkar A, Trivigno V, Zolkind PA, Matthew SM, Grin'kina N, Orynbayeva Z, Shaikh MF, Adler V, Michl J, Sarafraz-Yazdi E, Pincus MR, and Bowne WB. The anti-cancer peptide, PNC-27, induces tumor cell necrosis of a poorly differentiated non-solid tissue human leukemia cell line that depends on expression of HDM-2 in the plasma membrane of these cells. *Ann Clin Lab Sci.* 2014; 44(3):241–248.

73. Sarafraz-Yazdi E, Bowne WB, Adler V, Sookraj KA, Wu V, Shteyler V, Patel H, Oxbury W, Brandt-Rauf P, Zenilman ME, Michl J, and Pincus MR. Anticancer peptide PNC-27 adopts an HDM-2-binding conformation and kills cancer cells by binding to HDM-2 in their membranes. *Proc Natl Acad Sci.* USA: 2010 Feb 2; 107(5):1918-23.

74. Sinyukhin AB, Timoshinov GP, Komilov VA, and Shabanov PD. Delta sleep-inducing peptide analogue corrects the eNS functional state of children treated with antiblastomic therapy. *European Neuropsychopharmacology.* 2009; 19: S681–S682.

75. Popovich IG, Voitenkov BO, Anisimov VN, Ivanov VT, Mikhaleva II, Zabezhinski MA, Alimova IN, Baturin DA, Zavarzina NY, Rosenfeld SV, Semenchenko AV, and Yashin AI. Effect of delta-sleep inducing peptide-containing preparation Deltaran on biomarkers of aging, life span and spontaneous tumor incidence in female SHR mice. *Mechanisms of Ageing and Development.* 2003; 124 (6): 721–731.

76. Vetha, B.S.S., Kim, E., Oh, P. Kim SH, Lim ST, Sohn MY, and Jeong HW. Curcumin Encapsulated Micellar Nanoplatform for Blue Light Emitting Diode Induced Apoptosis as a New Class of Cancer Therapy. *Macromol.* 2019; Res. 27, 1179–1184.

77. Oh PS, Hwang H, Jeong HS, Kwon J, Kim HS, Kim M, Lim S, Sohn MH, and Jeong HJ. Blue light emitting diode induces apoptosis in lymphoid cells by stimulating autophagy. *The International Journal of Biochemistry & Cell Biology.* 2016 Jan; Volume 70: Pages 13-22.

78. Yan G, Zhang L, Feng C, Gong R, Idiiatullina E, Huang Q, He M, Guo S, Yang F, Li Y, Ding F, Ma W, Pavlov V, Han Z, Wang Z, Xu C, Cai B, Yuan Y, and Yang L. Blue light emitting diodes irradiation causes cell death in colorectal cancer by inducing ROS production and DNA damage. *Int J Biochem Cell Biol.* 2018 Oct; 103:81-88.

79. Sparsa A, Faucher K, Sol V, Durox H, Boulinguez S, Doffoel-Hantz V, Calliste CA, Cook-Moreau J, Krausz P, Sturtz FG, Bedane C, Jauberteau-Marchan MO, Ratinaud MH, and Bonnetblanc JM. Blue light is phototoxic for B16F10 murine melanoma and bovine endothelial cell lines by direct cytocidal effect. *Anticancer Res.* 2010 Jan; 30(1):143-7.

80. Zhuang J, Liu Y, Yuan Q, Liu J, Liu Y, Li H, and Wang D. Blue light-induced apoptosis of human promyelocytic leukemia cells via the mitochondrial-mediated signaling pathway. *Oncol Lett.* 2018 May; 15(5):6291-6296.

81. Ohara M, Kawashima Y, Watanabe H, and Kitajima S. Effects of blue-light-exposure on growth of extracorporeally circulated leukemic cells in rats with leukemia induced by 1-ethyl-1-nitrosourea. *Int J Mol Med.* 2002 Oct; 10(4):407-11.

82. Ohara M, Kawashima Y, Kitajima S, Mitsuoka C, and Watanabe H. Inhibition of lung metastasis of B16 melanoma cells exposed to blue light in mice. *Int J Mol Med.* 2002 Dec; 10(6):701-5.

83. Ohara M, Fujikura T, and Fujiwara H. Augmentation of the inhibitory effect of blue light on the growth of B16 melanoma cells by riboflavin. *Int J Oncol.* 2003 Jun; 22(6):1291-5.

84. Moan J and Berg K. Photochemotherapy of cancer: experimental research. *Photochem Photobiol.* 1992; 55(6):931–948.

85. Li MJ, Yin YC, Wang J, and Jiang YF. Green tea compounds in breast cancer prevention and treatment. *World J Clin Oncol.* 2014; 5(3):520-528.

86. Connors SK, Chornokur G, and Kumar NB. New insights into the mechanisms of green tea catechins in the chemoprevention of prostate cancer. *Nutr Cancer.* 2012; 64(1):4-22.

87. Atamna H, Nguyen A, Schultz C, Boyle K, Newberry J, Kato H, and Ames BN. Methylene blue delays cellular senescence and enhances key mitochondrial biochemical pathways. *FASEB J.* 2008 Mar; 22(3):703-12.

88. Dos Santos AF, Terra LF, Wailemann RA, Oliveira TC, Gomes VM, Mineiro MF, Meotti FC, Bruni-Cardoso A, Baptista MS, and Labriola L. Methylene blue photodynamic therapy induces selective and massive cell death in human breast cancer cells. *BMC Cancer.* 2017 Mar 15; 17(1):194.

89. Tardivo JP, Del Giglio A, de Oliveira CS, Gabrielli DS, Junqueira HC, Tada DB, Severino D, de Fátima Turchiello R, and Baptista MS. Methylene blue in photodynamic therapy: From basic mechanisms to clinical applications, *Photodiagnosis and Photodynamic Therapy.* 2005; Volume 2, Issue 3: Pages 175-191.

CHAPTER 23: LIGHT MEDICINE AND THE MERCY BLU ROOM PROGRAM

1. Sagner Rory. Healing With Light – The Blu Rooms. Figure 13. Copyright © 2018 Rory Sagner Photography.

2. Knight Judith Darlene. *Apparatus for providing light therapy United States*. Blu Room Enterprises, LLC. 2018. Yelm, WA: US 9919162. https://www.freepatentsonline.com/9919162.html.

3. Ramtha. *A Beginner's Guide to Creating Reality*, Third Edition. Yelm, WA: JZK Publishing, 2004; Pages 170–172.

4. Sykes Sophie. *The Radical Few, Ordinary People Manifesting The Extraordinary (Inspiring Stories Compiled by Sophie Sykes)*. Yelm, WA: Rosette Publishing, 2018.

5. Graf Irmgard. *Blu Room – Experience The Future Building Bridges With Light, Frequency, and Sound*. Lacey, WA: Blu Room Enterprises, LLC; 2017.

6. Phillips Stephen. *The Mathematical connection between Religion and Science*, Eastbourne: Anthony Rowe Publishing; 2009.

7. Rein Glen. Geometric resonance in DNA: The geometric continuum Model of Consciousness. *Frontier Perspectives*. Vol 7: pp.16-23.

8. Ramtha. *A Beginner's Guide to Creating Reality*, Third Edition. Yelm, WA: JZK Publishing, 2004; Page 286.

9. Krasylenko Y, Yemets A, and Blume Y. Cytoskeleton-mediated signaling pathways in UV-B perception by plant cell. *Emirates Journal of Food and Agriculture*. (2012) 24. 557-564.

10. Swanson Claude. *Life Force, The Scientific Basis, Breakthrough Physics of Energy Medicine, Healing, Chi and Quantum Consciousness*. Volume 2 of The Synchronized Universe Series. Poseida Press; 2010.

11. Binaday J, Gobres W, Abbarientos A, Diesta K, Marquez K, Palomillo R, Lobos AH, and Lita C. Increased Wound Healing Effect of 111 Hertz Sound Frequency in Male ICR Mice. Unpublished. 2015.

12. De Schutter E and Bower JM. An active membrane model of the cerebellar Purkinje cell II. Simulation of synaptic responses. *J Neurophysiol*. 1994 Jan; 71(1):401-19.

13. Ramtha. *A Beginner's Guide to Creating Reality*, Third Edition. Yelm, WA: JZK Publishing, 2004; Pages 248-258.

14. Finsen Niels Ryberg. The Nobel Prize in Physiology or Medicine 1903. https://www.nobelprize.org/prizes/medicine/1903/summary/ Accessed October 3, 2020.

15. Jussila A, Huotari-Orava R, Ylianttila L, Partonen T, and Snellman E. Narrow-band ultraviolet B radiation induces the expression of β-endorphin in human skin in vivo. *J Photochem Photobiol B*. 2016 Feb; 155:104-8.

16. Killgore WDS, Vanuk JR, Shane BR, Weber M, and Bajaj S. A randomized, double-blind, placebo-controlled trial of blue wavelength light exposure on sleep and recovery of brain structure, function, and cognition following mild traumatic brain injury. *Neurobiol Dis.* 2020 Feb; 134:104679.

17. Bosman ES, Albert AY, Lui H, Dutz JP, and Vallance BA. Skin Exposure to Narrow Band Ultraviolet (UVB) Light Modulates the Human Intestinal Microbiome. *Front Microbiol.* 2019; 10:2410.

18. Sasaki N, Yamashita T, Kasahara K, Fukunaga A, Yamaguchi T, Emoto T, Yodoi K, Matsumoto T, Nakajima K, Kita T, Takeda M, Mizoguchi T, Hayashi T, Sasaki Y, Hatakeyama M, Taguchi K, Washio K, Sakaguchi S, Malissen B, Nishigori C, and Hirata KI. UVB Exposure Prevents Atherosclerosis by Regulating Immunoinflammatory Responses. *Arterioscler Thromb Vasc Biol.* 2017 Jan; 37(1):66-74.

19. MacLaughlin J and Holick MF. Aging decreases the capacity of human skin to produce vitamin D3. *J Clin Invest.* 1985; 76:1536–1538.

20. Ramtha. Italy Advanced Retreat. Santa Sofia, Italy; August 19, 2015.

21. Swanson Claude. (2010).

22. Franskevych D, Palyvoda K, Petukhov D, Prylutska S, Grynyuk I, Schuetze C, Drobot L, Matyshevska O, and Ritter U. Fullerene C_{60} Penetration into Leukemic Cells and Its Photoinduced Cytotoxic Effects. *Nanoscale Res Lett.* 2017 Dec; 12(1):40.

23. Cutando A, López-Valverde A, Arias-Santiago S, DE Vicente J, and DE Diego RG. Role of melatonin in cancer treatment. *Anticancer Res.* 2012 Jul; 32(7):2747-53.

24. Yousefzadeh MJ, Zhu Y, McGowan SJ, Angelini L, Fuhrmann-Stroissnigg H, Xu M, Ling YY, Melos KI, Pirtskhalava T, Inman CL, McGuckian C, Wade EA, Kato JI, Grassi D, Wentworth M, Burd CE, Arriaga EA, Ladiges WL, Tchkonia T, Kirkland JL, Robbins PD, and Niedernhofer LJ. Fisetin is a senotherapeutic that extends health and lifespan. *EBioMedicine.* 2018 Oct; 36:18-28.

25. Castano AP, Demidova TN, and Hamblin MR. Mechanisms in photodynamic therapy: part one-photosensitizers, photochemistry and cellular localization. *Photodiagnosis Photodyn Ther.* 2004 Dec; 1(4):279-93.

26. Sengupta B, Pahari B, Blackmon L, and Sengupta PK. Prospect of bioflavonoid fisetin as a quadruplex DNA ligand: a biophysical approach. *PLoS One.* 2013 Jun 13; 8(6): e65383.

27. Cole SW, Nagaraja AS, Lutgendorf SK, Green PA, and Sood AK. Sympathetic nervous system regulation of the tumour microenvironment. *Nat Rev Cancer.* 2015 Sep; 15(9):563-72.

28. Khavinson VKh and Morozov VG. Peptides of pineal gland and thymus prolong human life. *Neuro Endocrinol Lett.* 2003 Jun-Aug; 24(3-4):233-40.

29. Fotino AD, Thompson-Paul AM, and Bazzano LA. Effect of coenzyme Q_{10} supplementation on heart failure: a meta-analysis. *Am J Clin Nutr.* 2013; 97(2):268-275.

30. Okuyama H, Langsjoen PH, Hamazaki T, Ogushi Y, Hama R, Kobayashi T, and Uchino H. Statins stimulate atherosclerosis and heart failure: pharmacological mechanisms. *Expert Rev Clin Pharmacol.* 2015 Mar; 8(2):189-99. Erratum in: *Expert Rev Clin Pharmacol.* 2015; 8(4):503-5.

31. Sykes Sophie. *The Radical Few: Ordinary People Manifesting the Extraordinary (Inspiring Stories Compiled by Sophie Sykes)* Yelm, WA: Rosette Publishing. 2015.

CHAPTER 24: FUTURE FRONTIERS AND CREATING SUPERHUMANS

1. Lévesque M, Gatien S, Finnson K, Desmeules S, Villiard E, Pilote M, Philip A, and Roy S. Transforming growth factor: beta signaling is essential for limb regeneration in axolotls. *PLoS One.* 2007. Nov 28; 2(11): e1227.

2. Gehrke AR, Neverett E, Luo YJ, Brandt A, Ricci L, Hulett RE, Gompers A, Ruby JG, Rokhsar DS, Reddien PW, and Srivastava M. Acoel genome reveals the regulatory landscape of whole-body regeneration. *Science.* 2019 Mar 15; 363(6432): eaau6173.

3. Alonge M and Schatz MC. A master regulator of regeneration. *Science.* 2019 Mar 15; 363(6432):1152-1153.

4. UniProtKB - P18146 (EGR1_HUMAN) https://www.uniprot.org/uniprot/P18146. Accessed October 5, 2020.

5. Mansour Joshua. Harvard Scientists one step closer to human regeneration. https://physiciansnews.com/2019/03/22/harvard-scientists-one-step-closer-to-human-regeneration/ Accessed October 10, 2020.

6. De Tullio MC. What is vitamin C? How does it function biochemically? Why can't humans synthesize it? The Mystery of Vitamin C. *Nature Education.* 2010; 3(9):48.

7. Nishikimi M and Yagi K. Molecular basis for the deficiency in humans of gulonolactone oxidase, a key enzyme for ascorbic acid biosynthesis. *Am J Clin Nutr.* 1991 Dec; 54(6 Suppl):1203S-1208S.

8. Chatterjee IB, Majumder AK, Nandi BK, and Subramanian N. Synthesis and Some Major Functions of Vitamin C in Animals. *Annals of the New York Academy of Sciences.* 258.1 Second Confer. 1975; 24-47.

9. Haupt S and Haupt Y. P53 at the start of the 21st century: lessons from elephants. *F1000Res.* 2017 Nov 22; 6:2041.

10. Tollis M, Robbins J, Webb AE, Kuderna LFK, Caulin AF, Garcia JD, Bèrubè M, Pourmand N, Marques-Bonet T, O'Connell MJ, Palsbøll PJ, and Maley CC. Return to the sea, get huge, beat cancer: an analysis of cetacean genomes including an assembly for the humpback whale (Megaptera novaeangliae). *Mol Biol Evol.* 2019 Aug 1; 36(8):1746-1763.

11. Ruhr IM, McCourty H, Bajjig A, Crossley DA 2nd, Shiels HA, and Galli GLJ. Developmental plasticity of cardiac anoxia-tolerance in juvenile common snapping turtles (Chelydra serpentina). *Proc Biol Sci.* 2019 Jun 26; 286(1905):20191072.

12. Liu Z, Qi FY, Zhou X, Ren HQ, and Shi P. Parallel sites implicate functional convergence of the hearing gene prestin among echolocating mammals. Mol Biol Evol. 2014 Sep; 31(9):2415-24.

13. Thaler L, De Vos R, Kish D, Antoniou M, Baker C, and Hornikx M. Human echolocators adjust loudness and number of clicks for detection of reflectors at various azimuth angles. *Proc Biol Sci.* 2018 Feb 28; 285(1873):20172735.

ARTHEMA SOPHIA PUBLISHING

A division of

AM Medical LLC
715 E Yelm Avenue, Suite #5
Yelm, WA 98597, U.S.A.
Phone: (360)960-8538 / Fax: (360) 252-7023
https://ammedicalmd.com/

Bringing Light Back Into Our World

Made in the USA
Middletown, DE
23 September 2023